The Bridge

Uniting traditions in
the worshipping church

Acknowledgements

The publishers wish to express their gratitude to the copyright holders who have granted permission to include their material in this book.

Every effort has been made to trace the copyright holders of all the songs in this collection and we hope that no copyright has been infringed. Apology is made and pardon sought if the contrary be the case, and a correction will be made in any reprint of this book.

Important Copyright Information

We would like to remind users of this hymnal that the reproduction of any song texts or music without the permission of the copyright holder is illegal. Details of all copyright holders are clearly indicated under each song.

Many of the song texts may be covered either by a Christian Copyright Licensing (CCL) licence or a Calamus licence. If you possess a CCL or Calamus licence, it is essential that you check your instruction manual to ensure that the song you wish to use is covered.

If you are not a member of CCL or Calamus, or the song you wish to reproduce is not covered by your licence, you must contact the copyright holder direct for their permission.

Christian Copyright Licensing (Europe) Ltd have also now introduced a Music Reproduction Licence. Again, if you hold such a licence it is essential that you check your instruction manual to ensure that the song you wish to reproduce is covered. The reproduction of any music not covered by your licence is both illegal and immoral.

If you are interested in joining CCL or Calamus they can be contacted at the following addresses:

Christian Copyright Licensing (Europe) Ltd, P.O. Box 1339, Eastbourne,
East Sussex BN 21 1AD
Tel: 01323 417711, Fax: 01323 417722

Calamus, 30 North Terrace, Mildenhall, Suffolk, IP28 7AB.
Tel: 01638 716579, Fax: 01638 510390

First published in Great Britain in 2001 by
KEVIN MAYHEW LIMITED
Buxhall, Stowmarket, Suffolk IP14 3BW
Compilation © Kevin Mayhew Ltd 2001

The right of Susie Hare to be identified as the compiler of this work has been asserted by her in accordance with the Copyright, Designs and Patents Act 1988.

The following editions are available:

Words edition   Catalogue No. 1400269
                     ISBN No. 1 84003 668 0
                     ISMN No. M 57004 804 5

Organ/Choir   Catalogue No. 1400270
                     ISBN No. 1 84003 669 9
                     ISMN No. M 57004 805 2

                     Music setter: Geoffrey Moore
                     Text setter: Fiona Connell Finch
                     Proof reader: Linda Ottewell
                     Cover design: Jonathan Stroulger

                     Printed in China

Foreword

Come, let us sing for joy to the Lord; let us shout aloud to the rock of our salvation. Let us come before him with thanksgiving and extol him with music and song.
Psalm 95:1-2.

It is inevitable that different streams of the Christian church should adopt distinctive styles of worship, thus creating their own tradition. Some churches are characterised by hymns which have stood the test of time, others by songs that were written yesterday. Neither is necessarily right or wrong but we are in danger of thinking that certain songs are exclusive to our particular tradition.

My heartfelt concern is for the many churches that seek to progress from the old but at the same time fight shy of the new. They find themselves in a gap between the two, often pursuing a style of worship that misses out on the richness of either and ends up being mediocre. We in the Christian family owe it to ourselves, and to the next generation, to embrace a greater diversity of musical expression, to be open to some 'cross-pollination' and thus to share in the blessings of God's gifts. We shall be sharing in the same songs when we worship the same Lord together in heaven; let's start now – here on earth!

The Bridge has been born out of a desire to cross the denominational, doctrinal and musical divide between churches and to provide worship leaders with a resource which aims to be imaginative, theologically sound and musically varied. It contains many hymns with which you will be familiar and, alongside their original tunes, some brand-new arrangements. It also includes many songs afforded us by the powerful outpouring of contemporary songwriters.

It has been a huge privilege to put together this compilation. I pray that you will find it meaningful, challenging and refreshingly different and that it will help to bring you into the presence of him who alone is worthy of our praise.

Susie Hare

Susie Hare is Music Director of St Mary's Church,
Eastrop, Basingstoke, Hampshire.

The Bridge

1 Abide with me

Henry Francis Lyte (1793-1847)　　　　　　　　　　William Henry Monk (1823-1889)

2. Swift to its close ebbs out life's little day;
   earth's joys grow dim, its glories pass away;
   change and decay in all around I see;
   O thou who changest not, abide with me.

3. I need thy presence ev'ry passing hour;
   what but thy grace can foil the tempter's pow'r?
   Who like thyself my guide and stay can be?
   Through cloud and sunshine, Lord, abide with me.

4. I fear no foe with thee at hand to bless;
   ills have no weight, and tears no bitterness.
   Where is death's sting? Where, grave, thy victory?
   I triumph still, if thou abide with me.

5. Hold thou thy cross before my closing eyes;
   shine through the gloom, and point me to the skies;
   heav'n's morning breaks, and earth's vain shadows flee;
   in life, in death, O Lord, abide with me.

2 Above the clash of creeds *No other way*

Graham Kendrick

Graham Kendrick (b.1950)

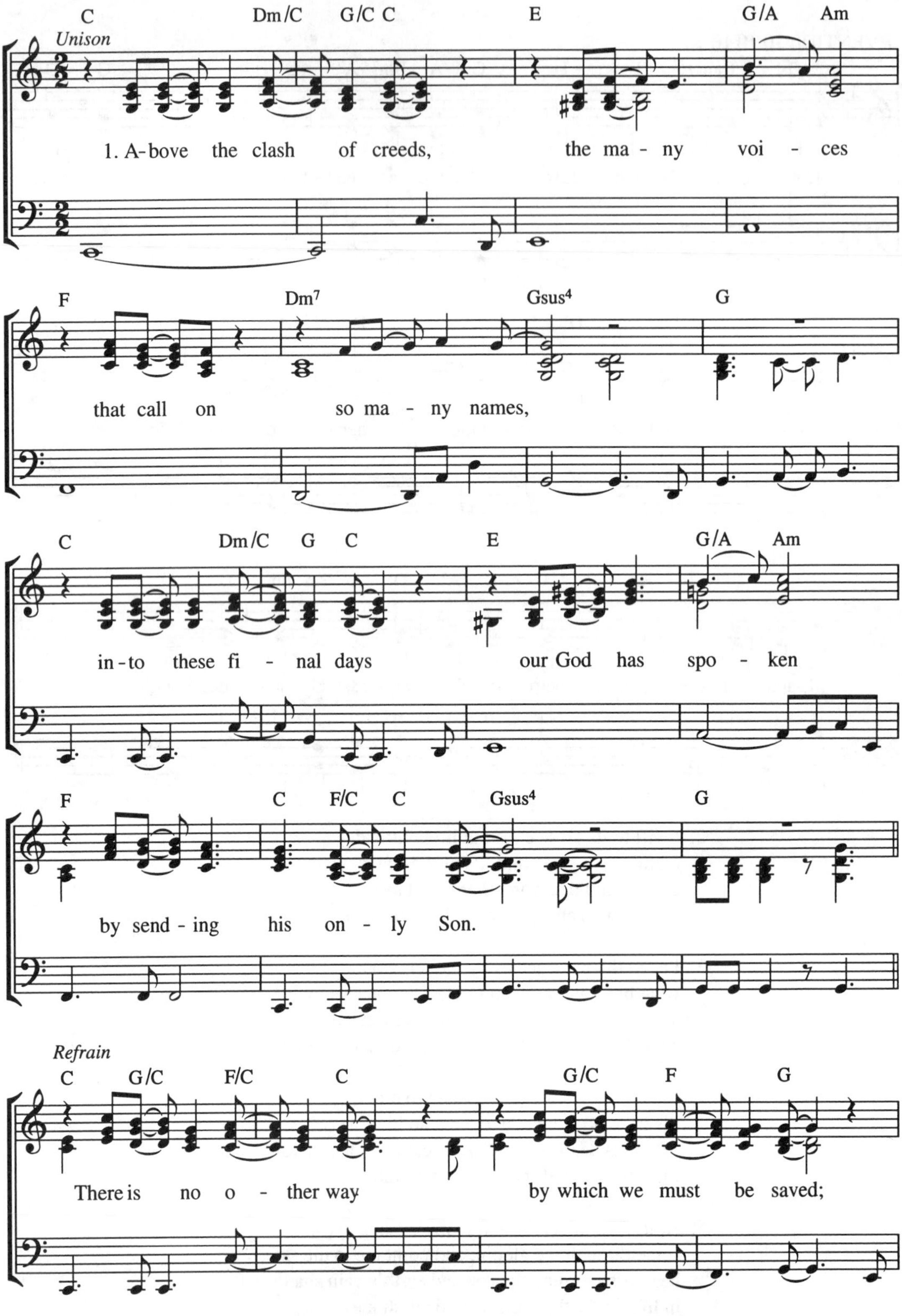
C Dm/C G/C C E G/A Am
Unison
1. A-bove the clash of creeds, the ma - ny voi - ces
F Dm7 Gsus4 G
that call on so ma - ny names,
C Dm/C G C E G/A Am
in-to these fi - nal days our God has spo - ken
F C F/C C Gsus4 G
by send - ing his on - ly Son.
Refrain
C G/C F/C C G/C F G
There is no o - ther way by which we must be saved;

his name is Je - sus, the on - ly Sa - viour; no o - ther sin -
- less life, no o - ther sac - ri - fice, in all cre -
a - tion no o - ther way.

2. Before we called he came
   to earth from heaven,
   our maker became a man;
   when no one else could pay,
   he bought our freedom,
   exchanging his life for ours.

3. Beneath the cross of Christ
   let earth fall silent
   in awe of this mystery;
   then let this song arise
   and fill the nations:
   O hear him call, 'Come to me.'

The Bridge

3 Abraham's Son

Hail to the King

Bob Baker

Bob Baker

4 Alas, and did my Saviour bleed

Isaac Watts

Bob Kauflin

2. Well might the sun in darkness hide and shut his glories in,
   when Christ, the mighty Maker, died for man the creature's sin.
   Thus might I hide my blushing face while his dear cross appears;
   dissolve my heart in thankfulness and melt my eyes to tears.

5 Alleluia, sing to Jesus!

William Chatterton Dix (1837-1898)

Rowland Huw Pritchard (1811-1887)
as in 'The Australian Hymn Book' 1977

HYFRYDOL 87 87 D

1. Al - le - lu - ia, sing to Je - sus! his the

scep - tre, his the throne; Al - le - lu - ia! - his the

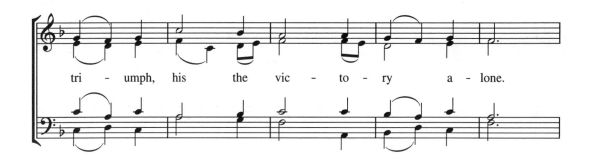

tri - umph, his the vic - to - ry a - lone.

Hear the songs of ho - ly Zi - on thun - der like a

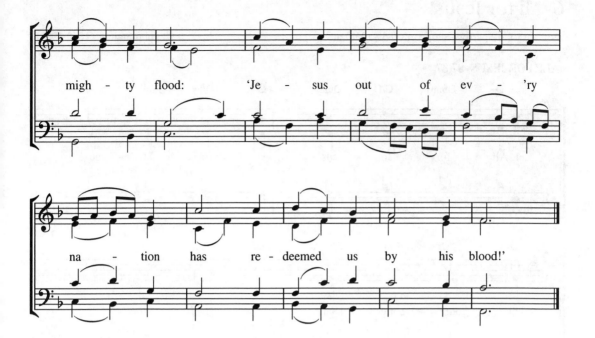

migh - ty flood: 'Je - sus out of ev - 'ry

na - tion has re - deemed us by his blood!'

2. Alleluia! – not as orphans
   are we left in sorrow now;
   Alleluia! – he is near us;
   faith believes, nor questions how.
   Though the cloud from sight received him
   whom the angels now adore,
   shall our hearts forget his promise,
   'I am with you evermore'?

3. Alleluia! – bread of heaven,
   here on earth our food, our stay;
   Alleluia! – here the sinful
   come to you from day to day.
   Intercessor, friend of sinners,
   earth's redeemer, plead for me,
   where the songs of all the sinless
   sweep across the crystal sea.

4. Alleluia, sing to Jesus!
   his the sceptre, his the throne;
   Alleluia! his the triumph,
   his the victory alone.
   Hear the songs of holy Zion
   thunder like a mighty flood:
   'Jesus out of ev'ry nation
   has redeemed us by his blood!'

6 All for Jesus!

William John Sparrow-Simpson (1859-1952) alt.

John Stainer (1840-1901)

ALL FOR JESUS 87 87

2. All for Jesus! thou wilt give us
   strength to serve thee hour by hour;
   none can move us from thy presence
   while we trust thy love and pow'r.

3. All for Jesus! at thine altar
   thou dost give us sweet content;
   there, dear Saviour, we receive thee
   in thy holy sacrament.

4. All for Jesus! thou hast loved us,
   all for Jesus! thou hast died,
   all for Jesus! thou art with us,
   all for Jesus, glorified!

5. All for Jesus! All for Jesus!
   This the Church's song shall be,
   till at last the flock is gathered
   one in love, and one in thee.

A lower setting

ALL FOR JESUS 87 87

2. All for Jesus! thou wilt give us
   strength to serve thee hour by hour;
   none can move us from thy presence
   while we trust thy love and pow'r.

3. All for Jesus! at thine altar
   thou dost give us sweet content;
   there, dear Saviour, we receive thee
   in thy holy sacrament.

4. All for Jesus! thou hast loved us,
   all for Jesus! thou hast died,
   all for Jesus! thou art with us,
   all for Jesus, glorified!

5. All for Jesus! All for Jesus!
   This the Church's song shall be,
   till at last the flock is gathered
   one in love, and one in thee.

The Bridge

7 All hail King Jesus!

Dave Moody

Dave Moody

Worshipfully with strength

All hail King Je - sus! All hail Em - man - u - el!

King of kings, Lord of lords, bright morn-ing star.

And through - out e - ter - ni - ty I'll sing your prai - ses,

and I'll reign with you through-out e - ter - ni - ty.

8 All hail the power of Jesus' name!

Edward Perronet (1726-1792)

William Shrubsole (1760-1806)

TUNE 1: MILES LANE CM

1. All hail the pow'r of Je-sus' name! let an-gels pros-trate fall; bring forth the roy-al di-a-dem and crown him, crown him, crown him, crown him Lord of all.

Edward Perronet (1726 - 1792)

James Ellor (1819-1899)

TUNE 2: DIADEM 86 86 extended

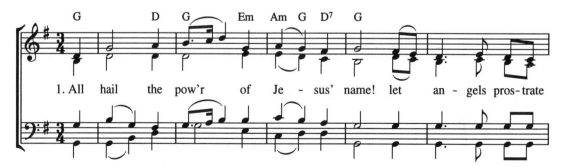

1. All hail the pow'r of Je-sus' name! let an-gels pros-trate

2. Crown him, ye martyrs of your God,
   who from his altar call,
   who from his altar call;
   praise him whose way of pain ye trod,
   and crown him, crown him, crown him,
   crown him Lord of all.

3. Ye prophets who our freedom won,
   ye searchers, great and small,
   ye searchers, great and small,
   by whom the work of truth is done,
   now crown him, crown him, crown him,
   crown him Lord of all.

4. Ye seed of Israel's chosen race,
   ye ransomed of the fall,
   ye ransomed of the fall,
   hail him who saves you by his grace,
   and crown him, crown him, crown him,
   crown him Lord of all.

5. Let ev'ry tribe and ev'ry tongue
   to him their hearts enthral,
   to him their hearts enthral;
   lift high the universal song,
   and crown him, crown him, crown him,
   crown him Lord of all.

6. O that, with yonder sacred throng,
   we at his feet may fall,
   we at his feet may fall,
   join in the everlasting song,
   and crown him, crown him, crown him,
   crown him Lord of all.

The Bridge

9 All heaven declares

Noel and Tricia Richards

Noel and Tricia Richards

1. All heav'n de - clares the glo - ry of the ri - sen Lord.
Who can com - pare with the beau - ty of the Lord?
For - e - ver he will be the Lamb up - on the throne.
I glad - ly bow the knee and wor - ship him a - lone.

2. I will proclaim
   the glory of the risen Lord.
   Who once was slain
   to reconcile us to God.
   For ever you will be
   the Lamb upon the throne.
   I gladly bow the knee
   and worship you alone.

10 All I once held dear

Knowing you

Graham Kendrick

Graham Kendrick (b.1950)

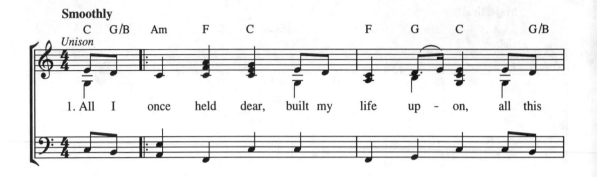

1. All I once held dear, built my life up - on, all this

world re - veres, and wars to own, all I once thought gain I have

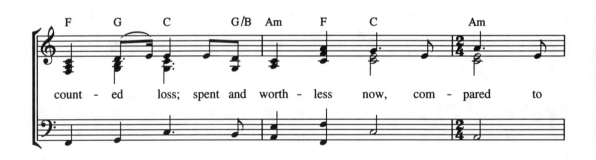

count - ed loss; spent and worth - less now, com - pared to

this. Know-ing you, Je-sus, know-ing you, there

2. Now my heart's desire
   is to know you more,
   to be found in you
   and known as yours.
   To possess by faith
   what I could not earn,
   all-surpassing gift
   of righteousness.

3. Oh, to know the pow'r
   of your risen life,
   and to know you in
   your sufferings.
   To become like you
   in your death, my Lord,
   so with you to live
   and never die.

11 All my days

Beautiful Saviour

Stuart Townend

Stuart Townend

1. All my days I will sing this song of glad - ness,
2. I will trust in the cross of my Re - deem - er,
3. I long to be where the praise is ne - ver - end - ing,

give my praise to the foun-tain of de - lights; for
I will sing of the blood that ne - ver fails, of
yearn to dwell where the glo - ry ne - ver fades, where

in my help - less - ness you heard my cry, and
sins for - gi - ven, of con - science cleansed, of
count - less wor - ship - pers will share one song, and

waves of mer - cy poured down on my life.
death de - fea - ted and life with - out end.
cries of 'wor-thy' will ho - nour the Lamb!

12 All my hope on God is founded

Paraphrased by Robert Bridges (1844-1930) alt.
based on 'Meine Hoffnung stehet feste'
by Joachim Neander (1650-1680)

Herbert Howells (1892-1983)

MICHAEL 87 87 33 7

2. Human pride and earthly glory,
   sword and crown betray his trust;
   what with care and toil he buildeth,
   tow'r and temple, fall to dust.
   But God's pow'r, hour by hour,
   is my temple and my tow'r.

3. God's great goodness aye endureth,
   deep his wisdom, passing thought:
   splendour, light and life attend him,
   beauty springeth out of naught.
   Evermore, from his store,
   new-born worlds rise and adore.

4. Still from earth to God eternal
   sacrifice of praise be done,
   high above all praises praising
   for the gift of Christ his Son.
   Christ doth call one and all:
   ye who follow shall not fall.

13 All people that on earth do dwell

William Kethe (d.1594), from 'Day's Psalter' (1560) alt.

From the 'Genevan Psalter' (1551)

OLD HUNDREDTH LM

1. All peo - ple that on earth do dwell, sing

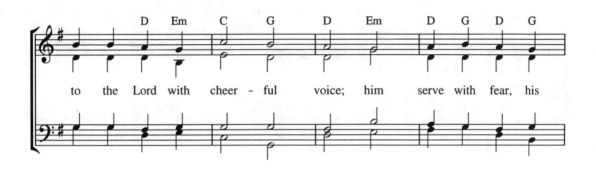

to the Lord with cheer - ful voice; him serve with fear, his

praise forth tell, come ye be - fore him and re - joice.

2. Know that the Lord is God indeed,
   without our aid he did us make;
   we are his flock, he doth us feed,
   and for his sheep he doth us take.

3. O enter then his gates with praise,
   approach with joy his courts unto;
   praise, laud and bless his name always,
   for it is seemly so to do.

4. For why? the Lord our God is good:
   his mercy is for ever sure;
   his truth at all times firmly stood,
   and shall from age to age endure.

5. Praise God from whom all blessings flow,
   praise him, all creatures here below,
   praise him above, ye heav'nly hosts:
   praise Father, Son and Holy Ghost.

14 All to Jesus I surrender

I surrender all

J.W. Van De Venter

W.S. Weedon

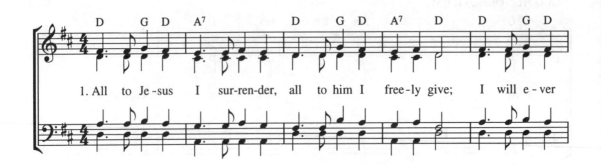

1. All to Je-sus I sur-ren-der, all to him I free-ly give; I will e-ver

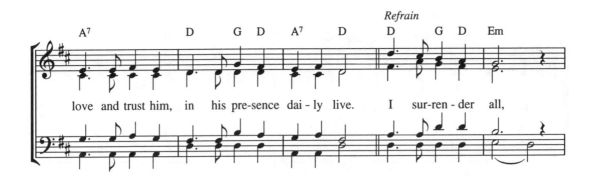

love and trust him, in his pre-sence dai-ly live. I sur-ren-der all,

I sur-ren-der all, all to thee, my bles-sed Sa-viour, I sur-ren-der all.

2. All to Jesus I surrender,
   humbly at his feet I bow;
   worldly pleasures all forsaken,
   take me, Jesus, take me now.

3. All to Jesus I surrender,
   make me, Saviour, wholly thine;
   let me feel the Holy Spirit,
   truly know that thou art mine.

4. All to Jesus I surrender,
   Lord, I give myself to thee;
   fill me with thy love and power,
   let thy blessing fall on me.

5. All to Jesus I surrender,
   now to feel the sacred flame;
   O, the joy of full salvation!
   Glory, glory to his name!

W.S. Weedon arr. Susie Hare

NEW ARRANGEMENT

1. All to Jesus I surrender, all to him I freely give;
I will ever love and trust him, in his presence daily live.

Refrain
I surrender all, I surrender all,
all to thee, my blessed Saviour, I surrender all.

2. All to Jesus I surrender,
humbly at his feet I bow;
worldly pleasures all forsaken,
take me, Jesus, take me now.

3. All to Jesus I surrender,
make me, Saviour, wholly thine;
let me feel the Holy Spirit,
truly know that thou art mine.

4. All to Jesus I surrender,
Lord, I give myself to thee;
fill me with thy love and power,
let thy blessing fall on me.

5. All to Jesus I surrender,
now to feel the sacred flame;
O, the joy of full salvation!
Glory, glory to his name!

15 Almighty God, my Redeemer

All things are possible

Darlene Zschech

Darlene Zschech

Lyrics underlaid in the music:

Al-migh-ty God, my Re-deem-er, my hid-ing-place,
My feet are plant-ed on this rock and I will not

my safe re-fuge, no o-ther name like Je-sus,
be sha-ken. My hope, it comes from you a-lone,

1. no pow'r can stand a-gainst you.

2. my Lord, and my sal-va-tion.

Your praise is al-ways on my lips, your word is liv-ing in my heart
You fill my life with grea-ter joy, yes, I de-light my-self in you

1, 3. and I will praise you with a new song, my soul will bless you, Lord.

16 Amazing grace!

vs. 1–4: John Newton alt.,
v.5: John Rees

American folk melody
arr. Richard Lloyd

AMAZING GRACE CM

2. 'Twas grace that taught my heart to fear,
   and grace my fears relieved.
   How precious did that grace appear
   the hour I first believed.

3. Through many dangers, toils and snares
   I have already come.
   'Tis grace that brought me safe thus far,
   and grace will lead me home.

4. The Lord has promised good to me,
   his word my hope secures;
   he will my shield and portion be
   as long as life endures.

5. Yes, when this heart and flesh shall fail,
   and mortal life shall cease,
   I shall possess within the veil
   a life of joy and peace.

6. When we've been there a thousand years,
   bright shining as the sun,
   we've no less days to sing God's praise
   than when we first begun.

American folk melody
arr. Susie Hare

NEW ARRANGEMENT

17 And can it be

Charles Wesley (1707-1788)

Thomas Campbell (1825-1876)

SAGINA 88 88 88 extended

1. And can it be that I should gain an in-t'rest in the Sa-viour's blood? Died he for me, who caused his pain? For me, who him to death pur-sued? A-maz-ing love! How can it be that thou, my God, shouldst die for

2. 'Tis myst'ry all! Th'Immortal dies:
   who can explore his strange design?
   In vain the first-born seraph tries
   to sound the depths of love divine!
   'Tis mercy all! Let earth adore,
   let angel minds inquire no more.

3. He left his Father's throne above
   so free, so infinite his grace;
   emptied himself of all but love,
   and bled for Adam's helpless race;
   'tis mercy all, immense and free;
   for, O my God, it found out me.

4. Long my imprisoned spirit lay
   fast bound in sin and nature's night;
   thine eye diffused a quick'ning ray,
   I woke, the dungeon flamed with light;
   my chains fell off, my heart was free;
   I rose, went forth, and followed thee.

5. No condemnation now I dread;
   Jesus, and all in him is mine!
   Alive in him, my living Head,
   and clothed in righteousness divine,
   bold I approach the eternal throne,
   and claim the crown, through Christ my own.

18 And he shall reign

Graham Kendrick

Graham Kendrick (b.1950)

2. He was given sov'reign power,
   glory and authority.
   Every nation, tribe and tongue
   worshipped him on bended knee.

3. On the throne for ever,
   see the Lamb who once was slain;
   wounds of sacrificial love
   for ever shall remain.

The Bridge

19 And now, O Father, mindful of the love

William Bright (1824-1901)

William Henry Monk (1823-1889)

UNDE ET MEMORES 10 10 10 10 10 10

1. And now, O Father, mindful of the love that bought us, once for all, on Cal-v'ry's tree, and hav-ing with us him that pleads a-bove, we here pre-sent, we here spread forth to thee that on-ly of-f'ring per-fect in thine eyes, the one true, pure, im-mor-tal sa-cri-fice.

2. Look, Father, look on his anointed face,
and only look on us as found in him;
look not on our misusings of thy grace,
our prayer so languid, and our faith so dim:
for lo, between our sins and their reward
we set the Passion of thy Son our Lord.

3. And then for those, our dearest and our best,
by this prevailing presence we appeal;
O fold them closer to thy mercy's breast,
O do thine utmost for their souls' true weal;
from tainting mischief keep them pure and clear,
and crown thy gifts with strength to persevere.

4. And so we come: O draw us to thy feet,
most patient Saviour, who canst love us still;
and by this food, so aweful and so sweet,
deliver us from ev'ry touch of ill:
in thine own service make us glad and free,
and grant us never more to part with thee.

20 Angels from the realms of glory

James Montgomery (1771-1854)

French or Flemish melody

IRIS 87 87 47

1. An-gels from the realms of glo - ry, wing your flight o'er all the earth;

ye, who sang cre - a - tion's sto - ry, now pro-claim Mes - si - ah's birth:

Refrain

Come

and wor - ship,

Come and

Christ, the new-born King; come

Come

and   wor - ship,   wor-ship Christ the   new - born King.

and

2. Shepherds in the field abiding,
   watching o'er your flocks by night,
   God with us is now residing,
   yonder shines the infant light:

3. Sages, leave your contemplations;
   brighter visions beam afar;
   seek the great desire of nations;
   ye have seen his natal star:

4. Saints, before the altar bending,
   watching long with hope and fear,
   suddenly the Lord, descending,
   in his temple shall appear:

21 Angel-voices ever singing

Francis Pott (1832-1909) alt.

Edwin George Monk (1819-1900)

ANGEL VOICES 85 85 843

1. An - gel - voi - ces e - ver sing - ing round thy throne of light,
an - gel - harps for e - ver ring - ing, rest not day nor night;
thou-sands on - ly live to bless thee, and con - fess thee Lord of might.

2. Thou who art beyond the farthest
   mortal eye can see,
   can it be that thou regardest
   our poor hymnody?
   Yes, we know that thou art near us
   and wilt hear us constantly.

3. Yea, we know that thou rejoicest
   o'er each work of thine;
   thou didst ears and hands and voices
   for thy praise design;
   craftsman's art and music's measure
   for thy pleasure all combine.

4. In thy house, great God, we offer
   of thine own to thee;
   and for thine acceptance proffer,
   all unworthily,
   hearts and minds and hands and voices
   in our choicest psalmody.

5. Honour, glory, might and merit
   thine shall ever be,
   Father, Son and Holy Spirit,
   blessèd Trinity.
   Of the best that thou hast given
   earth and heaven render thee.

22 As the deer pants

Martin J. Nystrom,
based on Psalm 42:1-2

Martin J. Nystrom

Flowing

Unison

1. As the deer pants for the wa-ter, so my soul longs af-ter you.

You a-lone are my heart's de-sire and I long to wor-ship you.

Refrain

You a-lone are my strength, my shield, to you a-lone may my spi-rit yield.

You a-lone are my heart's de-sire and I long to wor-ship you.

2. I want you more than gold or silver,
   only you can satisfy.
   You alone are the real joy-giver
   and the apple of my eye.

3. You're my friend and you are my brother,
   even though you are a King.
   I love you more than any other,
   so much more than anything.

23 As we see the world

Lex Loizides

Every place

Lex Loizides

Strong, slow 4

1. As we see the world in tat-ters, as we watch their

dreams break down, we can hear their qui-et an-guish: 'Come and

help us!' Brought to life by God's own Spi-rit, joined to-geth-er

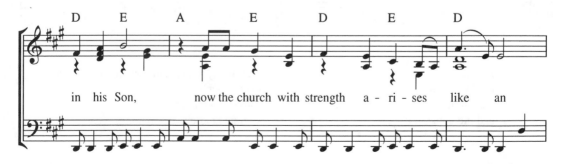

in his Son, now the church with strength a-ri-ses like an

2. In the midst of boastful darkness
   shines a light that cannot fail,
   and the blind behold his glory,
   Jesus! Jesus!
   Not content with restoration
   of the remnant in the land,
   he has filled us with his power
   for the nations.

24 At all times I will bless him

Let us exalt

Stuart Dauermann,
based on Psalm 34

Stuart Dauermann

Steadily ($\bullet$ = 116)

mf

1. At all times I will bless
(2.) an - gel of the Lord
(3.) child - ren, now and hear

him, his praise will be in my mouth – my soul makes its
en-camps round those who fear his name, to save them and de -
me if you would see long life: just keep your lips from

boast in the Lord. The hum - ble man will
li - ver them from harm. Though li - ons roar with
wick - ed - ness and lies. Do good and turn from

hear of him, the af - flict - ed will be glad and join with me to
hun - ger, we lack for no good thing: no won - der, then, we
e - vil, seek peace in - stead of strife, love right-eous-ness and

25 At the name of Jesus

Caroline Maria Noel (1817-1877) alt.

William Henry Monk (1823-1889)

TUNE 1: EVELYNS 65 65 D

1. At the name of Je - sus ev - 'ry knee shall bow,
ev - 'ry tongue con - fess him King of glo - ry now;
'tis the Fa - ther's plea - sure we should call him Lord,
who, from the be - gin - ning, was the migh - ty Word.

2. At his voice creation
   sprang at once to sight,
   all the angels' faces,
   all the hosts of light,
   thrones and dominations,
   stars upon their way,
   all the heav'nly orders
   in their great array.

3. Humbled for a season,
   to receive a name
   from the lips of sinners
   unto whom he came,
   faithfully he bore it,
   spotless to the last,
   brought it back victorious
   when from death he passed.

4. Bore it up triumphant,
   with its human light,
   through all ranks of creatures
   to the central height,
   to the throne of Godhead,
   to the Father's breast,
   filled it with the glory
   of that perfect rest.

5. All creation, name him,
   with love as strong as death;
   but with awe and wonder,
   and with bated breath.
   He is God the Saviour,
   he is Christ the Lord,
   ever to be worshipped,
   trusted and adored.

6. In your hearts enthrone him;
   there let him subdue
   all that is not holy,
   all that is not true;
   crown him as your captain
   in temptation's hour;
   let his will enfold you
   in its light and pow'r.

7. Truly, this Lord Jesus
   shall return again,
   with his Father's glory,
   with his angel train;
   for all wreaths of empire
   meet upon his brow,
   and our hearts confess him
   King of glory now.

Caroline Maria Noel (1817-1877) alt.

Michael Brierley (b.1932)

TUNE 2: CAMBERWELL 65 65 D

1. At the name of Je - sus ev - 'ry knee shall bow, ev - 'ry tongue con - fess him King of glo - ry now; 'tis the Fa - ther's plea - sure we should call him Lord, who, from the be - gin - ning, was the migh - ty Word. now.

26 At this time of giving

The giving song

Graham Kendrick

Graham Kendrick (b.1950)

Accelerating with each verse

Unison

At this time of giv-ing, glad-ly now we bring

gifts of good-ness and mer-cy from a heav'n-ly King.

1. Earth could not con-tain the trea-sures hea-ven holds for you,

per-fect joy and last-ing plea-sures,

love   so   strong   and   true.

2. May his tender love surround you
   at this Christmastime;
   may you see his smiling face
   that in the darkness shines.

3. But the many gifts he gives
   are all poured out from one;
   come, receive the greatest gift,
   the gift of God's own Son.

Last two refrains and verses:
   Lai, lai, lai . . . *etc.*

27 At your feet we fall

David Fellingham

David Fellingham

With steady strength

1. At your feet we fall, migh-ty ri-sen Lord, as we come be-fore your throne to wor-ship you. By your Spi-rit's pow'r you now draw our hearts, and we hear your voice in

2. There we see you stand, mighty risen Lord,
   clothed in garments pure and holy, shining bright.
   Eyes of flashing fire, feet like burnished bronze,
   and the sound of many waters is your voice.

3. Like the shining sun in its noonday strength,
   we now see the glory of your wondrous face.
   Once that face was marred, but now you're glorified,
   and your words like a two-edged sword have mighty pow'r.

28 Awake, awake, O Zion

Our God reigns

Nathan Fellingham

Nathan Fellingham

With strength
Unison Capo 3
B♭ G C A Dm7 Bm7 B♭ G C A Dm7 Bm7
1. A - wake, a - wake, O Zi - on, and clothe your - self with strength, shake
you have been re - deemed by the pre - cious blood of Je - sus, and
B♭ G C A
1. Dm7 Bm7 C/E A/C♯ Fsus4 Dsus4 F D
off your dust and fix your eyes on him. For
now you sit en -
2. Dm7 Bm7 C/E A/C♯ Fsus4 Dsus4 F D
Refrain
F D C/E A/C♯
throned with him. Our God reigns, he is
voice and
B♭2 G2 Csus4 Asus4 C A F D C/E A/C♯
king of all the earth, our God reigns, and he's
sing a song of praise, our God reigns, the

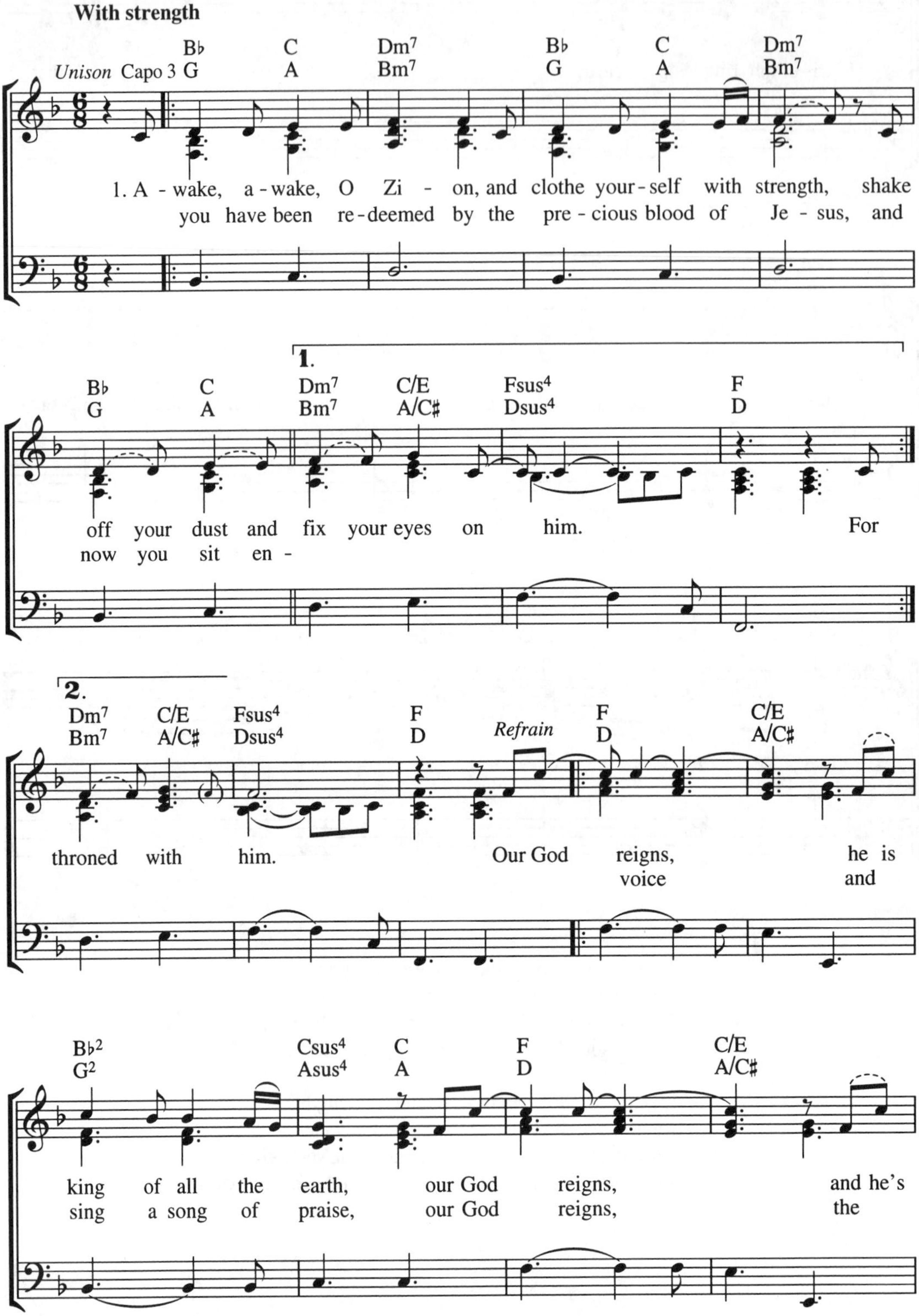

2. How beautiful the feet are
   of those who bring good news,
   for they proclaim the peace that comes from God.
   Rise up you holy nation,
   proclaim the great salvation,
   and say to Zion: 'Your God reigns'.

3. The watchmen lift their voices,
   and raise a shout of joy,
   for he will come again.
   Then all eyes will see the
   salvation of our God,
   for he has redeemed Jerusalem.

29 Beautiful Lord, wonderful Saviour   *The Potter's hand*

Darlene Zschech

Darlene Zschech

Beau - ti -ful Lord, won - der - ful Sa - viour, I know for sure

all of my days are held in your hand, craft-ed in - to your

per - fect plan. You gent-ly call me

in - to your pre - sence, guid-ing me by your Ho - ly Spi - rit;

teach me, dear Lord, to live all of my life through your

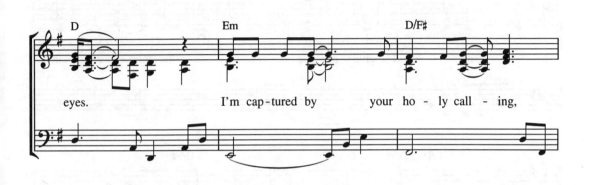

eyes. I'm cap-tured by your ho - ly call - ing,

set me a - part, I know you're draw - ing me to your-self;

lead me, Lord, I pray.

The Bridge

30 Before the throne of God above

Charitie L. Bancroft (1841-92)

Vikki Cook

Majestically

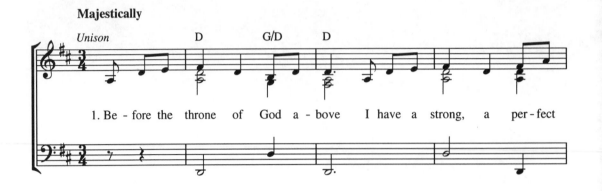

1. Be - fore the throne of God a - bove I have a strong, a per - fect

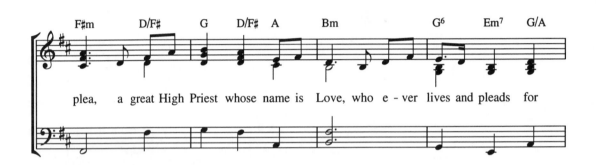

plea, a great High Priest whose name is Love, who e - ver lives and pleads for

me. My name is gra - ven on his hands, my name is writ - ten on his

heart; I know that while in heav'n he stands no tongue can

bid me thence de – part, no tongue can bid me thence de – part.

2. When Satan tempts me to despair,
   and tells me of the guilt within,
   upward I look and see him there
   who made an end to all my sin.
   Because the sinless Saviour died,
   my sinful soul is counted free;
   for God the Just is satisfied
   to look on him and pardon me,
   to look on him and pardon me.

3. Behold him there! The risen Lamb,
   my perfect, spotless righteousness;
   the great unchangeable I Am,
   the King of glory and of grace!
   One with himself I cannot die,
   my soul is purchased with his blood;
   my life is hid with Christ on high,
   with Christ, my Saviour and my God,
   with Christ, my Saviour and my God.

31 Before the world began

So you would come

Russell Fragar

Russell Fragar

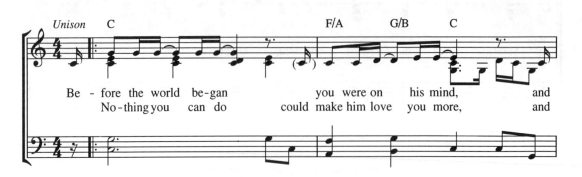

Be - fore the world be-gan you were on his mind, and
No-thing you can do could make him love you more, and

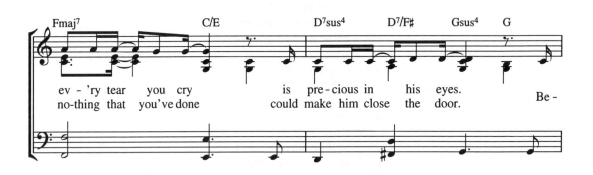

ev - 'ry tear you cry is pre-cious in his eyes.
no-thing that you've done could make him close the door. Be -

cause of his great love, he gave his on - ly Son;

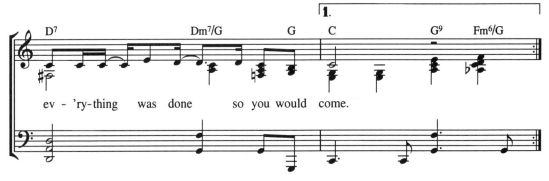

ev - 'ry-thing was done so you would come.

2.

Refrain

come. Come to the Fa - ther though your gift is small,

bro - ken hearts, bro - ken lives, he will take them all. The

pow - er of the word, the pow - er of his blood,

ev - 'ry-thing was done so you would come.

32 Beneath the cross of Jesus

Elizabeth Cecilia Clephane (1830-1869)   Ira David Sankey (1840-1908)

BENEATH THE CROSS OF JESUS 76 86 86 86

1. Be - neath the cross of Je - sus I fain would take my stand; the
sha - dow of a migh - ty rock with - in a wea - ry land. A
home with - in a wild - er - ness, a rest up - on the way, from the
burn - ing of the noon - tide heat and the bur - den of the day.

2. Upon that cross of Jesus
   mine eye, at times, can see
   the very dying form of one
   who suffered there for me.
   And from my stricken heart, with tears
   two wonders I confess:
   the wonders of redeeming love,
   and my own unworthiness.

3. I take, O cross, thy shadow,
   for my abiding place!
   I ask no other sunshine than
   the sunshine of his face;
   content to let the world go by,
   to know no gain nor loss:
   my sinful self my only shame,
   my glory all, the cross.

Ira David Sankey (1840-1908)
arr. Susie Hare

NEW ARRANGEMENT

Unison

1. Be - neath the cross of Je - sus I fain would take my stand; the
sha - dow of a migh - ty rock with - in a wea - ry land. A
home with - in a wild - er - ness, a rest up - on the way, from the
burn - ing of the noon - tide heat and the bur - den of the day.

2. Upon that cross of Jesus
   mine eye, at times, can see
   the very dying form of one
   who suffered there for me.
   And from my stricken heart, with tears
   two wonders I confess:
   the wonders of redeeming love,
   and my own unworthiness.

3. I take, O cross, thy shadow,
   for my abiding place!
   I ask no other sunshine than
   the sunshine of his face;
   content to let the world go by,
   to know no gain nor loss:
   my sinful self my only shame,
   my glory all, the cross.

The Bridge

33 Be still, for the presence of the Lord

David J. Evans

David J. Evans (b.1957)

2. Be still, for the glory of the Lord is shining all around;
   he burns with holy fire, with splendour he is crowned.
   How awesome is the sight, our radiant King of light!
   Be still, for the glory of the Lord is shining all around.

3. Be still, for the power of the Lord is moving in this place;
   he comes to cleanse and heal, to minister his grace.
   No work too hard for him, in faith receive from him.
   Be still, for the power of the Lord is moving in this place.

34 Be still, my soul

Katharina Von Schlegal (b.1697)
trans. Jane L. Borthwick, alt.

Jean Sibelius (1865-1957)

FINLANDIA 10 10 10 10 10 10

1. Be still, my soul: the Lord is on your side; bear pa-tient-

ly the cross of grief and pain; leave to your God to

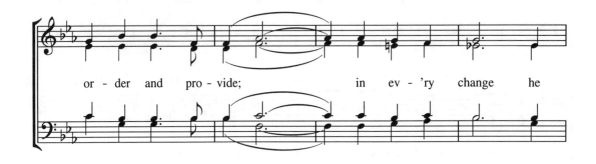

or - der and pro - vide; in ev - 'ry change he

faith-ful will re - main. Be still, my soul: your best, your heav'n - ly

friend, through thor - ny ways, leads to a joy - ful end.

2. Be still, my soul: your God will undertake
   to guide the future as he has the past.
   Your hope, your confidence let nothing shake,
   all now mysterious shall be clear at last.
   Be still, my soul: the tempests still obey
   his voice, who ruled them once on Galilee.

3. Be still, my soul: the hour is hastening on
   when we shall be for ever with the Lord,
   when disappointment, grief and fear are gone,
   sorrow forgotten, love's pure joy restored.
   Be still, my soul: when change and tears are past,
   all safe and blessèd we shall meet at last.

35 Be still my soul (Noblitt)

Kim Noblitt,
based on Psalm 46

Kim Noblitt

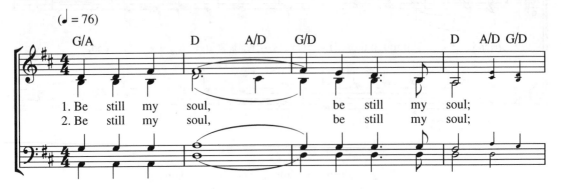

1. Be still my soul, be still my soul;
2. Be still my soul, be still my soul;

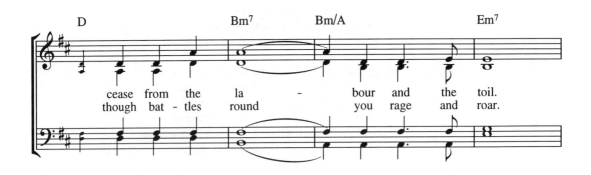

cease from the la - bour and the toil.
though bat - tles round you rage and roar.

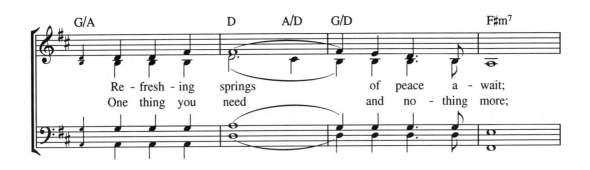

Re - fresh - ing springs of peace a - wait;
One thing you need and no - thing more;

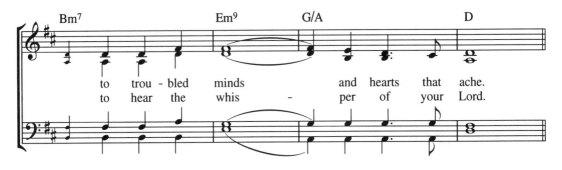

to trou - bled minds and hearts that ache.
to hear the whis - per of your Lord.

Refrain

Be still my soul, God knows your way;
'Be still, my child, I know your way;

and he will guide for his name's sake.
and I will guide for my name's sake.

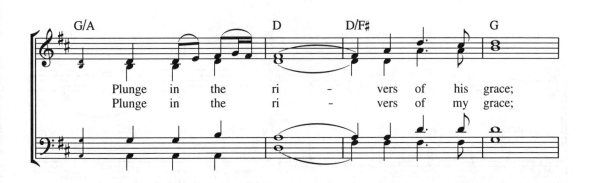

Plunge in the ri - vers of his grace;
Plunge in the ri - vers of my grace;

rest in the arms of his em - brace.
rest in the arms of my em - brace.'

36 Be thou my vision

Irish (c.8th century)
trans. Mary Byrne and Eleanor Hull

Traditional Irish melody
arr. Colin Hand

2. Be thou my wisdom, be thou my true word,
   I ever with thee and thou with me, Lord;
   thou my great Father, and I thy true heir;
   thou in me dwelling, and I in thy care.

3. Be thou my breastplate, my sword for the fight,
   be thou my armour, and be thou my might,
   thou my soul's shelter, and thou my high tow'r,
   raise thou me heav'nward, O Pow'r of my pow'r.

4. Riches I need not, nor all the world's praise,
   thou my inheritance through all my days;
   thou, and thou only, the first in my heart,
   high King of heaven, my treasure thou art!

5. High King of heaven, when battle is done,
   grant heaven's joys to me, O bright heav'n's sun;
   Christ of my own heart, whatever befall,
   still be my vision, O Ruler of all.

See over for another arrangement.

Traditional Irish melody
arr. Susie Hare

NEW ARRANGEMENT

1. Be thou my vi - sion, O Lord of my

heart, be all else but naught to me,

save that thou art; be thou my best

thought in the day and the night, both

wa - king and sleep - ing, thy pre - sence my

light.   light.

2. Be thou my wisdom, be thou my true word,
   be thou ever with me and I with thee, Lord;
   be thou my great Father, and I thy true heir;
   be thou in me dwelling, and I in thy care.

3. Be thou my breastplate, my sword for the fight;
   be thou my whole armour, be thou my true might;
   be thou my soul's shelter, be thou my strong tow'r;
   O raise thou me heav'nward, great Pow'r of my pow'r.

4. Riches I need not, nor all the world's praise;
   be thou my inheritance now and always;
   be thou, and thou only, the first in my heart;
   O Sov'reign of heaven, my treasure thou art.

5. High King of heaven, thou heaven's bright sun,
   O grant me its joys after vict'ry is won;
   great heart of my own heart, whatever befall,
   still thou be my vision, O Ruler of all.

Verse 5 descant

5. High King of hea - ven, thou hea - ven's bright sun, O

grant me its joys af - ter vic - t'ry is won; great

heart of my own heart, what - e - ver be - fall, still

thou be my vi - sion, O Ru - ler of all.

37 Blessed assurance

Frances Jane van Alstyne
(Fanny J. Crosby) (1820-1915)

Pheobe Palmer Knapp (1839-1908)

BLESSED ASSURANCE Irregular

1. Bles - sed as - sur - ance, Je - sus is mine: O what a

fore - taste of glo - ry di - vine! Heir of sal - va - tion, pur - chase of

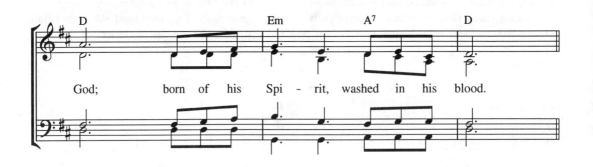

God; born of his Spi - rit, washed in his blood.

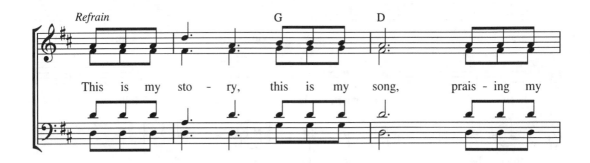

Refrain

This is my sto - ry, this is my song, prais - ing my

Sa - viour all the day long. This is my sto - ry, this is my

song, prais - ing my Sa - viour all the day long.

2. Perfect submission, perfect delight,
   visions of rapture burst on my sight;
   angels descending, bring from above
   echoes of mercy, whispers of love.

3. Perfect submission, all is at rest,
   I in my Saviour am happy and blessed;
   watching and waiting, looking above,
   filled with his goodness, lost in his love.

See over for another arrangement.

Pheobe Palmer Knapp (1839-1908)
arr. Susie Hare

NEW ARRANGEMENT

Worshipfully

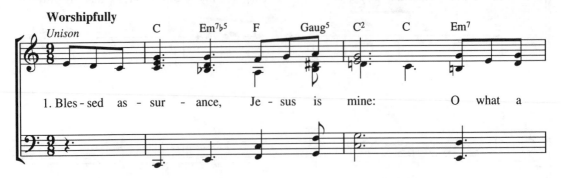

1. Bles - sed as - sur - ance, Je - sus is mine: O what a

fore - taste of glo - ry di - vine! Heir of sal - va - tion, pur-chase of

God; born of his Spi - rit, washed in his blood.

Refrain

This is my sto - ry, this is my song, prais - ing my

2. Perfect submission, perfect delight,
   visions of rapture burst on my sight;
   angels descending, bring from above
   echoes of mercy, whispers of love.

3. Perfect submission, all is at rest,
   I in my Saviour am happy and blessed;
   watching and waiting, looking above,
   filled with his goodness, lost in his love.

38 Blessing and honour

Ancient of Days

Gary Sadler and Jamie Harvill

Gary Sadler and Jamie Harvill

With an 'island' feel

Bless - ing and ho - nour, glo - ry and pow - er be un - to the An - cient of Days; from ev - 'ry na - tion, all of cre - a - tion bow be - fore the An - cient of Days. Ev-'ry tongue in hea-ven and earth shall de - clare your glo - ry, ev - 'ry knee shall bow at your throne

The Bridge

39 Break thou the bread of life

Mary A. Lathbury (1841-1913)

W.F. Sherwin (1826-1888)

LATHBURY 10 10 10 10

1. Break thou the bread of life, dear Lord, to me, as thou didst break the loaves be-side the sea: be-yond the sa-cred page I seek thee, Lord; my spi-rit pants for thee, O liv-ing Word.

2. Thou art the Bread of Life,
   O Lord, to me,
   thy holy word the truth
   that saveth me;
   give me to eat and live
   with thee above,
   teach me to love thy truth,
   for thou art love.

3. O send thy Spirit, Lord,
   now unto me,
   that he may touch my eyes
   and make me see;
   show me the truth concealed
   within thy word,
   and in thy book revealed,
   I see thee, Lord.

4. Bless thou the truth, dear Lord,
   to me, to me,
   as thou didst bless the loaves
   by Galilee;
   then shall all bondage cease,
   all fetters fall,
   and I shall find my peace,
   my all in all.

40 Breathe on me, Breath of God

Edwin Hatch (1835-1889),
adapted by David Fellingham

David Fellingham

1. Breathe on me, Breath of God, and fill my life a-new; that I may love as you love, and do the works that you do. Ho-ly Spi-rit, breathe on me.

2. Breathe on me, Breath of God,
   until my heart is pure;
   until my will is one with yours
   let holiness and love endure.
   Holy Spirit, breathe on me.

The Bridge

41 Breathe on me, Breath of God

Edwin Hatch (1835-1889)   Charles Lockhart (1745-1815)

CARLISLE SM

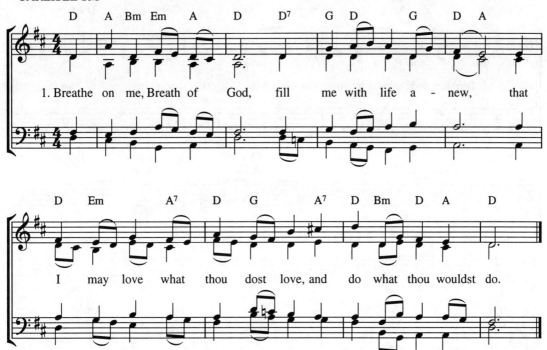

1. Breathe on me, Breath of God, fill me with life a - new, that I may love what thou dost love, and do what thou wouldst do.

2. Breathe on me, Breath of God,
   until my heart is pure:
   until with thee I have one will
   to do and to endure.

3. Breathe on me, Breath of God,
   till I am wholly thine,
   until this earthly part of me
   glows with thy fire divine.

4. Breathe on me, Breath of God,
   so shall I never die,
   but live with thee the perfect life
   of thine eternity.

42 Broken and melted

The past is done

Susie Hare

Susie Hare

2. Broken for ever are the chains that held
the life which once was cold before you.
Yielding to you, a heart which once rebelled;
your Spirit's love has made me new.

43 Broken for me

Janet Lunt

2. Come to my table and with me dine;
   eat of my bread and drink of my wine.

3. This is my body given for you;
   eat it remembering I died for you.

4. This is my blood I shed for you,
   for your forgiveness, making you new.

44 By your side

Noel and Tricia Richards

Noel and Tricia Richards

Tenderly

By your side I would stay;

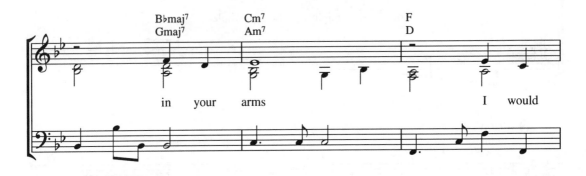

in your arms I would

lay. Je - sus, lo - ver of my

soul, no - thing from you

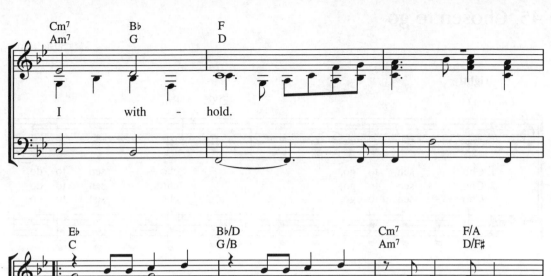

I with - hold.

Lord, I love you, and a - dore you; what more can I

say? You cause my love to grow strong - er

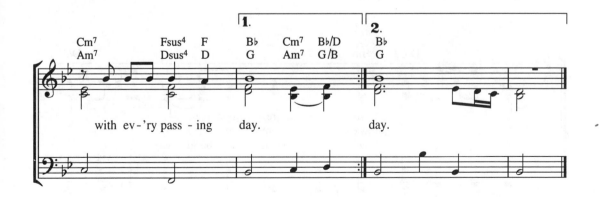

with ev - 'ry pass - ing day. day.

45 Chosen to go

Susie Hare

Susie Hare

Brightly

1. Cho - sen to go, cho - sen to do,
2. Cho - sen to go, cho - sen to do,
3. Cho - sen to go, cho - sen to do,

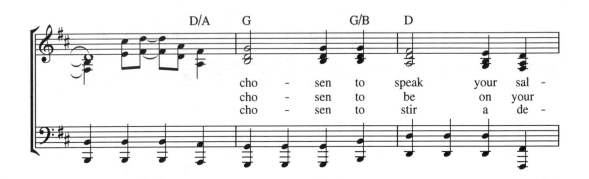

cho - sen to speak your sal -
cho - sen to be on your
cho - sen to stir a de -

va - tion; we are your hands,
mis - sion; we want to give,
sire; we want to reach,

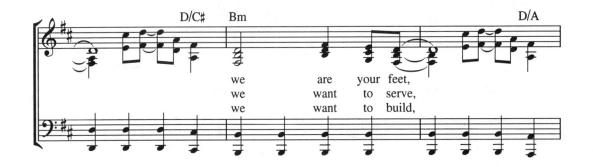

we are your feet,
we want to serve,
we want to build,

The Bridge

46 Christians, awake!

John Byrom (1692-1763) alt.

John Wainwright (1723-1768)

YORKSHIRE (STOCKPORT) 10 10 10 10 10 10

1. Christ - ians, a - wake! sa - lute the hap - py morn, where - on the

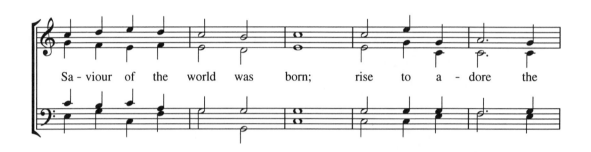

Sa - viour of the world was born; rise to a - dore the

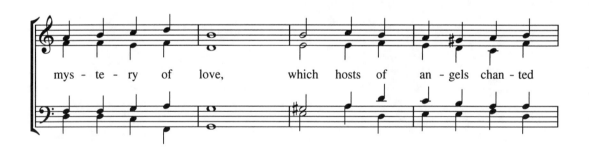

mys - te - ry of love, which hosts of an - gels chan - ted

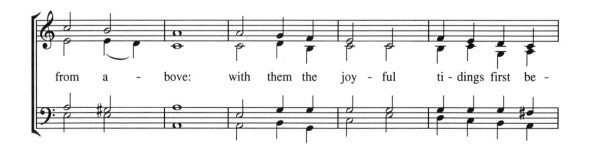

from a - bove: with them the joy - ful ti - dings first be -

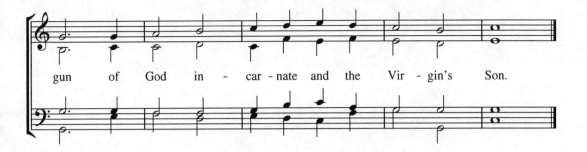

gun of God in - car - nate and the Vir - gin's Son.

2. Then to the watchful shepherds it was told,
   who heard th'angelic herald's voice, 'Behold,
   I bring good tidings of a Saviour's birth
   to you and all the nations on the earth:
   this day hath God fulfilled his promised word,
   this day is born a Saviour, Christ the Lord.'

3. He spake; and straightway the celestial choir
   in hymns of joy, unknown before, conspire;
   the praises of redeeming love they sang,
   and heav'n's whole orb with alleluias rang:
   God's highest glory was their anthem still,
   peace on the earth, in ev'ry heart good will.

4. To Bethl'em straight th' enlightened shepherds ran,
   to see, unfolding, God's eternal plan,
   and found, with Joseph and the blessèd maid,
   her Son, the Saviour, in a manger laid:
   then to their flocks, still praising God, return,
   and their glad hearts with holy rapture burn.

5. O may we keep and ponder in our mind
   God's wondrous love in saving lost mankind;
   trace we the babe, who hath retrieved our loss,
   from his poor manger to his bitter cross;
   tread in his steps, assisted by his grace,
   till our first heav'nly state again takes place.

6. Then may we hope, th'angelic hosts among,
   to sing, redeemed, a glad triumphal song:
   he that was born upon this joyful day
   around us all his glory shall display;
   saved by his love, incessant we shall sing
   eternal praise to heav'n's almighty King.

The Bridge

47 Christ is made the sure foundation

'Urbs beata Jerusalem' (c.7th century)
trans. John Mason Neale (1818-1866) alt.

Henry Purcell (1659-1695)
arr. E. Hawkins (1802-1868)

WESTMINSTER ABBEY 87 87 87

1. Christ is made the sure foun-da-tion, Christ the head and cor-ner-stone, cho-sen of the Lord, and pre-cious, bind-ing all the Church in one, ho-ly Zi-on's help for e-ver, and her con-fi-dence a-lone.

2. To this temple, where we call you,
   come, O Lord of hosts, today;
   you have promised loving kindness,
   hear your servants as we pray,
   bless your people now before you,
   turn our darkness into day.

3. Hear the cry of all your people,
   what they ask and hope to gain;
   what they gain from you, for ever
   with your chosen to retain,
   and hereafter in your glory
   evermore with you to reign.

4. Praise and honour to the Father,
   praise and honour to the Son,
   praise and honour to the Spirit,
   ever Three and ever One,
   One in might and One in glory,
   while unending ages run.

48 Christ triumphant

Michael Saward (b.1932)   Michael Baughen (b.1930)

TUNE 1: CHRIST TRIUMPHANT 85 85 and Refrain

1. Christ tri-um-phant, e-ver reign-ing, Sa-viour, Mas-ter, King.
Lord of heav'n, our lives sus-tain-ing, hear us as we sing:

Refrain
Yours the glo-ry and the crown, the high re-nown, the e-ter-nal name.

2. Word incarnate, truth revealing,
Son of Man on earth!
Pow'r and majesty concealing
by your humble birth:

3. Suff'ring servant, scorned, ill-treated,
victim crucified!
Death is through the cross defeated,
sinners justified:

4. Priestly King, enthroned for ever
high in heav'n above!
Sin and death and hell shall never
stifle hymns of love:

5. So, our hearts and voices raising
through the ages long,
ceaselessly upon you gazing,
this shall be our song:

Michael Saward (b.1932)　　　　　　　　　　　　　　　　　John Barnard (b.1948)

TUNE 2: GUITING POWER 85 85 and Refrain

Unison

1. Christ tri-um-phant, e - ver reign-ing, Sa - viour, Mas - ter, King. Lord of heav'n, our lives sus - tain - ing, hear us as we sing:

Refrain

Yours the glo - ry and the crown, the high re-nown, the e - ter - nal name.

2. Word incarnate, truth revealing,
   Son of Man on earth!
   Pow'r and majesty concealing
   by your humble birth:

3. Suff'ring servant, scorned, ill-treated,
   victim crucified!
   Death is through the cross defeated,
   sinners justified:

4. Priestly King, enthroned for ever
   high in heav'n above!
   Sin and death and hell shall never
   stifle hymns of love:

5. So, our hearts and voices raising
   through the ages long,
   ceaselessly upon you gazing,
   this shall be our song:

49 Come and see

We worship at your feet

Graham Kendrick

Graham Kendrick (b.1950)

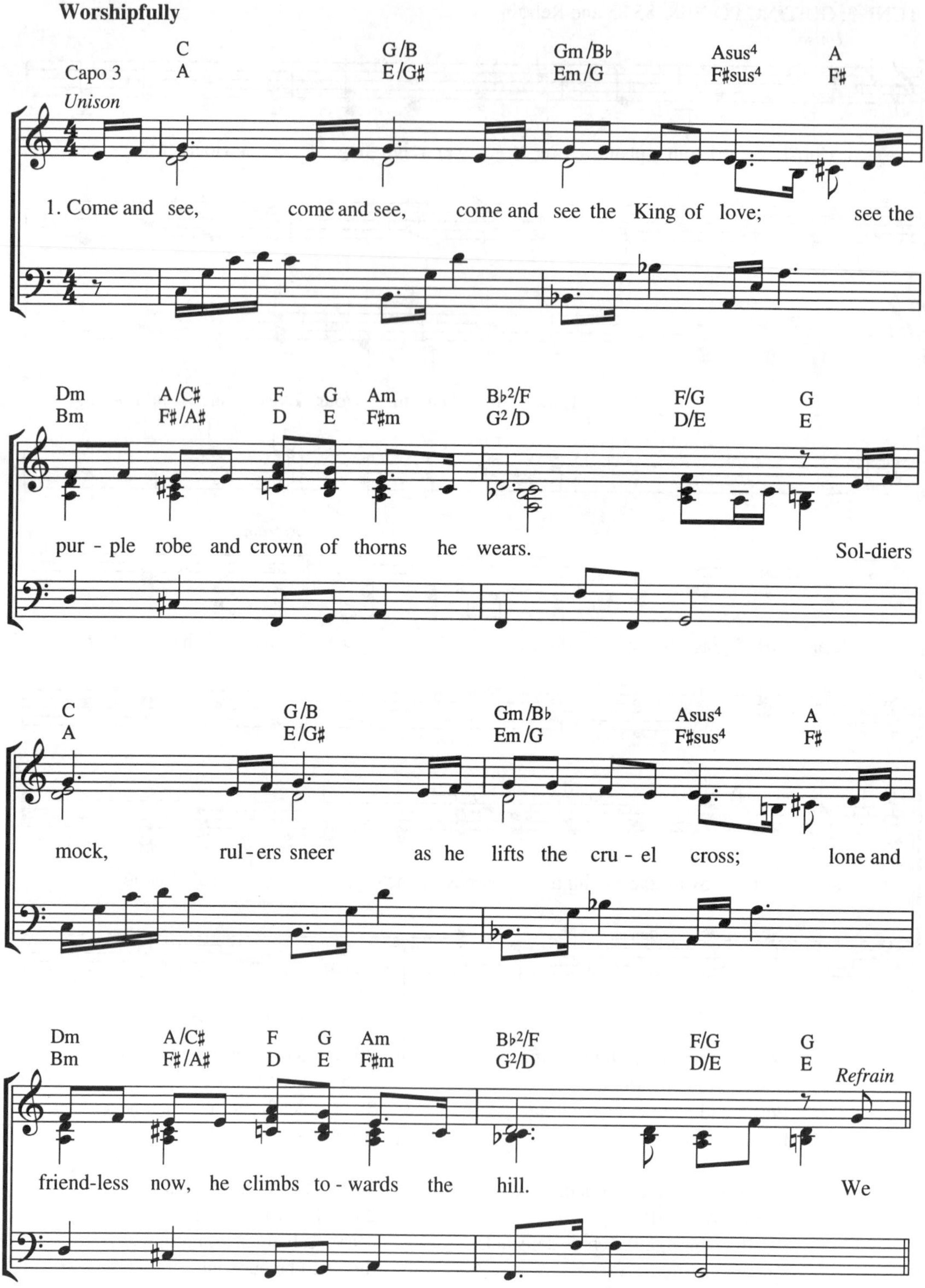
Worshipfully
Capo 3
C A
G/B E/G♯
Gm/B♭ Em/G
Asus4 F♯sus4
A F♯
Unison
1. Come and see, come and see, come and see the King of love; see the
Dm Bm
A/C♯ F♯/A♯
F D
G E
Am F♯m
B♭2/F G2/D
F/G D/E
G E
pur - ple robe and crown of thorns he wears. Sol-diers
C A
G/B E/G♯
Gm/B♭ Em/G
Asus4 F♯sus4
A F♯
mock, rul - ers sneer as he lifts the cru - el cross; lone and
Dm Bm
A/C♯ F♯/A♯
F D
G E
Am F♯m
B♭2/F G2/D
F/G D/E
G E
Refrain
friend-less now, he climbs to - wards the hill. We

2. Come and weep, come and mourn
   for your sin that pierced him there;
   so much deeper than the wounds of thorn and nail.
   All our pride, all our greed,
   all our fallenness and shame;
   and the Lord has laid the punishment on him.

3. Man of heaven, born to earth
   to restore us to your heaven.
   Here we bow in awe beneath your searching eyes.
   From your tears comes our joy,
   from your death our life shall spring;
   by your resurrection power we shall rise.

50 Come down, O Love divine

'Discendi, amor santo' by Bianco da Siena (d.1434)
trans. Richard F. Littledale (1833-1890) alt.

Ralph Vaughan Williams (1872-1958)

TUNE 1: DOWN AMPNEY 66 11 D

1. Come down, O Love di - vine, seek thou this soul of

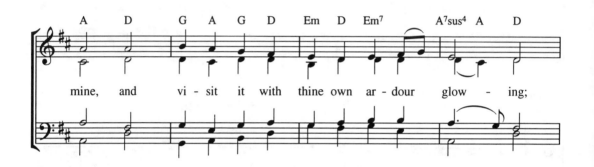

mine, and vi - sit it with thine own ar - dour glow - ing;

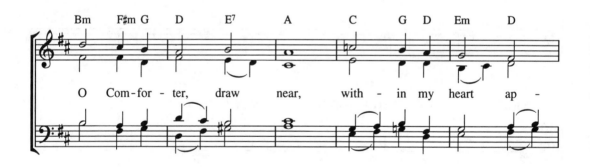

O Com - for - ter, draw near, with - in my heart ap -

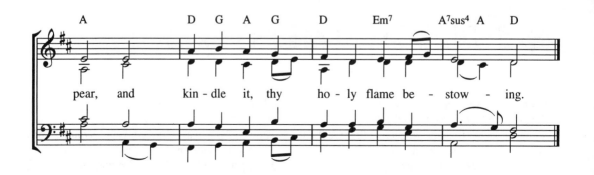

pear, and kin - dle it, thy ho - ly flame be - stow - ing.

2. O let it freely burn,
    till earthly passions turn
    to dust and ashes in its heat consuming;
    and let thy glorious light
    shine ever on my sight,
    and clothe me round, the while my path illuming.

3. Let holy charity
    mine outward vesture be,
    and lowliness become mine inner clothing;
    true lowliness of heart,
    which takes the humbler part,
    and o'er its own shortcomings weeps with loathing.

4. And so the yearning strong,
    with which the soul will long,
    shall far outpass the pow'r of human telling;
    nor can we guess its grace,
    till we become the place
    wherein the Holy Spirit makes his dwelling.

See over for another tune.

'Discendi, amor santo' by Bianco da Siena (d.1434)
trans. Richard F. Littledale (1833-1890) alt.

Roger Mayor

TUNE 2: YEARNING

2. O let it freely burn,
   till earthly passions turn
   to dust and ashes in its heat consuming;
   and let thy glorious light
   shine ever on my sight,
   and clothe me round, the while my path illuming.

3. Let holy charity
   mine outward vesture be,
   and lowliness become mine inner clothing;
   true lowliness of heart,
   which takes the humbler part,
   and o'er its own shortcomings weeps with loathing.

4. And so the yearning strong,
   with which the soul will long,
   shall far outpass the pow'r of human telling;
   nor can we guess its grace,
   till we become the place
   wherein the Holy Spirit makes his dwelling.

The Bridge

51 Come, let us join our cheerful songs

Isaac Watts (1674-1748) alt.

Henry Lahee (1826-1912)

NATIVITY CM

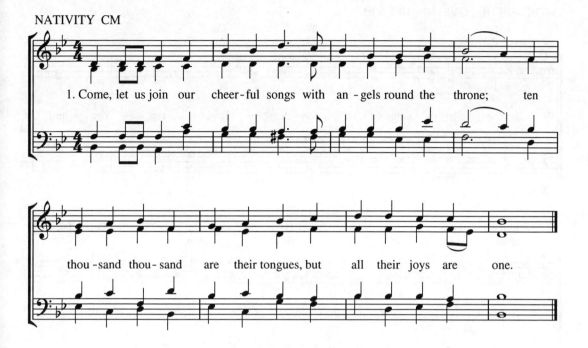

1. Come, let us join our cheer-ful songs with an - gels round the throne; ten thou -sand thou- sand are their tongues, but all their joys are one.

2. 'Worthy the Lamb that died,' they cry,
   'to be exalted thus.'
   'Worthy the Lamb,' our lips reply,
   'for he was slain for us.'

3. Jesus is worthy to receive
   honour and pow'r divine;
   and blessings, more than we can give,
   be, Lord, for ever thine.

4. Let all creation join in one
   to bless the sacred name
   of him that sits upon the throne,
   and to adore the Lamb.

52 Come, let us sing

Robert Walmsley (1831-1905) F. Luke Wiseman (1858-1944)

WONDERFUL LOVE 10 4 10 7 4 10

1. Come, let us sing of a won-der-ful love, ten - der and true; out of the heart of the Fa-ther a - bove, stream-ing to me and to you: won - der - ful love dwells in the heart of the Fa-ther a - bove.

2. Jesus, the Saviour, this gospel to tell,
   joyfully came;
   came with the helpless and hopeless to dwell,
   sharing their sorrow and shame;
   seeking the lost,
   saving, redeeming at measureless cost.

3. Jesus is seeking the wanderers yet;
   why do they roam?
   Love only waits to forgive and forget;
   home! weary wanderer, home!
   Wonderful love
   dwells in the heart of the Father above.

4. Come to my heart, O thou wonderful love,
   come and abide,
   lifting my life till it rises above
   envy and falsehood and pride;
   seeking to be
   lowly and humble, a learner of thee.

See over for another arrangement.

F. Luke Wiseman (1858-1944)
arr. Susie Hare

NEW ARRANGEMENT

With a gentle lilt

Unison

1. Come, let us sing of a won-der-ful love, ten - der and
2. Je - sus, the Sa-viour, this gos-pel to tell, joy - ful - ly
3. Je - sus is seek-ing the wan-der-ers yet; why do they

true; out of the heart of the Fa - ther a - bove,
came; came with the help - less and hope - less to dwell,
roam? Love on - ly waits to for - give and for - get;

stream - ing to me and to you: won - der - ful
shar - ing their sor - row and shame; seek - ing the
home, wea - ry wan - der - er, home! Won - der - ful

love dwells in the heart of the Fa - ther a - bove.
lost, sav - ing, re - deem - ing at mea - sure - less cost.
love dwells in the heart of the Fa - ther a - bove.

1, 2.   *D.C.*   **3.**

4. Come to my heart O thou won-der-ful love, come and a-bide, lift-ing my life, till it ri-ses a-bove en-vy and false-hood and pride; seek-ing to be low-ly and hum-ble, a learn-er of thee, low-ly and hum-ble, a learn-er of thee.

53 Come, now is the time to worship

Brian Doerksen

Brian Doerksen

Come, now is the time to wor - ship.

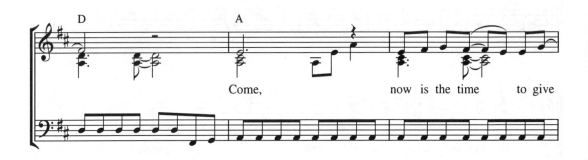

Come, now is the time to give

your heart. Come,

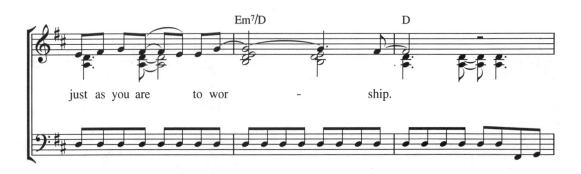

just as you are to wor - ship.

54 Come on and celebrate

Celebrate

Patricia Morgan and Dave Bankhead

Patricia Morgan and Dave Bankhead

Very lively

Come on and ce-le-brate his gift of love, we will

ce-le-brate the Son of God who loved us

and gave us life. We'll shout your

praise, O King, you give us joy no-thing else can bring,

55 Come, rest in the love of Jesus

Susie Hare

Susie Hare

The Bridge

56 Come, ye thankful people, come

Henry Alford (1810-1871) alt.

George Job Elvey (1816-1893)

ST GEORGE'S WINDSOR 77 77 D

1. Come, ye thank-ful peo-ple, come, raise the song of har-vest-home! All is safe-ly ga-thered in, ere the win-ter storms be-gin; God, our ma-ker, doth pro-vide for our wants to be sup-plied; come to God's own tem-ple, come; raise the song of har-vest-home!

2. We ourselves are God's own field,
   fruit unto his praise to yield;
   wheat and tares together sown,
   unto joy or sorrow grown;
   first the blade and then the ear,
   then the full corn shall appear:
   grant, O harvest Lord, that we
   wholesome grain and pure may be.

3. For the Lord our God shall come,
   and shall take his harvest home,
   from his field shall purge away
   all that doth offend, that day;
   give his angels charge at last
   in the fire the tares to cast,
   but the fruitful ears to store
   in his garner evermore.

4. Then, thou Church triumphant, come,
   raise the song of harvest-home;
   all be safely gathered in,
   free from sorrow, free from sin,
   there for ever purified
   in God's garner to abide:
   come, ten thousand angels, come,
   raise the glorious harvest-home!

57 Creation is awaiting

Chris Bowater and Ian Taylor

Chris Bowater and Ian Taylor

1. Cre-a-tion is a-wait-ing the re-turn of the King. The trees are poised to clap their hands for joy. The moun-tains stand ma-jes-tic to sa-lute their God; the des-ert lies in wait to burst in-to bloom. The King is com-ing, the King is

2. The church is awaiting the return of the King.
   The people joined together in his love.
   Redeemed by his blood,
   washed in his word.
   As a bride longs for her bridegroom
   the church looks to God.
   Refrain
   The King is coming, the King is coming,
   the King is coming to receive his bride. *(x2)*

3. The world is awaiting the return of the King.
   The earth is a footstool for his feet.
   Ev'ry knee will bow down,
   ev'ry tongue confess,
   that Jesus Christ is Lord
   of heaven and earth.
   Refrain
   The King is coming, the King is coming,
   the King is coming to reign in majesty. *(x2)*

58 Creation sings!

Martin Leckebusch

Susie Hare

EASTROP 88 88 88

2. Creation speaks a message true,
   reminds us we are creatures, too:
   to serve as stewards is our role,
   despite our dreams of full control –
   when we disparage what God owns,
   in turmoil, all creation groans.

3. Creation groans to see the day
   which ends all bondage, all decay:
   frustrated now, it must await
   the Lord who comes to recreate
   till round the universe there rings
   the song his new creation sings!

59 Crown him with many crowns

Matthew Bridges (1800-1894)

George Job Elvey (1816-1893)

DIADEMATA DSM

1. Crown him with many crowns, the Lamb upon his throne; hark,

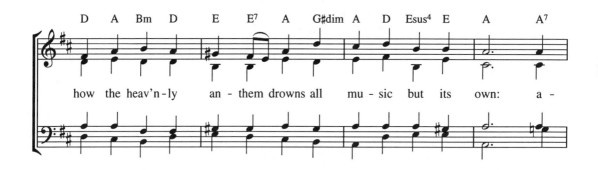

how the heav'n-ly an-them drowns all music but its own: a-

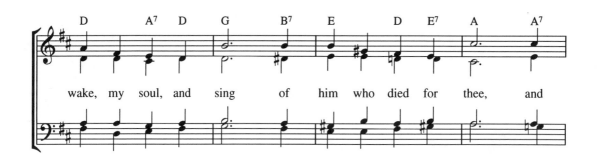

wake, my soul, and sing of him who died for thee, and

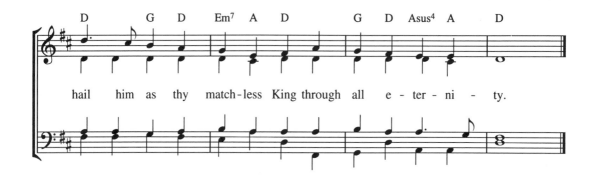

hail him as thy match-less King through all e-ter-ni-ty.

2. Crown him the Lord of life,
   who triumphed o'er the grave,
   and rose victorious in the strife
   for those he came to save.
   His glories now we sing,
   who died and rose on high;
   who died eternal life to bring,
   and lives that death may die.

3. Crown him the Lord of love;
   behold his hands and side,
   rich wounds, yet visible above,
   in beauty glorified:
   no angel in the sky
   can fully bear that sight,
   but downward bends each burning eye
   at mysteries so bright.

4. Crown him the Lord of peace,
   whose pow'r a sceptre sways
   from pole to pole, that wars may cease,
   and all be prayer and praise:
   his reign shall know no end,
   and round his piercèd feet
   fair flow'rs of paradise extend
   their fragrance ever sweet.

5. Crown him the Lord of years,
   the Potentate of time,
   Creator of the rolling spheres,
   ineffably sublime.
   All hail, Redeemer, hail!
   for thou hast died for me;
   thy praise shall never, never fail
   throughout eternity.

See over for another arrangement.

George Job Elvey (1816-1893)
arr. Susie Hare

NEW ARRANGEMENT

2. Crown him the Lord of life,
who triumphed o'er the grave,
and rose victorious in the strife
for those he came to save.
His glories now we sing,
who died and rose on high;
who died eternal life to bring,
and lives that death may die.

3. Crown him the Lord of love;
behold his hands and side,
rich wounds, yet visible above,
in beauty glorified:
no angel in the sky
can fully bear that sight,
but downward bends each burning eye
at mysteries so bright.

4. Crown him the Lord of peace,
whose pow'r a sceptre sways
from pole to pole, that wars may cease,
and all be prayer and praise:
his reign shall know no end,
and round his piercèd feet
fair flow'rs of paradise extend
their fragrance ever sweet.

5. Crown him the Lord of years,
the Potentate of time,
Creator of the rolling spheres,
ineffably sublime.
All hail, Redeemer, hail!
for thou hast died for me;
thy praise shall never, never fail
throughout eternity.

The Bridge

60 Dear Lord and Father of mankind

John Greenleaf Whittier (1807-1892)

Charles Hastings Parry (1848-1918)

REPTON 86 88 6

1. Dear Lord and Fa - ther of man-kind, for - give our fool-ish ways! Re - clothe us in our right-ful mind, in pur - er lives thy ser - vice find, in deep - er rev - 'rence praise, in deep - er rev - 'rence praise.

2. In simple trust like theirs who heard,
   beside the Syrian sea,
   the gracious calling of the Lord,
   let us, like them, without a word,
   rise up and follow thee,
   rise up and follow thee.

3. O Sabbath rest by Galilee!
   O calm of hills above,
   where Jesus knelt to share with thee
   the silence of eternity,
   interpreted by love,
   interpreted by love!

4. Drop thy still dews of quietness,
   till all our strivings cease;
   take from our souls the strain and stress,
   and let our ordered lives confess
   the beauty of thy peace,
   the beauty of thy peace.

5. Breathe through the heats of our desire
   thy coolness and thy balm;
   let sense be dumb, let flesh retire;
   speak through the earthquake, wind and fire,
   O still small voice of calm,
   O still small voice of calm!

61 Depth of mercy!

Charles Wesley (1707-1788)

Bob Kauflin

1. Depth of mer - cy! Can there be mer - cy reach - ing

e - ven me? God, the just, his wrath for - bears,

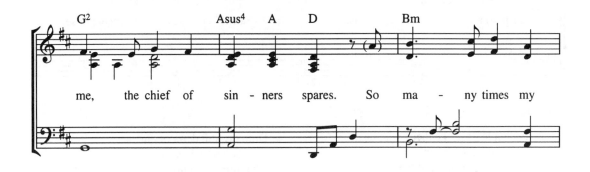

me, the chief of sin - ners spares. So ma - ny times my

heart has strayed from his kind and per - fect ways,

mak - ing clear my des - p'rate need for his blood poured

out for me.

1st time D.C.

2. Give me grace, Lord, let me own
   all the wrongs that I have done.
   Let me now my sins deplore,
   look to you and sin no more.
   There, for me, the Saviour stands
   holding forth his wounded hands,
   scars which ever cry for me;
   once condemned but now set free.

62 Don't let me waste your sacrifice

Susie Hare

Susie Hare

Fa - ther's loss,   lift up my eyes   to see your cross;
I might still   hold to a life   that binds your will;

show me the pain   of Cal - va - ry: Je - sus, you did   it
don't let me waste   the price you paid,   I want to walk   the

Refrain

all for me.
path you made.   I want to re - build the al - tar of

my heart,   give you my first   and give you my last,

yours is the death that brought me life; don't let me waste your

sac - ri -fice, don't let me waste your sac - ri -fice.

1.

D.S.

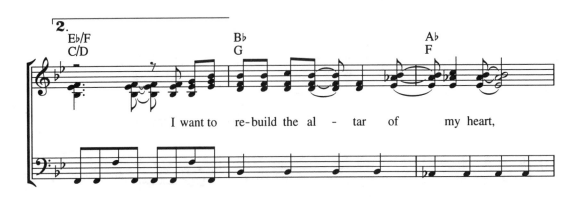

2.

I want to re-build the al – tar of my heart,

63 Down the mountain the river flows · *The river is here*

Andy Park

Andy Park

1. Down the moun - tain the ri - ver flows, and it brings re - fresh - ing wher - e-ver it goes. Through the val - leys and o - ver the fields, the
2. The ri - ver of God is teem - ing with life, and all who touch it can be re - vived. And those who lin - ger on this ri - ver's shore will
3. Up to the moun - tain we love to go to find the pre - sence of the Lord. A - long the banks of the ri - ver we run, we

64 Draw me close to the cross

Geoff and Judith Roberts

Geoff and Judith Roberts

Meditatively

Draw me close to the cross, to the place of your

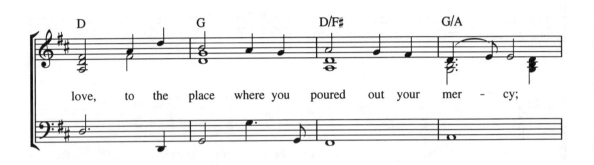

love, to the place where you poured out your mer - cy;

where the ri - ver of life that flows from your wound - ed

side brings re - fresh - ing to those who draw near.

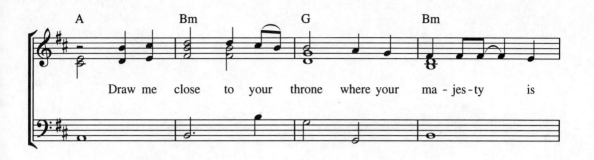

Draw me close to your throne where your ma-jes-ty is

shown, where the crown of my life I lay down.

Draw me close to your side, where my heart is sa-tis-

fied, draw me close to you, Lord, draw me close.

The Bridge

65 Faithful God

Chris Bowater

Chris Bowater

Worshipfully and unhurried

Faith - ful God, faith - ful God, all - suf - fi - cient one, I wor-ship you. Sha-lom my peace, my strong de - li - ve - rer, I lift you up, faith - ful God.

66 Faithful One

Brian Doerksen

Brian Doerksen

Faith - ful One, so un-chang - ing,
Age - less One, you're my rock of peace.
Lord of all, I de - pend on you,
I call out to you a-gain and a-gain,
I call out to you a-gain and a-

67 Far above all other loves

David Fellingham

David Fellingham

With strength

1. Far a-bove all o-ther loves,
far be-yond all o-ther joys,
hea-ven's bles - sings poured on me,
by the Ho - ly Spi - rit's pow'r.

Refrain
Love's com-pel - ling pow - er draws my heart in - to yours;

2. All ambition now has gone,
   pleasing you my only goal;
   motivated by your grace,
   living for eternity.

3. Looking with the eye of faith
   for the day of your return;
   in that day I want to stand
   unashamed before your throne.

68 Far and near

Graham Kendrick

Say it loud

Graham Kendrick (b.1950)

1. Far and near hear the call, wor - ship
   wide is the love hea - ven

him, Lord of all; fa - mi - lies of na - tions,
sent from a - bove; God's own Son, for sin - ners

come, ce - le - brate what God has done. 2. Deep and
died, rose a - gain — he is a -

live. Say it loud, say it strong, tell the

3. At his name, let praise begin;
   oceans roar, nature sing,
   for he comes to judge the earth
   in righteousness and in his truth.

69 Father God, I wonder

I will sing your praises

Ian Smale

Ian Smale

Lively

Fa-ther God, I won-der how I man-aged to ex - ist with-out the know-ledge of your pa-rent-hood and your lov-ing care. But now I am your child, I am a - dopt-ed in your fa-mi-ly and I can ne-ver be a-lone, 'cause, Fa-ther God, you're there be-side me. I will sing your prai-ses, I will sing your prai-ses, I will sing your prai-ses, for e-ver - more. for e-ver - more.

70 Father in heaven, how we love you
Blessed be the Lord God Almighty

Bob Fitts

Bob Fitts

Majestically

Unison

Fa-ther in hea-ven, how we love you, we lift your name in all the earth. May your king-dom be es-tab-lished in our prai-ses as your peo-ple de-clare your migh-ty works. Bles-sed be the Lord God Al-migh-ty, who was and is and is to come. Bles-sed be the Lord God Al-migh-ty, who reigns for e-ver-more.

71 Father of creation

Let your glory fall

David Ruis

David Ruis

2. Ruler of the nations,
   the world has yet to see
   the full release of your promise,
   the church in victory.

Turn to us, Lord, and touch us,
make us strong in your might.
Overcome our weakness,
that we could stand up and fight.

72 Father of life, draw me closer *Let the peace of God reign*

Darlene Zschech

Darlene Zschech

Fa - ther of life, draw me clo - ser,
O Ho - ly Spi - rit, Lord, my com - fort,

Lord, my heart is set on you; let me
strength - en me, hold my head up high; and I'll

run the race of time with your life en - fold - ing mine and let the
stand up - on your truth, bring - ing glo - ry un - to you,

peace of God, let it reign. reign.

O Lord, I hun - ger for more of you, rise up with-in me, let me

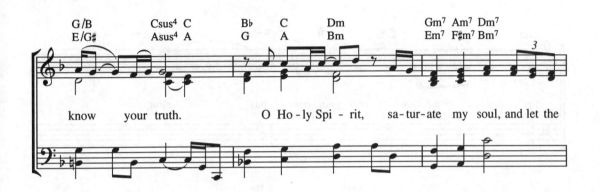

know your truth. O Ho - ly Spi - rit, sa - tur-ate my soul, and let the

life of God fill me now, let your heal - ing pow'r bring

life and make me whole and let the peace of God, let it reign.

73 Father, we have received

Neighbours to nations

John Gibson and Dave Bankhead

John Gibson and Dave Bankhead
arr. L. Hills

1. Father, we have received of the fire of your love and your compassion; stir our hearts to believe that your power in us can move in this nation as we raise a standard for your Son. From

2. Father, we shall arise,
and reach out for the healing of our nation;
may each day of our lives
be inspired to fulfil your call and commission
to disciple ev'ry tribe and tongue.

The Bridge

74 Father, we love you

Glorify your name

Donna Adkins

Donna Adkins (b.1940)

Worshipfully

1. Fa - ther, we love you, we wor - ship and a - dore you,
glo - ri - fy your name in all the earth.
Glo - ri - fy your name, glo - ri - fy your name,
glo - ri - fy your name in all the earth.

2. Jesus, we love you . . .

3. Spirit, we love you . . .

75 Fight the good fight

John Samuel Bewley Monsell (1811-1875) alt.

Melody attributed to
John Hatton (d.1793)

TUNE 1: DUKE STREET LM

1. Fight the good fight with all thy might; Christ is thy strength, and Christ thy right;
lay hold on life, and it shall be thy joy and crown e - ter - nal - ly.

2. Run the straight race through God's good grace,
   lift up thine eyes and seek his face;
   life with its way before us lies;
   Christ is the path, and Christ the prize.

3. Cast care aside, lean on thy guide;
   his boundless mercy will provide;
   trust, and thy trusting soul shall prove
   Christ is its life, and Christ its love.

4. Faint not nor fear, his arms are near;
   he changeth not, and thou art dear;
   only believe, and thou shalt see
   that Christ is all in all to thee.

John Samuel Bewley Monsell (1811-1875) alt.

Susie Hare

TUNE 2: CRONDALL LM

Steady

Unison

1. Fight the good fight with all thy might;
Christ is thy strength, and Christ thy right;
lay hold on life, and it shall be thy joy and crown e-
ter-nal - ly, thy joy and crown e - ter-nal - ly.

2. Run the straight race through God's good grace,
lift up thine eyes and seek his face;
life with its way before us lies;
Christ is the path, and Christ the prize.

3. Cast care aside, lean on thy guide;
his boundless mercy will provide;
trust, and thy trusting soul shall prove
Christ is its life, and Christ its love.

4. Faint not nor fear, his arms are near;
he changeth not, and thou art dear;
only believe, and thou shalt see
that Christ is all in all to thee.

76 Filled with compassion

For all the people who live on the earth

Noel and Tricia Richards

Noel and Tricia Richards

Gently
A Bm7 A/C♯ D A/C♯ E Bm/A A
Unison
1. Filled with com - pas - sion for all cre - a - tion,
A Bm7 A/C♯ D A/C♯ E
Je - sus came in - to a world that was lost.
A Bm7 A/C♯ D A/C♯ E Bm/A A
There was but one way that he could save us,
A Bm7 A/C♯ D A/C♯ E A Bm7 A/C♯
on - ly through suf - fer - ing death on a cross.
Refrain D A/C♯ E Bm7 A
God, you are wait - ing, your heart is break - ing

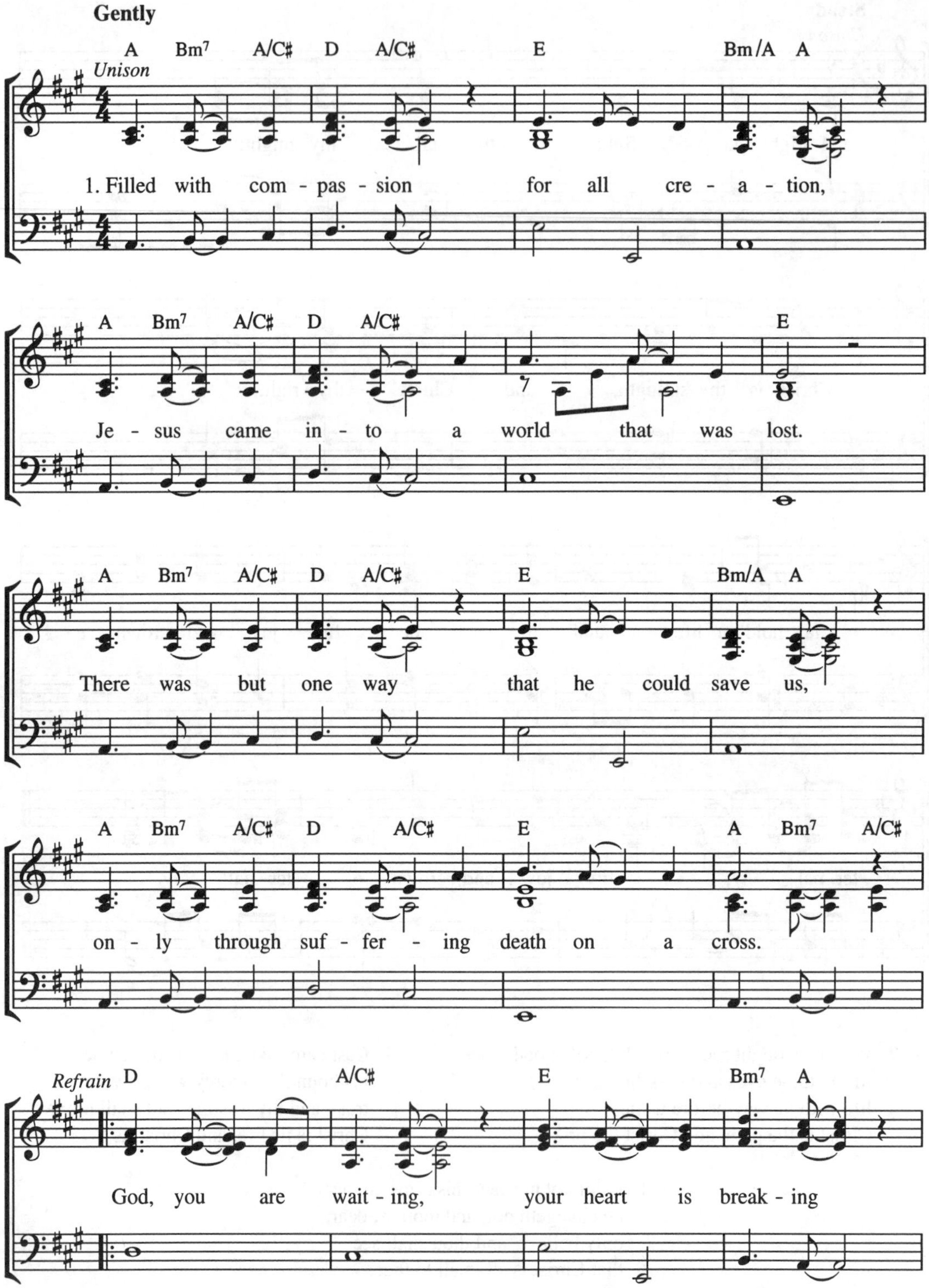

2. Great is your passion for all the people
   living and dying without knowing you.
   Having no saviour, they're lost for ever,
   if we don't speak out and lead them to you.

3. From ev'ry nation we shall be gathered,
   millions redeemed shall be Jesus' reward.
   Then he will turn and say to his Father:
   'Truly my suffering was worth it all.'

77 Fill thou my life, O Lord my God

Horatius Bonar (1808-1889) alt.

Melody adapted from
Thomas Haweis (1734-1820)

RICHMOND CM

1. Fill thou my life, O Lord my God, in ev - 'ry part with praise, that my whole be - ing may pro - claim thy be - ing and thy ways.

2. Not for the lip of praise alone,
   nor e'en the praising heart,
   I ask, but for a life made up
   of praise in ev'ry part.

3. Praise in the common things of life,
   its goings out and in;
   praise in each duty and each deed,
   however small and mean.

4. Fill ev'ry part of me with praise:
   let all my being speak
   of thee and of thy love, O Lord,
   poor though I be and weak.

5. So shalt thou, Lord, receive from me
   the praise and glory due;
   and so shall I begin on earth
   the song for ever new.

6. So shall each fear, each fret, each care,
   be turnèd into song;
   and ev'ry winding of the way
   the echo shall prolong.

7. So shall no part of day or night
   unblest or common be;
   but all my life, in ev'ry step,
   be fellowship with thee.

78 Focus my eyes

Ian White

Ian White

Gently

1. Fo-cus my eyes on you, O Lord, fo-cus my eyes on you; to wor-ship in spi-rit and in truth, fo-cus my eyes on you.

2. Turn round my life to you, O Lord,
   turn round my life to you;
   to know from this night you've made me new,
   turn round my life to you.

3. Fill up my heart with praise, O Lord,
   fill up my heart with praise;
   to speak of your love in ev'ry place,
   fill up my heart with praise.

79 For all the saints

William Walsham How (1823-1897)

Ralph Vaughan Williams (1872-1958)

SINE NOMINE 10 10 10 4

1. For all the saints who from their la-bours rest, who
2. Thou wast their rock, their fort-ress and their might;
3. O may thy sol-diers, faith-ful, true and bold,

thee by faith be-fore the world con-fessed, thy
thou, Lord, their cap-tain in the well-fought fight;
fight as the saints who no-bly fought of old, and

name, O Je-sus, be for e-ver blest.
thou in the dark-ness drear their one true light. Al-
win, with them, the vic-tor's crown of gold.

-le-lu-ia, al-le-lu-ia!

Harmony

4. O blest com - mu - nion! fel - low - ship di - vine!
5. And when the strife is fierce, the war - fare long,
6. The gol - den eve - ning bright - ens in the west;

we fee - bly strug - gle, they in glo - ry shine; yet
steals on the ear the dis - tant tri - umph - song, and
soon, soon to faith - ful war - riors com - eth rest;

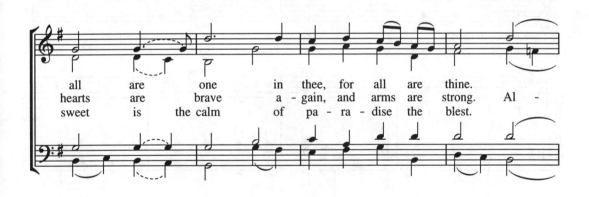

all are one in thee, for all are thine. Al -
hearts are brave a - gain, and arms are strong. Al -
sweet is the calm of pa - ra - dise the blest.

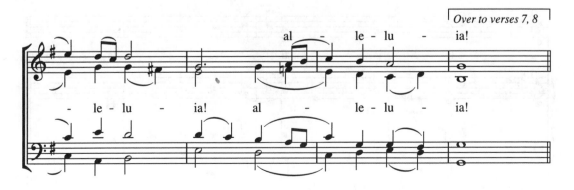

Over to verses 7, 8

al - le - lu - ia!

- le - lu - ia! al - le - lu - ia!

7. But lo! There breaks a yet more glo-rious day; the
8. From earth's wide bounds, from o-cean's far-thest coast, through

saints tri - um - phant rise in bright ar - ray: the
gates of pearl streams in the count-less host,

King of glo - ry pas - ses on his way. Al -
sing - ing to Fa - ther, Son and Ho - ly Ghost.

- le - lu - ia. al - le - lu - ia.

80 For all you have done

Susie Hare

Susie Hare

Unhurried

1. For
all you have done in our lives, Je - sus, for
be - ing our strength in times of weak - ness, for
know - ing our lives are in your keep - ing, for

all that your love has brought us through, for
be - ing our guide when paths are new, for
know - ing your hand in all we do, for

all that is past and all that's to come,
be - ing our rock and be - ing our hope,
know - ing your peace and know - ing your grace,

we are so grate - ful to you.

81 For riches of salvation

Give thanks

Martin E. Leckebusch

Susie Hare

FROYLE 75 75 777 7

Brightly

1. For rich - es of sal-va - tion give thanks to the Lord; re -

lease from con-dem-na - tion, give thanks to the Lord; for

love which tru - ly frees us be - cause the Fa - ther sees us i -

den - ti - fied with Je - sus— give thanks, give thanks to the Lord!

2. For

2. For courage and endurance
   give thanks to the Lord;
   the Spirit's reassurance,
   give thanks to the Lord;
   for fatherly correction,
   the call to share perfection,
   the hope of resurrection –
   give thanks, give thanks to the Lord!

3. For life in all its fullness
   give thanks to the Lord;
   for all that leads to wholeness,
   give thanks to the Lord;
   he knows our ev'ry feeling
   and speaks in grace, revealing
   his comfort and his healing –
   give thanks, give thanks to the Lord!

4. For justice with compassion
   give thanks to the Lord,
   and freedom from oppression,
   give thanks to the Lord;
   for holiness unending,
   a kingdom still extending,
   all earthly pow'r transcending –
   give thanks, give thanks to the Lord!

82 For the joys and for the sorrows

For this I have Jesus

Graham Kendrick

Graham Kendrick (b.1950)

1. For the joys and for the sorrows, the best and worst of times, for this mo - ment, for to - mor - row, for all that lies be - hind; fears that crowd a - round me, for the fail - ure of my plans, for the dreams of all I hope to be, the truth of what I am:

2. For the tears that flow in secret,
   in the broken times,
   for the moments of elation,
   or the troubled mind;
   for all the disappointments,
   or the sting of old regrets,
   all my prayers and longings,
   that seem unanswered yet:

3. For the weakness of my body,
   the burdens of each day,
   for the nights of doubt and worry
   when sleep has fled away;
   needing reassurance
   and the will to start again,
   a steely-eyed endurance,
   the strength to fight and win:

83 For this purpose

Graham Kendrick

Graham Kendrick (b.1950)

1. For this pur - pose Christ was re - veal'd to des - troy all the works of the ev - il one. Christ in us has o - ver - come, so with glad-ness we sing and wel-come his king-dom in. O-ver

2. In the name of Jesus we stand,
   by the power of his blood
   we now claim this ground.
   Satan has no authority here,
   pow'rs of darkness must flee,
   for Christ has the victory.

The Bridge

84 Friend of sinners

Matt Redman

Matt Redman

Gently

Capo 2

Unison

1. Friend of sin-ners, Lord of truth, I am fal-ling in love with you.

Friend of sin-ners, Lord of truth, I have fal-len in love with you. Je -

Refrain

sus, I love your name, the name by which we're saved. Je -

sus, I love your name, the name by which we're saved.

2. Friend of sinners, Lord of truth,
   I am giving my life to you.
   Friend of sinners, Lord of truth,
   I have given my life to you.

85 From all that dwell below the skies

Isaac Watts (1674-1748),
based on Psalm 117

Melody from 'Geistliche Kirchengesang',
Cologne (1623)
arr. Ralph Vaughan Williams (1872-1958)

LASST UNS ERFREUEN   88 44 88 and Alleluias

1. From all that dwell be-low the skies let the Cre-a-tor's praise a-

Harmony   *Unison*

rise: Al-le-lu - ia, al-le-lu - ia! Let

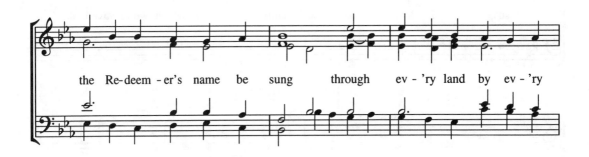

the Re-deem-er's name be sung through ev-'ry land by ev-'ry

Refrain
Harmony

tongue. Al-le-lu - ia, al-le-lu - ia, al-le-

lu - ia, al - le - lu - ia, al - le - lu - ia!

2. Eternal are thy mercies, Lord;
   eternal truth attends thy word:
   > Alleluia.
   Thy praise shall sound from shore to shore,
   till suns shall rise and set no more,
   > Alleluia.

86 From heaven you came

The Servant King

Graham Kendrick

Graham Kendrick (b.1950)

Worshipfully

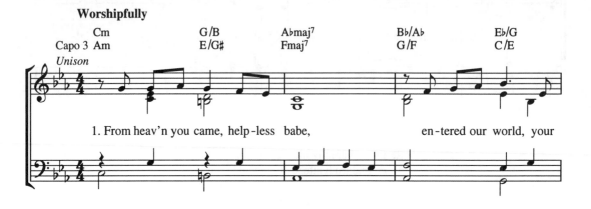

1. From heav'n you came, help-less babe, en-tered our world, your

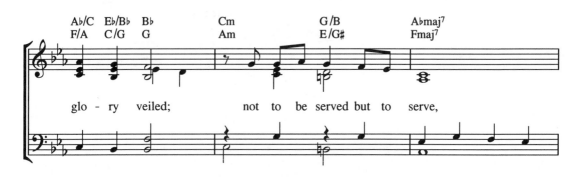

glo - ry veiled; not to be served but to serve,

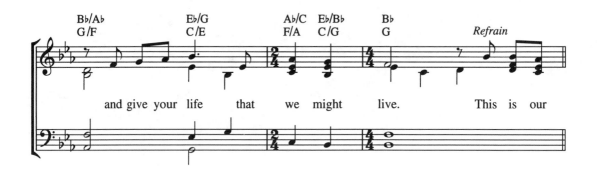

and give your life that we might live. This is our

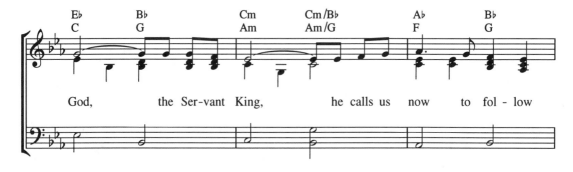

God, the Ser-vant King, he calls us now to fol - low

him, to bring our lives as a dai-ly of-fer-ing of wor-ship

To next verse　　*Last time*

to the Ser-vant King. King.

2. There in the garden of tears,
   my heavy load he chose to bear;
   his heart with sorrow was torn.
   'Yet not my will but yours,' he said.

3. Come see his hands and his feet,
   the scars that speak of sacrifice,
   hands that flung stars into space,
   to cruel nails surrendered.

4. So let us learn how to serve,
   and in our lives enthrone him;
   each other's needs to prefer,
   for it is Christ we're serving.

87 From the heights of glory

What a gift

Susie Hare

Susie Hare

2. From a humble stable, to a world of shame,
   the friend of sinners, who calls my name
   brought the love of heaven to the hearts of men
   and it gave lives hope again.

3. From a life, so perfect, to a cruel cross,
   the world's redemption, the Father's loss;
   and the nails were driven and the blood flowed free
   in the hands outstretched for me.

4. From the grave he's risen, ever glorified,
   to take his place at his Father's side;
   and the greatest glory will be ours to own
   when he comes to take us home.

   What a hope, what a hope we are given,
   sacrifice of the Father for us.
   What a song to proclaim: 'He is risen!
   King of kings, Lord of lords, Jesus!
   King of kings, Lord of lords, Jesus!

88 From the squalor of a borrowed stable

Immanuel

Stuart Townend

Stuart Townend

With a 'celtic' feel

1. From the squa-lor of a bor-rowed sta - ble, by the Spi-rit and a vir - gin's faith; to the an-guish and the shame of scan - dal came the Sa - viour of the hu – man race! But the skies were filled with the praise of heav'n, shep - herds lis - ten as the

an - gels tell of the Gift of God come down to man

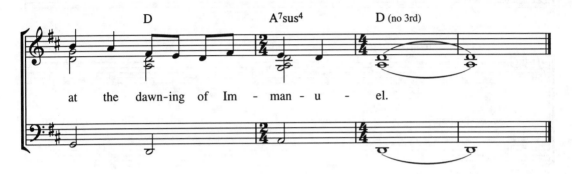

at the dawn-ing of Im - man - u - el.

2. King of heaven now the friend of sinners,
   humble servant in the Father's hands,
   filled with power and the Holy Spirit,
   filled with mercy for the broken man.
   Yes, he walked my road and he felt my pain,
   joys and sorrows that I know so well;
   yet his righteous steps give me hope again –
   I will follow my Immanuel!

3. Through the kisses of a friend's betrayal,
   he was lifted on a cruel cross;
   he was punished for a world's transgressions,
   he was suffering to save the lost.
   He fights for breath, he fights for me,
   loosing sinners from the claims of hell;
   and with a shout our souls are free –
   death defeated by Immanuel!

4. Now he's standing in the place of honour,
   crowned with glory on the highest throne,
   interceding for his own belovèd
   till his Father calls to bring them home!
   Then the skies will part as the trumpet sounds
   hope of heaven or the fear of hell;
   but the Bride will run to her Lover's arms,
   giving glory to Immanuel!

89 Giver of grace

You are good to me

Stuart Townend

Stuart Townend

Gently and rhythmic

1. Gi-ver of grace, how price-less your love for me, pur-er than sil-ver, more cost-ly than gold. Gi-ver of life, all that I'll e-ver need, strength for my bo-dy and food for my soul. Oh, you are good, so good to me. Yes, you are good, so good to me. Oh, you are good, so good to me. Yes, you are good, so

good to me. I've ne-ver known a love so perfect in its faith-ful-ness; it lifts me up to the high - est place. A glimpse of hea-ven and a taste of my in - he - ri-tance, I know that one day I'll be with you.

2. Giver of hope, rock of salvation,
   tower of refuge, yet there in my pain.
   Now I'm secure, loved for eternity,
   showered with blessings
   and lavished with grace.

90 Give thanks with a grateful heart

Henry Smith

Henry Smith

Give thanks with a grateful heart. Give thanks to the Holy One. Give thanks because he's given Jesus Christ, his Son. Give Son. And now let the weak say, 'I am strong', let the

The Bridge

91 Gloria

Traditional

Jacques Berthier (1923-1994)

This setting may be sung as a canon with entries as indicated

92 Glorious things of thee are spoken

John Newton (1725-1807)
based on Isaiah 33:20-21, alt.

Croatian folk melody adapted by
Franz Joseph Haydn (1732-1809)

TUNE 1: AUSTRIA 87 87 D

1. Glo - rious things of thee are spo - ken, Zi - on, ci - ty of our God;

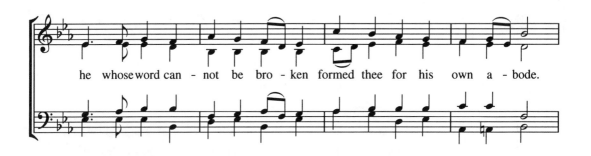

he whose word can - not be bro - ken formed thee for his own a - bode.

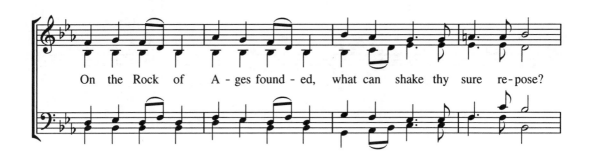

On the Rock of A - ges found - ed, what can shake thy sure re - pose?

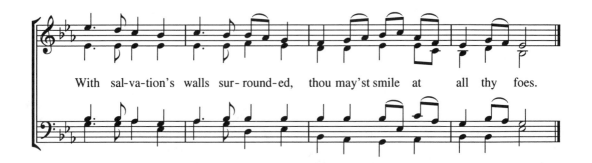

With sal - va - tion's walls sur - round-ed, thou may'st smile at all thy foes.

2. See, the streams of living waters,
   springing from eternal love,
   well supply thy sons and daughters,
   and all fear of want remove.
   Who can faint while such a river
   ever flows their thirst to assuage?
   Grace which, like the Lord, the giver,
   never fails from age to age.

3. Round each habitation hov'ring,
   see the cloud and fire appear
   for a glory and a cov'ring,
   showing that the Lord is near.
   Thus they march, the pillar leading,
   light by night and shade by day;
   daily on the manna feeding
   which he gives them when they pray.

4. Saviour, if of Zion's city
   I through grace a member am,
   let the world deride or pity,
   I will glory in thy name.
   Fading is the worldling's pleasure,
   boasted pomp and empty show;
   solid joys and lasting treasure
   none but Zion's children know.

See over for another tune.

John Newton (1725-1807)
based on Isaiah 33:20-21, alt.

Cyril Vincent Taylor (1907-1991)

TUNE 2: ABBOT'S LEIGH 87 87 D

1. Glo - rious things of thee are spo - ken, Zi - on,

ci - ty of our God; he whose word can - not be

bro - ken formed thee for his own a - bode.

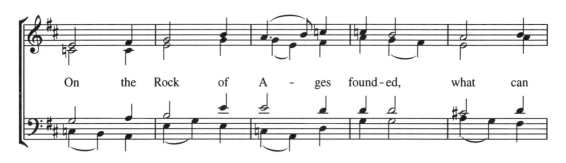

On the Rock of A - ges found - ed, what can

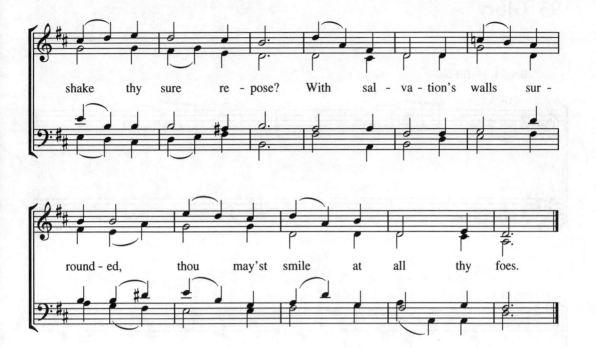

shake thy sure re - pose? With sal - va - tion's walls sur -
round - ed, thou may'st smile at all thy foes.

2. See, the streams of living waters,
   springing from eternal love,
   well supply thy sons and daughters,
   and all fear of want remove.
   Who can faint while such a river
   ever flows their thirst to assuage?
   Grace which, like the Lord, the giver,
   never fails from age to age.

3. Round each habitation hov'ring,
   see the cloud and fire appear
   for a glory and a cov'ring,
   showing that the Lord is near.
   Thus they march, the pillar leading,
   light by night and shade by day;
   daily on the manna feeding
   which he gives them when they pray.

4. Saviour, if of Zion's city
   I through grace a member am,
   let the world deride or pity,
   I will glory in thy name.
   Fading is the worldling's pleasure,
   boasted pomp and empty show;
   solid joys and lasting treasure
   none but Zion's children know.

93 Glory

Danny Daniels   Danny Daniels

Bright, joyful feel

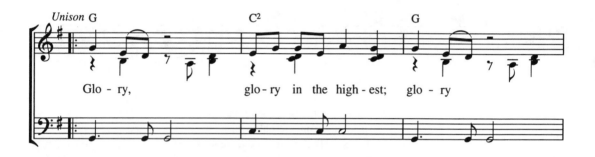

Glo - ry, glo - ry in the high - est; glo - ry

to the Al - migh - ty; glo - ry to the Lamb of God, and

glo - ry to the liv - ing Word; glo - ry

94 Glory to the King of kings!

Geoff Bullock

2. Jesus, Lord, with eyes unveiled
   we will see your throne.
   Jesus, Prince of Peace,
   Son of God, Emmanuel.

95 God forgave my sin

Freely, freely

Carol Owens

Carol Owens

1. God for - gave my sin in Je - sus'

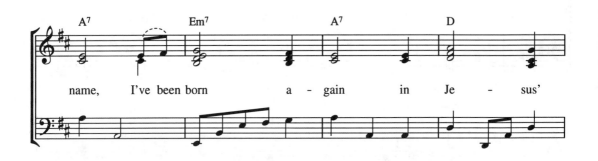

name, I've been born a - gain in Je - sus'

name; and in Je - sus' name I come to

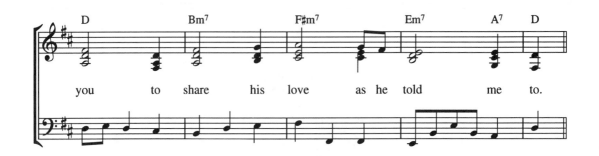

you to share his love as he told me to.

2. All pow'r is given in Jesus' name,
   in earth and heav'n in Jesus' name;
   and in Jesus' name I come to you
   to share his pow'r as he told me to.

96 God is good

Graham Kendrick

Graham Kendrick (b.1950)

Fast and rhythmic

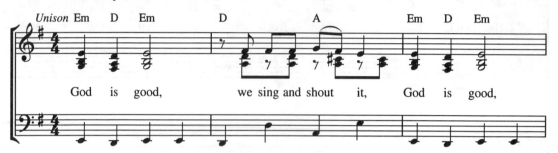

God is good, we sing and shout it, God is good,

we ce-le-brate. God is good, no more we doubt it,

God is good, we know it's true.

And when I think of his love for me, my heart

fills   with   praise   and   I   feel   like   danc - ing.

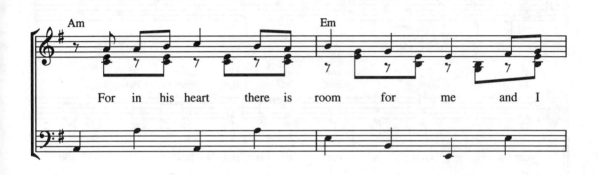

For   in   his   heart   there   is   room   for   me   and   I

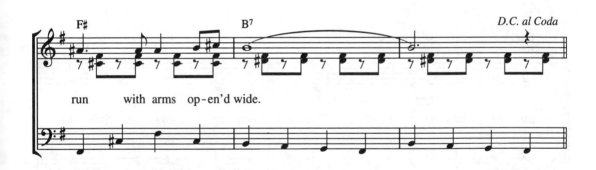

D.C. al Coda

run   with   arms   op-en'd wide.

CODA

(shout)

we know it's   true.   Hey!

97 God is working his purpose out

Arthur Campbell Ainger (1841-1919,
adapted by Michael Forster

Millicent Kingham (1866-1894)
in 'Church Hymns' (1903)

BENSON 86 87 87 12 8

1. God is work-ing his pur-pose out as year suc-ceeds to year. God is work-ing his pur-pose out, and the day is draw-ing near. Near-er and near-er draws the time, the time that shall sure-ly be, when the earth shall be filled with the

glo - ry of God as the wa - ters co -ver the sea.

2. From the east to the utmost west
wherever foot has trod,
through the mouths of his messengers
echoes forth the voice of God:
'Listen to me, ye continents,
ye islands, give ear to me,
that the earth shall be filled with the glory of God
as the waters cover the sea.'

3. March we forth in the strength of God,
his banner is unfurled;
let the light of the gospel shine
in the darkness of the world:
strengthen the weary, heal the sick
and set ev'ry captive free,
that the earth shall be filled with the glory of God
as the waters cover the sea.

4. All our efforts are nothing worth
unless God bless the deed;
vain our hopes for the harvest tide
till he brings to life the seed.
Yet ever nearer draws the time,
the time that shall surely be,
when the earth shall be filled with the glory of God
as the waters cover the sea.

98 God of glory, we exalt your name

David Fellingham

David Fellingham

Brightly with strength and feeling

God of glo - ry, we ex - alt your name,

you who reign in ma-jes - ty. We

lift our hearts to you and we will wor - ship, praise and

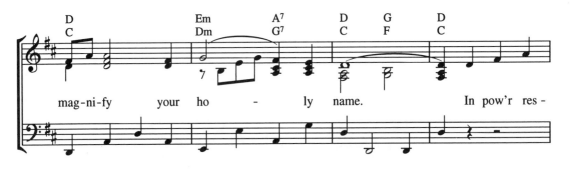

mag-ni-fy your ho - ly name. In pow'r res-

99 God of glory, you are worthy

Fire of God's glory

Simon and Tina Triffitt

Simon and Tina Triffitt

God of glo - ry, you are wor - thy, you

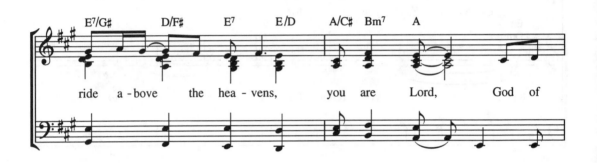

ride a - bove the hea - vens, you are Lord, God of

fi - re, my de - si - re is to

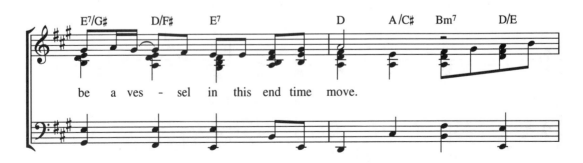

be a ves - sel in this end time move.

Fi - re of God's glo - ry, fall on me,

burn a - way the chaff of self and set me free;

make me pure and ho - ly, a light for all to see;

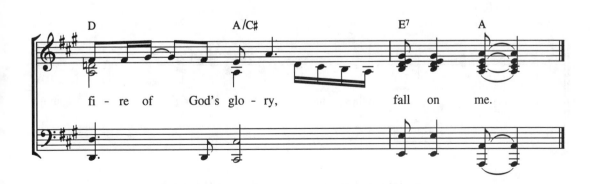

fi - re of God's glo - ry, fall on me.

100 God of grace

I stand complete in you

Chris Bowater

Chris Bowater

With feeling

God of grace,   I turn my face   to you,   I can-not
Striv-ings and   all an-guished dreams   in rags   lie at my

hide;   my na-ked-ness,   my shame, my guilt,   are
feet;   and on-ly grace   pro-vides the way   for

all be-fore   your   eyes.
me to stand com -   plete.   And your

grace   clothes   me   in   right - eous-

ness, and your mer - cy co-vers me in

love. Your life a-dorns

and beau - ti - fies, I

stand com-plete in you.

101 God of mercy, God of grace

Henry Francis Lyte (1793-1847)
based on Psalm 67, alt.

Henry Smart (1813-1879)

HEATHLANDS 77 77 77

1. God of mer - cy, God of grace, show the bright-ness of thy face;
shine u - pon us, Sa - viour, shine, fill thy Church with light di - vine;
and thy sav - ing health ex - tend un - to earth's re - mo - test end.

2. Let the people praise thee, Lord;
   be by all that live adored;
   let the nations shout and sing
   glory to their Saviour King;
   at thy feet their tribute pay,
   and thy holy will obey.

3. Let the people praise thee, Lord;
   earth shall then her fruits afford;
   God to us his blessing give,
   we to God devoted live;
   all below, and all above,
   one in joy and light and love.

A lower setting

1. God of mer - cy, God of grace, show the bright-ness of thy face;
shine u - pon us, Sa - viour, shine, fill thy Church with light di - vine;
and thy sav - ing health ex - tend un - to earth's re - mo - test end.

102 Greater grace

Chris Bowater   Chris Bowater

103 Great is the darkness

Come, Lord Jesus

Noel Richards and Gerald Coates

Noel Richards and Gerald Coates

Growing in strength

1. Great is the dark-ness that cov-ers the earth, op-pres-sion, in-jus-tice and

pain. Na-tions are slip-ping in hope-less des-pair, though

ma-ny have come in your name. Watch-ing while sa-ni-ty

dies, touched by the mad-ness and lies.

2. May now your church rise with power and love,
   this glorious gospel proclaim.
   In ev'ry nation salvation will come
   to those who believe in your name.
   Help us bring light to this world
   that we might speed your return.

3. Great celebrations on that final day
   when out of the heavens you come.
   Darkness will vanish, all sorrow will end,
   and rulers will bow at your throne.
   Our great commission complete,
   then face to face we shall meet.

104 Great is the Lord and most worthy of praise

Steve McEwan   Steve McEwan

Worshipfully

Great is the Lord and most wor-thy of praise, the

ci-ty of our God, the ho-ly place, the joy of the whole earth.

Great is the

Lord, in whom we have the vic - to - ry. He

aids us a-gainst the e - ne - my, we

105 Great is thy faithfulness

Thomas Obadiah Chisholm (1866-1960)

William Marion Runyan (1870-1957)

FAITHFULNESS (RUNYAN) 11 10 11 10 and Refrain

Morn - ing by morn - ing new mer - cies I see;
all I have need - ed thy hand has pro - vi - ded,
great is thy faith - ful - ness, Lord, un - to me!

2. Summer and winter, and springtime and harvest,
   sun, moon and stars in their courses above,
   join with all nature in manifold witness
   to thy great faithfulness, mercy and love.

3. Pardon for sin and a peace that endureth,
   thine own dear presence to cheer and to guide;
   strength for today and bright hope for tomorrow,
   blessings all mine, with ten thousand beside!

The Bridge

106 Guide me, O thou great Redeemer

William Williams (1717-1791)
trans. Peter Williams (1727-1796) and others

John Hughes (1873-1932)

CWM RHONDDA 87 87 47

1. Guide me, O thou great Re-deem-er, pil-grim through this bar-ren land; I am weak, but thou art migh-ty, hold me with thy pow'r-ful hand: Bread of Hea-ven, Bread of Hea-ven, feed me till I want no more, (want no more,) feed me till I want no more. (want no more,)

2. Open now the crystal fountain,
whence the healing stream doth flow;
let the fire and cloudy pillar
lead me all my journey through;
strong deliv'rer, strong deliv'rer,
be thou still my strength and shield,
be thou still my strength and shield.

3. When I tread the verge of Jordan,
bid my anxious fears subside;
death of death, and hell's destruction,
land me safe on Canaan's side;
songs of praises, songs of praises,
I will ever give to thee,
I will ever give to thee.

107 Hail, thou once despisèd Jesus

John Bakewell (1721-1819) alt.

Arthur Seymour Sullivan (1842-1900)

LUX EOI 87 87 D

1. Hail, thou once de - spi - sèd Je - sus, hail, thou Ga - li - le - an King!

Thou didst suf - fer to re - lease us; thou didst free sal - va - tion bring.

Hail, thou u - ni - ver - sal Sa - viour, bear - er of our sin and shame;

by thy me - rits we find fa - vour; life is gi - ven through thy name.

2. Paschal Lamb, by God appointed,
   all our sins on thee were laid;
   by almighty love anointed,
   thou hast full atonement made.
   All thy people are forgiven
   through the virtue of thy blood;
   opened is the gate of heaven,
   we are reconciled to God.

3. Jesus, hail! enthroned in glory,
   there for ever to abide;
   all the heav'nly hosts adore thee,
   seated at thy Father's side:
   there for sinners thou art pleading,
   there thou dost our place prepare;
   ever for us interceding,
   till in glory we appear.

4. Worship, honour, pow'r and blessing,
   thou art worthy to receive;
   loudest praises, without ceasing,
   it is right for us to give:
   help, ye bright angelic spirits!
   bring your sweetest, noblest lays;
   help to sing our Saviour's merits,
   help to chant Immanuel's praise.

108 Hail to the Lord's anointed

James Montgomery (1771-1854),
based on Psalm 72

From a melody in Johann Crüger's 'Gesangbuch',
adapted by William Henry Monk (1823-1889)

CRÜGER 76 76 D

1. Hail to the Lord's a - noint - ed, great Da - vid's great - er son! Hail, in the time ap - point - ed, his reign on earth be - gun! He comes to break op - pres - sion, to set the cap - tive free; to take a - way trans - gres - sion, and rule in e - qui - ty.

2. He comes with succour speedy
   to those who suffer wrong;
   to help the poor and needy,
   and bid the weak be strong;
   to give them songs for sighing,
   their darkness turn to light,
   whose souls, condemned and dying,
   were precious in his sight.

3. He shall come down like showers
   upon the fruitful earth,
   and love, joy, hope, like flowers,
   spring in his path to birth:
   before him on the mountains
   shall peace the herald go;
   and righteousness in fountains
   from hill to valley flow.

4. Kings shall fall down before him,
   and gold and incense bring;
   all nations shall adore him,
   his praise all people sing;
   to him shall prayer unceasing
   and daily vows ascend;
   his kingdom still increasing,
   a kingdom without end.

5. O'er ev'ry foe victorious,
   he on his throne shall rest,
   from age to age more glorious,
   all-blessing and all-blest;
   the tide of time shall never
   his covenant remove;
   his name shall stand for ever;
   that name to us is love.

109 Hark, my soul, it is the Lord

William Cowper (1731-1800)
based on John 21:16

John Bacchus Dykes (1823-1876)

ST BEES 77 77

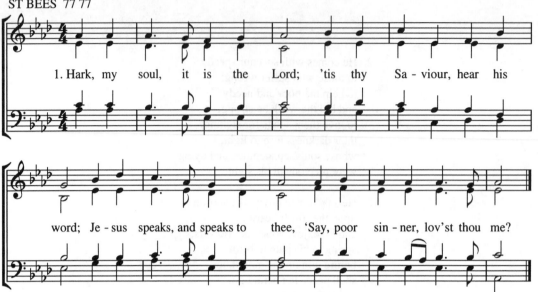

1. Hark, my soul, it is the Lord; 'tis thy Sa-viour, hear his word; Je-sus speaks, and speaks to thee, 'Say, poor sin-ner, lov'st thou me?

2. 'I delivered thee when bound,
and, when wounded, healed thy wound;
sought thee wand'ring, set thee right,
turned thy darkness into light.

3. 'Can a woman's tender care
cease towards the child she bare?
yes, she may forgetful be,
yet will I remember thee.

4. 'Mine is an unchanging love,
higher than the heights above,
deeper than the depths beneath,
free and faithful, strong as death.

5. 'Thou shalt see my glory soon,
when the work of grace is done;
partner of my throne shalt be:
say, poor sinner, lov'st thou me?'

6. Lord, it is my chief complaint
that my love is weak and faint;
yet I love thee, and adore;
O for grace to love thee more!

110 Hark, the herald-angels sing

Charles Wesley (1707-1788), George Whitefield (1714-1770),
Martin Madan (1726-1790) and others, alt.

Adapted from
Felix Mendelssohn (1809-1847)
by William Hayman Cummings (1831-1915)

MENDELSSOHN 77 77 D and Refrain

1. Hark, the he-rald-an-gels sing glo-ry to the new-born King; peace on earth and mer-cy mild, God and sin-ners re-con-ciled: joy-ful, all ye na-tions rise, join the tri-umph of the skies, with th'an-ge-lic host pro-claim, 'Christ is born in Beth-le-hem.' Hark, the he-rald-an-gels sing glo-ry to the new-born King.

2. Christ, by highest heav'n adored,
Christ, the everlasting Lord,
late in time behold him come,
offspring of a virgin's womb!
Veiled in flesh the Godhead see,
hail, th'incarnate Deity!
Pleased as man with us to dwell,
Jesus, our Emmanuel.

3. Hail, the heav'n-born Prince of Peace!
Hail, the Sun of Righteousness!
Light and life to all he brings,
ris'n with healing in his wings;
mild he lays his glory by,
born that we no more may die,
born to raise us from the earth,
born to give us second birth.

111 Have you not said *Fill us up and send us out*

Matt Redman — Matt Redman

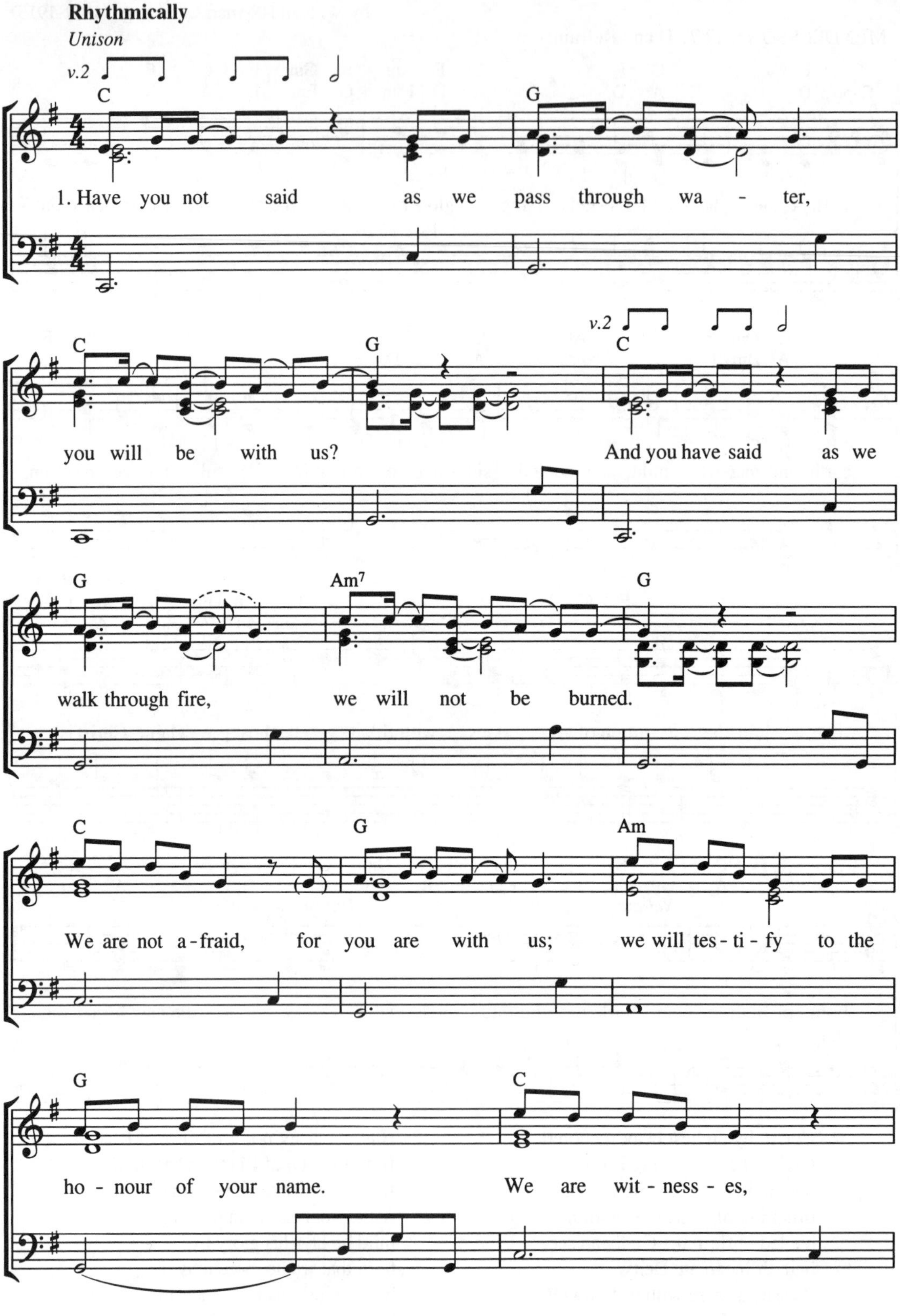
Rhythmically
Unison
v.2
C G
1. Have you not said as we pass through wa - ter,
C G C
you will be with us? And you have said as we
G Am7 G
walk through fire, we will not be burned.
C G Am
We are not a-fraid, for you are with us; we will tes-ti-fy to the
G C
ho - nour of your name. We are wit - ness - es,

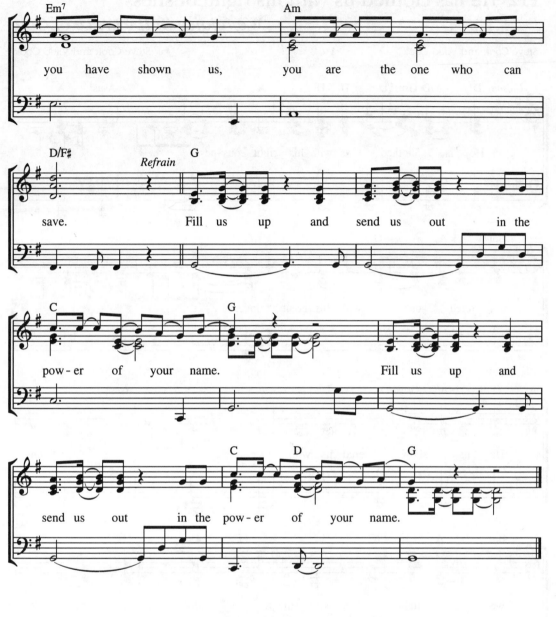

Em⁷ ... Am

you have shown us, you are the one who can

D/F♯ ... *Refrain* ... G

save. Fill us up and send us out in the

C ... G

pow-er of your name. Fill us up and

C ... D ... G

send us out in the pow-er of your name.

2. Bring them from the west, sons and daughters,
   call them for your praise.
   Gather from the east all your children,
   coming home again.
   Bring them from afar, all the nations,
   from the north and south,
   drawing all the peoples in.
   Corners of the earth, come to see there's
   only one Saviour and King.

112 He has clothed us with his righteousness

We rejoice in the grace of God

Steve Cook and Vikki Cook

Steve Cook and Vikki Cook

1. He has clothed us with his right-eous-ness, cov-ered us with his great love. He has show-ered us with mer-cy, and we de-light to know the glo-rious fa-vour, won-drous fa-vour of God.

2. He's brought us into his family,
   made us heirs with his own Son.
   All good things he freely gives us
   and we cannot conceive what God's preparing,
   God's preparing for us.

113 He has risen

Gerald Coates, Noel Richards
and Tricia Richards

Gerald Coates, Noel Richards
and Tricia Richards

2. In the grave God did not leave him,
   for his body to decay;
   raised to life, the great awakening,
   Satan's pow'r he overcame.

3. If there were no resurrection,
   we ourselves could not be raised;
   but the Son of God is living,
   so our hope is not in vain.

4. When the Lord rides out of heaven,
   mighty angels at his side,
   they will sound the final trumpet,
   from the grave we shall arise.

5. He has given life immortal,
   we shall see him face to face;
   through eternity we'll praise him,
   Christ the champion of our faith.

The Bridge

114 He is exalted

Twila Paris

Twila Paris

115 He is here

Graham Kendrick

Graham Kendrick (b.1950)

116 He is Lord

Unknown

Unknown

Triumphantly

He is Lord, he is Lord, he is ri-sen from the dead and he is Lord. Ev-'ry knee shall bow, ev-'ry tongue con - fess that Je - sus Christ is Lord.

117 Here I am

I will always love your name

Paul Oakley

Paul Oakley

Rhythmically

Unison D²

1. Here I am, and I have come to thank you Lord, for
(2.) took my sin, you took my shame, you drank my cup, you
(3.) bid me come, you make me whole, you give me peace, you re-

all you've done: thank you,
bore my pain: thank you,
store my soul: thank you,

Lord; you paid the price at
Lord; you broke the curse, you
Lord; you fill me up, and

Cal-va-ry, you shed your blood, you set me free:
broke the chains, in vic-to-ry from death you rose a-gain:
when I'm full you give me more till I o-ver-flow:

thank you, Lord;
thank you, Lord;
thank you, Lord;

no great-er love was e - ver shown, no
and not by works, but by your grace you
you're ma-king me to be like you, to

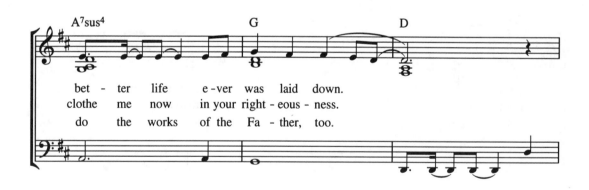

bet - ter life e -ver was laid down.
clothe me now in your right - eous - ness.
do the works of the Fa - ther, too.

And I will al - ways love your

The Bridge

118 Here is love

William Rees

Robert Lowry (1826-1899)

DIM OND IESU 87 87 D

1. Here is love vast as the o-cean, lov-ing kind-ness as the flood. When the
Prince of Life, our ran-som, shed for us his pre-cious blood. Who his
love will not re-mem-ber? Who can cease to sing his praise? He can
ne - ver be for-got-ten, through-out heav'n's e-ter-nal days.

2. On the mount of crucifixion
   fountains opened deep and wide;
   through the floodgates of God's mercy
   flowed a vast and gracious tide.
   Grace and love, like mighty rivers,
   poured incessant from above,
   and heaven's peace and perfect justice
   kissed a guilty world in love.

119 Here is the risen Son

Michael Sandeman

Michael Sandeman

Strong and majestic

Unison

Here is the ri-sen Son ride-ing out in glo-ry,

ra-di-a-ting light all a-round.

Here is the Ho-ly Spi-rit, poured out for the na-tions,

glo-ri-fy-ing Je-sus the Lamb.

We will stand as a peo-ple who are up-right and

120 He walked where I walk

God with us

Graham Kendrick

Graham Kendrick (b.1950)

Quite quick, with a steady rhythm

3 times

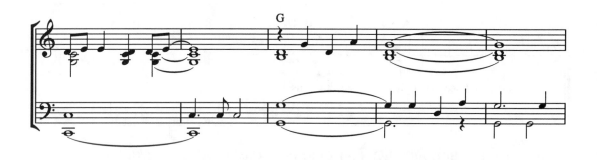

Unison

(Leader)   *(echo)*

1. He walked where I walk   (he walked where I walk).
He knows my frail - ty   (he knows my frail - ty),

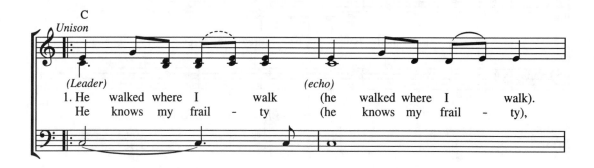

He stood where I stand   (he stood where I stand). He felt what I feel
shared my hu - ma - ni - ty   (shared my hu - ma - ni - ty),   tempt - ed in ev - 'ry way

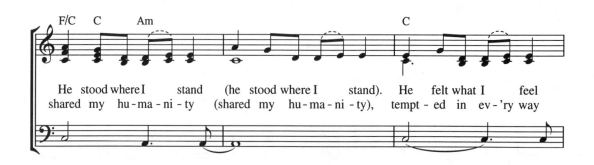

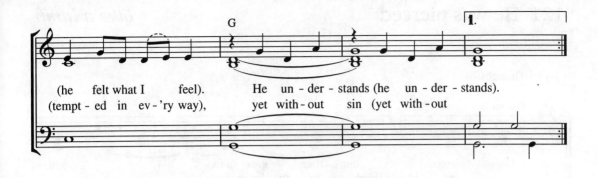

(he felt what I feel). He un - der - stands (he un - der - stands).
(tempt - ed in ev - 'ry way), yet with - out sin (yet with - out

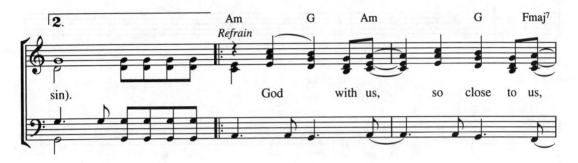

sin). God with us, so close to us,

God with us, Im - man - u - el!

(Leader)	(All)
2. One of a hated race,	(echo)
stung by the prejudice,	(echo)
suff'ring injustice,	(echo)
yet he forgives.	(echo)
Wept for my wasted years,	(echo)
paid for my wickedness,	(echo)
he died in my place,	(echo)
that I might live.	(echo)

121 He was pierced

Like a lamb

Maggi Dawn

Maggi Dawn

Thoughtful

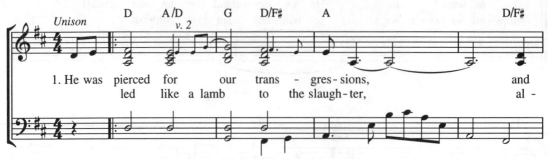

1. He was pierced for our trans-gres-sions, and
led like a lamb to the slaugh-ter, al-

bruised for our in-i-qui-ties; and to
though he was in-no-cent of crime; and cut

bring us peace he was pun-ished, and
off from the land of the liv-ing, he

by his stripes we are healed. 2. He was
paid for the guilt that was mine.

1. *To next verse*

The Bridge

122 He who began a good work

Jon Mohr

Jon Mohr

night, you can be sure that the Lord

has his hand on you, safe and se - cure, he will

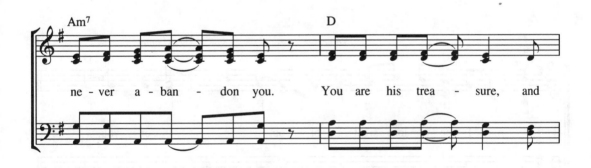

ne - ver a - ban - don you. You are his trea - sure, and

he finds his plea - sure in you.

123 Hold me closer to you — *May I never lose sight of you*

Noel and Tricia Richards

Noel and Tricia Richards

Tenderly

Unison
Refrain

Hold me clos-er to you each day; may my love for you ne -

- ver fade. Keep my fo-cus on all that's true;

To verses *Last time*

may I ne-ver lose sight of you. of you.

1. In my fail-ure, in my suc - cess,

if in sad-ness or hap - pi - ness, be the hope I am cling-

- ing to, for my heart be - longs to you.

2. You are only a breath away,
   watching over me ev'ry day;
   in my heart I am filled with peace
   when I hear you speak to me.

3. No one loves me in the way you do,
   no one cares for me like you do.
   Feels like heaven has broken through;
   God, you know how I love you.

The Bridge

124 Holiness unto the Lord

Danny Daniels

Danny Daniels

2. I love you, I love your ways,
   I love your name.
   I love you, and all my days
   I'll proclaim:

125 Holy, holy, holy is the Lord

Unknown

Unknown
arr. Susie Hare

1. Ho - ly, ho - ly, ho - ly is the Lord, ho - ly is the Lord God al - migh - ty.

Ho - ly, ho - ly, ho - ly is the Lord, ho - ly is the Lord God al - migh - ty: who

2. Jesus, Jesus, Jesus is the Lord,
   Jesus is the Lord God almighty.
   Jesus, Jesus, Jesus is the Lord,
   Jesus is the Lord God almighty:
   who was, and is, and is to come;
   Jesus, Jesus, Jesus is the Lord.

3. Worthy, worthy, worthy is the Lord,
   worthy is the Lord God almighty.
   Worthy, worthy, worthy is the Lord,
   worthy is the Lord God almighty:
   who was, and is, and is to come;
   worthy, worthy, worthy is the Lord.

4. Glory, glory, glory to the Lord,
   glory to the Lord God almighty.
   Glory, glory, glory to the Lord,
   glory to the Lord God almighty:
   who was, and is, and is to come;
   glory, glory, glory to the Lord.

126 Holy, holy, holy, Lord God almighty!

Reginald Heber (1783-1826)   John Bacchus Dykes (1823-1876)

NICAEA 11 12 12 10

1. Holy, holy, holy, Lord God almighty!
Early in the morning our song shall rise to thee;
only thou art holy, merciful and mighty,
God in three persons, blessed Trinity!

2. Holy, holy, holy! All the saints adore thee,
   casting down their golden crowns around the glassy sea;
   cherubim and seraphim falling down before thee,
   who were, and are, and evermore shall be.

3. Holy, holy, holy! Though the darkness hide thee,
   though the sinful mortal eye thy glory may not see;
   only thou art holy, there is none beside thee,
   perfect in pow'r, in love and purity.

4. Holy, holy, holy! Lord God almighty!
   All thy works shall praise thy name, in earth, and sky and sea;
   Holy, holy, holy! Merciful and mighty,
   God in three persons, blessèd Trinity!

See over for another arrangement.

John Bacchus Dykes (1823-1876)
arr. Susie Hare

NEW ARRANGEMENT

1. Ho - ly, ho - ly, ho - ly, Lord God Al - migh - ty!

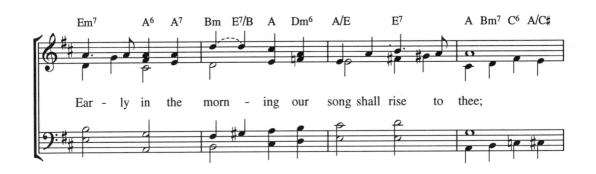

Ear - ly in the morn - ing our song shall rise to thee;

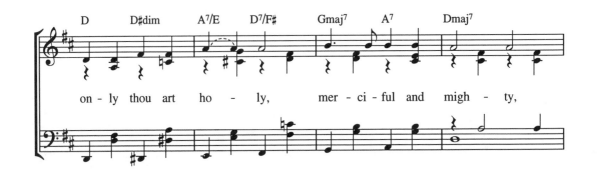

on - ly thou art ho - ly, mer - ci - ful and migh - ty,

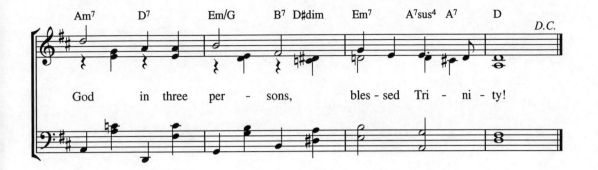

D.C.

God in three per - sons, bles - sed Tri - ni - ty!

2. Holy, holy, holy! All the saints adore thee,
   casting down their golden crowns around the glassy sea;
   cherubim and seraphim falling down before thee,
   who were, and are, and evermore shall be.

3. Holy, holy, holy! Though the darkness hide thee,
   though the sinful mortal eye thy glory may not see;
   only thou art holy, there is none beside thee,
   perfect in pow'r, in love, and purity.

4. Holy, holy, holy! Lord God almighty!
   All thy works shall praise thy name, in earth, and sky and sea;
   Holy, holy, holy! Merciful and mighty,
   God in three persons, blessèd Trinity!

The Bridge

127 Hosanna

Carl Tuttle

Carl Tuttle

Lively

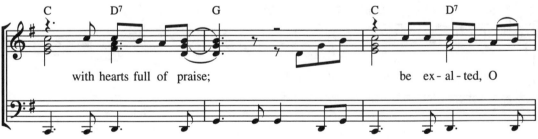

128 How can I be free from sin?

Lead me to the cross

Graham Kendrick and Steve Thompson

Graham Kendrick (b.1950) and Steve Thompson

1. How can I be free from sin? Lead me to the cross of Je - sus, from the guilt, the pow'r, the pain, lead me to the cross of Je - sus.

There's no o - ther way, no price that I could pay,

simp - ly to the cross I cling.

This is all I need, this is all I plead,

that his blood was shed for me.

2. How can I know peace within?
   Lead me to the cross of Jesus,
   sing a song of joy again,
   lead me to the cross of Jesus.

   Flowing from above,
   all-forgiving love,
   from the Father's heart to me.
   What a gift of grace,
   his own righteousness,
   clothing me in purity.

3. How can I live day by day?
   Lead me to the cross of Jesus,
   following his narrow way,
   lead me to the cross of Jesus.

129 How deep the Father's love for us

Stuart Townend

Stuart Townend

Thoughtfully

Unison

1. How deep the Fa-ther's love for us, how vast be-yond all mea - sure, that he should give his on - ly Son to make a wretch his trea - sure. How great the pain of sear - ing loss, the Fa - ther turns his face a - way, as wounds which mar the Cho - sen One bring

ma - ny sons to glo - ry.

2. Behold the man upon a cross,
   my sin upon his shoulders;
   ashamed, I hear my mocking voice
   call out among the scoffers.
   It was my sin that held him there
   until it was accomplished;
   his dying breath has brought me life –
   I know that it is finished.

3. I will not boast in anything,
   no gifts, no pow'r, no wisdom;
   but I will boast in Jesus Christ,
   his death and resurrection.
   Why should I gain from his reward?
   I cannot give an answer,
   but this I know with all my heart,
   his wounds have paid my ransom.

The Bridge

130 How good is the God we adore!

Joseph Hart (1712-1768)

'Lancashire Sunday School Songs' (1857)

CELESTE LM

1. How good is the God we a-dore! Our faith-ful, un-change-a-ble friend: his love is as great as his pow'r and knows nei-ther mea-sure nor end.

2. For Christ is the first and the last;
   his Spirit will guide us safe home;
   we'll praise him for all that is past
   and trust him for all that's to come.

A lower setting

1. How good is the God we a-dore! Our faith-ful, un-change-a-ble friend: his love is as great as his pow'r and knows nei-ther mea-sure nor end.

131 How lovely on the mountains

Our God reigns

Based on Isaiah 52,
v.1: Leonard E. Smith Jnr.; vs. 2-4: unknown

Leonard E. Smith Jnr. (b.1942)

Triumphantly, with pace

1. How love-ly on the moun-tains are the feet of him who brings good news, good news, pro-claim-ing peace, an-noun-cing news of hap-pi-ness: our God reigns, our God reigns, our God reigns, our God reigns, our God reigns, our God reigns!

2. You watchmen, lift your voices joyfully as one,
   shout for your King, your King.
   See eye to eye the Lord restoring Zion:
   your God reigns, your God reigns!

3. Waste places of Jerusalem, break forth with joy,
   we are redeemed, redeemed.
   The Lord has saved and comforted his people:
   your God reigns, your God reigns!

4. Ends of the earth, see the salvation of your God,
   Jesus is Lord, is Lord.
   Before the nations he has bared his holy arm:
   your God reigns, your God reigns!

132 How sweet the name of Jesus sounds

John Newton (1725-1807) alt.

Alexander Robert Reinagle (1799-1877)

TUNE 1: SAINT PETER CM

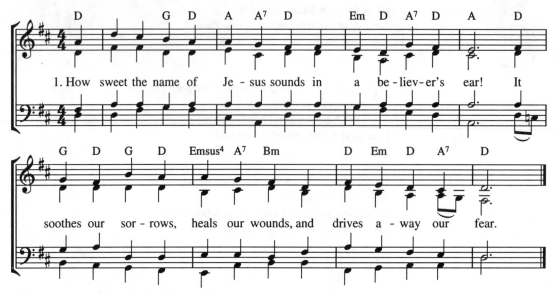

1. How sweet the name of Je - sus sounds in a be - liev - er's ear! It soothes our sor - rows, heals our wounds, and drives a - way our fear.

The verses are sung in pairs for the second setting.

2. It makes the wounded spirit whole,
   and calms the troubled breast;
   'tis manna to the hungry soul,
   and to the weary, rest.

3. Dear name! the rock on which I build,
   my shield and hiding-place,
   my never-failing treas'ry filled
   with boundless stores of grace.

4. Jesus! my Shepherd, Saviour, Friend,
   my Prophet, Priest, and King,
   my Lord, my life, my way, my end,
   accept the praise I bring.

5. Weak is the effort of my heart,
   and cold my warmest thought;
   but when I see thee as thou art,
   I'll praise thee as I ought.

6. Till then I would thy love proclaim
   with ev'ry fleeting breath;
   and may the music of thy name
   refresh my soul in death.

John Newton (1725-1807) alt.

Chris Bowater

TUNE 2: RACHEL CM

133 How wondrous is your presence, Lord

Your holiness is beautiful

Mark Altrogge

Mark Altrogge

Flowing and gentle

1. How won-drous is your pre - sence, Lord, too
long to see your splen - dour, Lord, you've

awe - some to be - hold. The se - ra - phim must turn
burned it in my heart. My hung - er won't be sat -

a - way, the an - gels are not bold. For
- is - fied to wor - ship from a - far. Oh

who can bear the bright - ness of your ho - ly dwell - ing - place?
cause your face to shine on me and take the veil a - way;

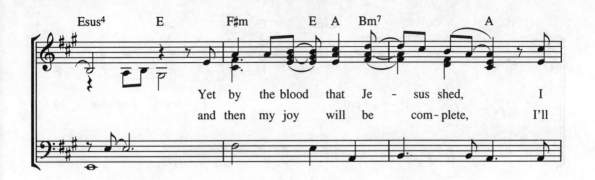

Yet by the blood that Je - sus shed, I
and then my joy will be com - plete, I'll

dare to lift my gaze. Your
sing e - ter - nal praise.

ho - li - ness is beau - ti - ful, O Lord.

Your ho - li - ness is beau - ti - ful, my

glo - ri -ous Lord. I see you now by

faith, but soon, Lord, face to face. Your

ho - li - ness is beau - ti - ful, my

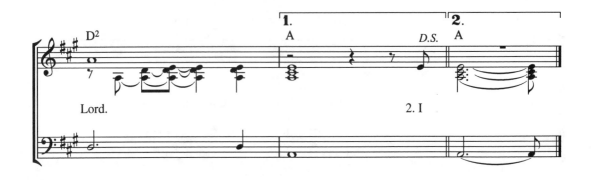

Lord. 2. I

134 Humble yourselves

Susie Hare

Susie Hare

135 I am a new creation

Dave Bilbrough

Dave Bilbrough

136 I am learning

Susie Hare

Susie Hare

1. I am learn-ing, Lord, that in your plan for me,
some things won't be quite the same as I would have them be;
I am learn-ing, Lord, your pur-pos-es to know;
a-ny hard-ship you al-low will help my faith to grow. For
I can do all things in him who strength-ens me; in the

power of Jesus is where my strength shall be. For I can do all things in him who strength-ens me; in the power of Jesus is where my strength shall be.

2. I am learning, Lord, that in your plan for me,
   I must learn acceptance of the things that are to be;
   I am learning, Lord, whatever life may ask,
   you will give me strength enough
   to arm me for my task.

3. I am learning, Lord, that in your plan for me,
   all that I will ever do should for your glory be;
   I am learning, Lord, to put my trust in you;
   even when the way is hard,
   your grace will take me through.

137 I believe in Jesus

Marc Nelson

Marc Nelson

With conviction

I be-lieve in Je - sus;
I be-lieve in you, Lord;

I be-lieve he is the Son of God.
I be-lieve you are the Son of God.

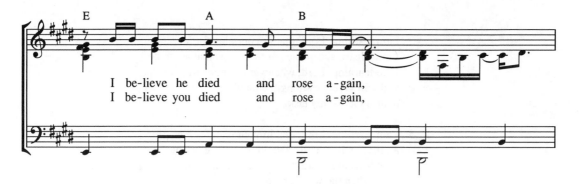

I be-lieve he died and rose a - gain,
I be-lieve you died and rose a - gain,

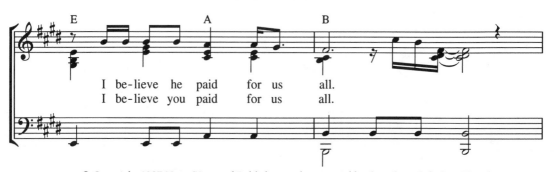

I be-lieve he paid for us all.
I be-lieve you paid for us all.

138 I believe there is a God in heaven

Dave Bilbrough

Dave Bilbrough

With a lilt

I be-lieve there is a God in heav'n who paid the price for all my sin; shed his blood to o-pen up the way for me to walk with him. him. Gave his life up-on a cross, took the pun-ish-ment for

139 I cannot tell

William Young Fullerton (1857-1932), alt.

Traditional Irish melody
arr. Noel Rawsthorne

LONDONDERRY AIR 11 10 11 10 11 10 11 12

1. I can-not tell how he whom an-gels wor - ship should stoop to love the peo-ples of the earth, or why as shep - herd he should seek the wand - 'rer with his mys - te - rious pro-mise of new birth. But this I know, that he was born of Ma - ry, when Beth-l'em's man - ger was his on - ly

home, and that he lived at Na - za - reth and la - boured, and so the Sa-viour, Sa-viour of the world, is come.

2. I cannot tell how silently he suffered,
   as with his peace he graced this place of tears,
   or how his heart upon the cross was broken,
   the crown of pain to three and thirty years.
   But this I know, he heals the broken-hearted,
   and stays our sin, and calms our lurking fear,
   and lifts the burden from the heavy laden,
   for yet the Saviour, Saviour of the world, is here.

3. I cannot tell how he will win the nations,
   how he will claim his earthly heritage,
   how satisfy the needs and aspirations
   of east and west, of sinner and of sage.
   But this I know, all flesh shall see his glory,
   and he shall reap the harvest he has sown,
   and some glad day his sun shall shine in splendour
   when he the Saviour, Saviour of the world, is known.

4. I cannot tell how all the lands shall worship,
   when, at his bidding, ev'ry storm is stilled,
   or who can say how great the jubilation
   when ev'ry heart with perfect love is filled.
   But this I know, the skies will thrill with rapture,
   and myriad, myriad human voices sing,
   and earth to heav'n, and heav'n to earth will answer:
   'At last the Saviour, Saviour of the world is King!'

140 I come into your presence, Holy King

Reign in me

Susie Hare

Susie Hare

Unhurried

1. I come into your pre-sence, Ho-ly King, and
(2.) come be-fore your throne of sov'reign-ty, and
(3.) come, no long-er cap-tive to the fears that

at your feet, sur-ren-der ev-'ry-thing; my
give my life to your au-tho-ri-ty; may
bound my stub-born heart in wast-ed years; for-

pride, in bro-ken-ness to you I bring; reign in me,
there be more of you and less of me; reign in me,
give - ness wash-es me in heal-ing tears; reign in me,

reign in me. I come, as clay with-in the pot-ter's hand, and
reign in me. I come, with no-where left to hide my face, to
reign in me. I come, with all my hopes and dreams laid down; I

141 I give you all the honour

I worship you

Carl Tuttle

Carl Tuttle

2. As your Spirit moves upon me now,
   you meet my deepest need,
   and I lift my hands up to your throne,
   your mercy I've received.

3. You have broken chains that bound me,
   you've set this captive free,
   I will lift my voice to praise your name
   for all eternity.

The Bridge

142 I have a destiny

Mark Altrogge

Mark Altrogge

pared for me. You've gi – ven me a part
bund – ant-ly. I know you will com – plete

to play in his – to-ry to
the work be – gun in me, by the

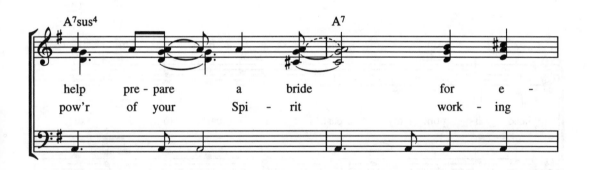

help pre – pare a bride for e –
pow'r of your Spi – rit work – ing

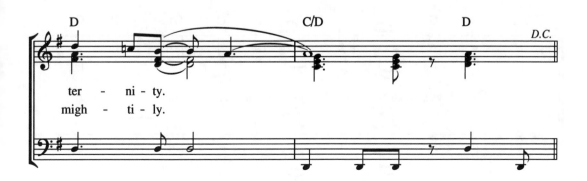

ter – ni – ty.
migh – ti – ly.

143 I heard the voice of Jesus say

Horatius Bonar (1808-1889)

Traditional English melody collected by Lucy Broadwater (1858-1929)
adapted and arr. Ralph Vaughan Williams (1872-1958)

TUNE 1: KINGSFOLD DCM

1. I heard the voice of Je-sus say, 'Come un-to me and rest; lay down, thou wea-ry one, lay down thy head u-pon my breast.' I came to Je-sus as I was, so wea-ry, worn and sad; I

found in him a rest - ing - place, and he has made me glad.

2. I heard the voice of Jesus say,
   'Behold, I freely give
   the living water, thirsty one;
   stoop down and drink and live.'
   I came to Jesus, and I drank
   of that life-giving stream;
   my thirst was quenched, my soul revived,
   and now I live in him.

3. I heard the voice of Jesus say,
   'I am this dark world's light;
   look unto me, thy morn shall rise,
   and all thy day be bright.'
   I looked to Jesus, and I found
   in him my star, my sun;
   and in that light of life I'll walk
   till trav'lling days are done.

See over for another tune

Horatius Bonar (1808-1889)

Susie Hare

TUNE 2: NYMPSFIELD DCM

Thoughtfully

1. I heard the voice of Je - sus say, 'Come un - to me and rest; lay down, thou wea - ry one, lay down thy head up - on my breast.' I came to Je - sus as I was, so wea - ry, worn and sad; I found in him a rest - ing - place, and he has made me

2. I heard the voice of Jesus say,
'Behold, I freely give
the living water, thirsty one;
stoop down and drink and live.'
I came to Jesus, and I drank
of that life-giving stream;
my thirst was quenched, my soul revived,
and now I live in him.

3. I heard the voice of Jesus say,
'I am this dark world's light;
look unto me, thy morn shall rise,
and all thy day be bright.'
I looked to Jesus, and I found
in him my star, my sun;
and in that light of life I'll walk
till trav'lling days are done.

144 I know a place

At the cross

Randy and Terry Butler

Randy and Terry Butler

I know a place, a won-der-ful place,

where ac - cused and con - demned

find mer - cy and grace, where the

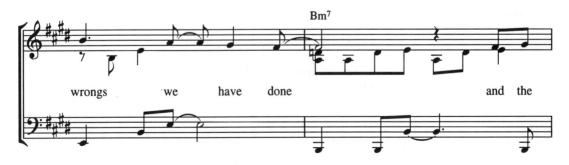

wrongs we have done and the

145 I know not why

I know whom I have believed

D.W. Whittle (1840-1901)

James McGranahan (1840-1907)

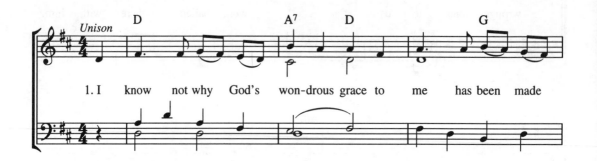

1. I know not why God's won-drous grace to me has been made

known; nor why, un-wor - thy as I am, he

claimed me for his own. But 'I know whom I have be -

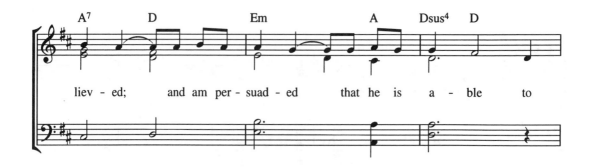

liev - ed; and am per - suad - ed that he is a - ble to

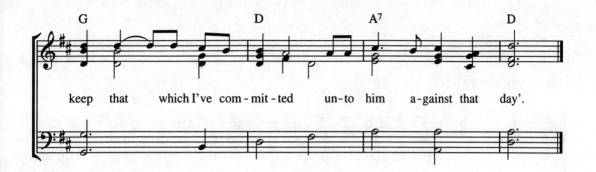

keep that which I've com-mit-ted un-to him a-gainst that day'.

2. I know not how this saving faith
   to me he did impart;
   or how believing in his word
   wrought peace upon my heart.

3. I know not how the Spirit moves,
   convincing us of sin;
   revealing Jesus through the word,
   creating faith in him.

4. I know not what of good or ill
   may be reserved for me –
   of weary ways or golden days
   before his face I see.

See over for another arrangement.

James McGranahan (1840-1907)
arr. Susie Hare

NEW ARRANGEMENT

1. I know not why God's won - drous grace to

me has been made known; nor why, un - wor - thy

as I am, he claimed me for his own. But 'I

know whom I have be - liev - ed; and am per - suad - ed that he is

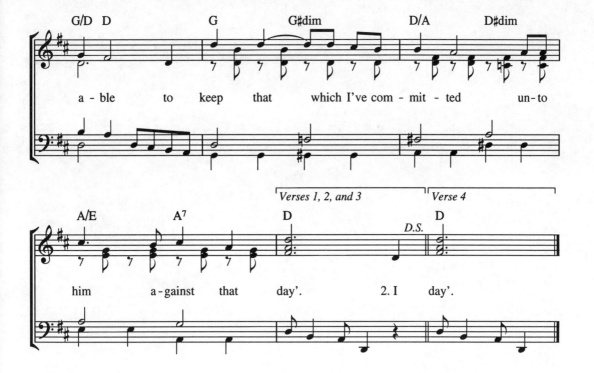

able to keep that which I've com - mit - ted un - to him a-gainst that day'. 2. I day'.

Verses 1, 2, and 3

Verse 4

D.S.

2. I know not how this saving faith
   to me he did impart;
   or how believing in his word
   wrought peace upon my heart.

3. I know not how the Spirit moves,
   convincing us of sin;
   revealing Jesus through the word,
   creating faith in him.

4. I know not what of good or ill
   may be reserved for me –
   of weary ways or golden days
   before his face I see.

The Bridge

146 I lift my hands

I will serve no foreign god

Andre Kempen

Andre Kempen

147 I'm accepted, I'm forgiven

Rob Hayward

Rob Hayward

Worshipfully

Unison Capo 4

I'm ac-cep - ted, I'm for-gi - ven, I am
fa - thered by the true and liv-ing God. I'm ac-cep-
- ted, no con-dem-na - tion, I am
loved by the true and liv-ing God. There's no

guilt or fear as I draw near to the

Sa-viour and Cre-a - tor of the world. There is

joy and peace as I re - lease my

wor - ship to you, O Lord.

The Bridge

148 Immortal, invisible, God only wise

Walter Chalmers Smith (1824-1908),
based on 1 Timothy 1:17

Traditional Welsh hymn melody (1839)

SAINT DENIO 11 11 11 11

1. Im - mor - tal, in - vi - si - ble, God on - ly wise, in light in - ac - ces - si - ble hid from our eyes, most bless - ed, most glo - rious, the An - cient of Days, al - migh - ty, vic - to - rious, thy great name we praise.

2. Unresting, unhasting, and silent as light,
   nor wanting, nor wasting, thou rulest in might;
   thy justice like mountains high soaring above
   thy clouds which are fountains of goodness and love.

3. To all life thou givest, to both great and small;
   in all life thou livest, the true life of all;
   we blossom and flourish as leaves on the tree,
   and wither and perish; but naught changeth thee.

4. Great Father of glory, pure Father of light,
   thine angels adore thee, all veiling their sight;
   all laud we would render, O help us to see
   'tis only the splendour of light hideth thee.

5. *repeat 1st verse*

149 I need thee every hour

Annie Sherwood Hawks (1835-1918)

Robert Lowry (1826-1899)

I NEED THEE 10 10 and Refrain

1. I need thee ev-'ry hour, most gra - cious Lord; no ten - der voice like thine can peace af - ford. I need thee, O I need thee! Ev - 'ry hour I need thee; O bless me now, my Sa - viour! I come to thee.

2. I need thee ev'ry hour,
   stay thou near by;
   temptations lose their pow'r
   when thou art nigh.

3. I need thee ev'ry hour,
   in joy or pain;
   come quickly and abide,
   or life is vain.

4. I need thee ev'ry hour,
   teach me thy will;
   and thy rich promises
   in me fulfil.

5. I need thee ev'ry hour,
   most Holy One;
   O make me thine indeed,
   thou blessèd Son!

NEW ARRANGEMENT

Robert Lowry (1826-1899)
arr. Susie Hare

150 In every circumstance

David Fellingham David Fellingham

With a 12/8 feel

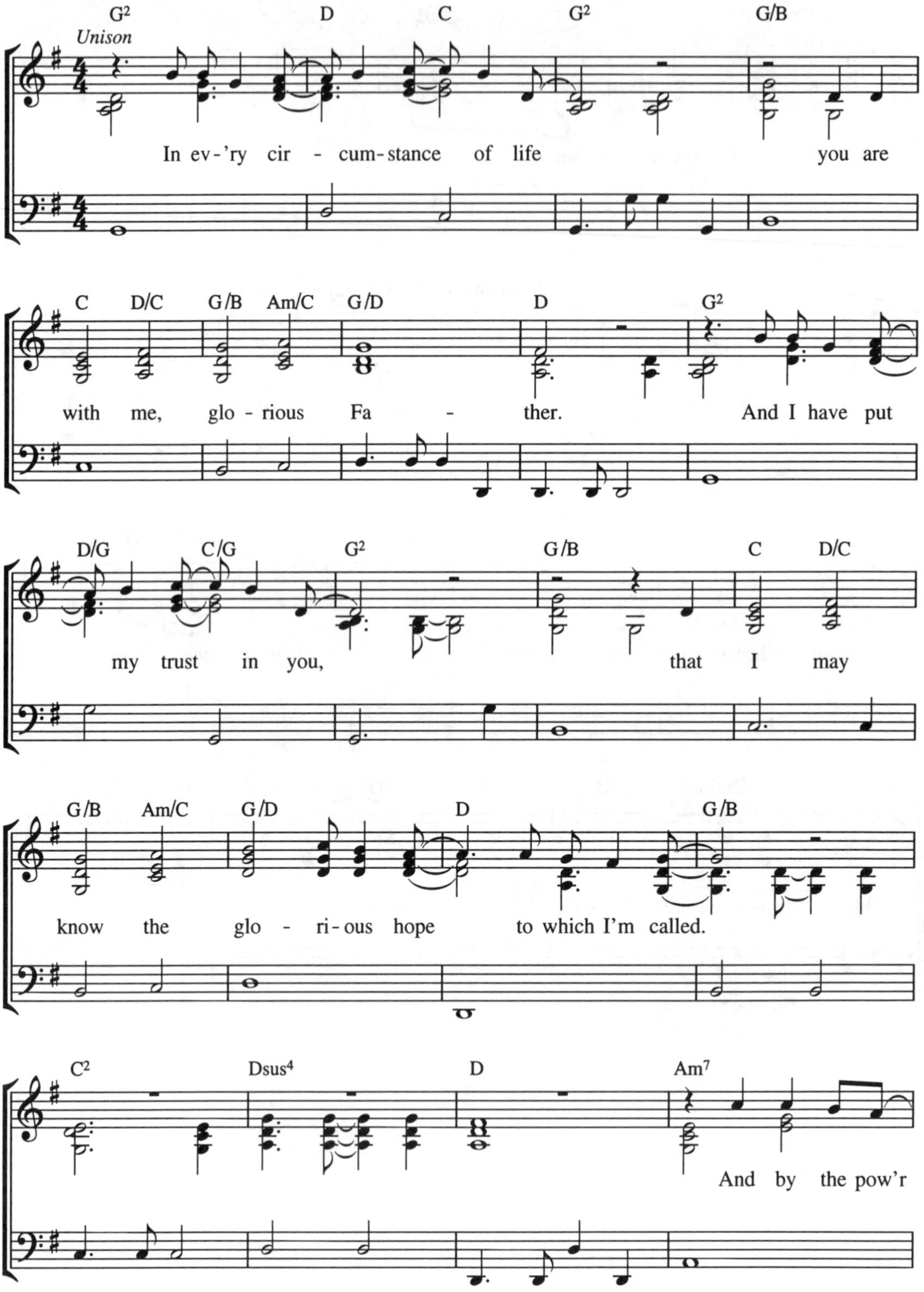

G2 D C G2 G/B
Unison
In ev-'ry cir - cum-stance of life you are
C D/C G/B Am/C G/D D G2
with me, glo - rious Fa - ther. And I have put
D/G C/G G2 G/B C D/C
my trust in you, that I may
G/B Am/C G/D D G/B
know the glo - ri-ous hope to which I'm called.
C2 Dsus4 D Am7
And by the pow'r

151 In heavenly armour · *The battle belongs to the Lord*

Jamie Owens-Collins

Jamie Owens-Collins

With strength

Unison

1. In hea-ven-ly ar - mour we'll en- -ter the land, the bat - tle be - longs to the Lord.

No wea - pon that's fash - ion'd a - gainst us will stand, the bat - tle be - longs to the Lord.

Refrain

And we sing glo - ry, hon - our,

power and strength to the Lord. We sing glo - ry,

hon - our, pow - er and strength to the Lord.

Last time

2. When the power of darkness comes in like a flood,
   the battle belongs to the Lord.
   He'll raise up a standard, the power of his blood,
   the battle belongs to the Lord.

3. When your enemy presses in hard, do not fear,
   the battle belongs to the Lord.
   Take courage, my friend, your redemption is near,
   the battle belongs to the Lord.

152 In heavenly love abiding

Anna Laetitia Waring (1820-1910)
based on Psalm 23

David Jenkins (1848-1915)

PENLAN 76 76 D

1. In heav'n-ly love a - bi - ding, no change my heart shall

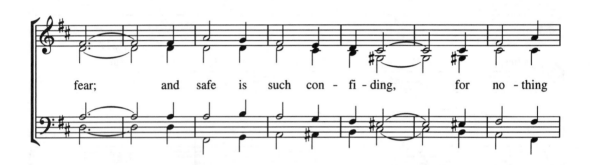

fear; and safe is such con - fi - ding, for no - thing

chan - ges here. The storm may roar with - out me, my

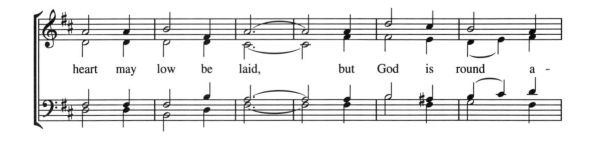

heart may low be laid, but God is round a -

bout me, and can I be dis - mayed?

2. Wherever he may guide me,
   no want shall turn me back;
   my Shepherd is beside me,
   and nothing shall I lack.
   His wisdom ever waketh,
   his sight is never dim,
   he knows the way he taketh,
   and I will walk with him.

3. Green pastures are before me,
   which yet I have not seen;
   bright skies will soon be o'er me,
   where the dark clouds have been.
   My hope I cannot measure,
   my path to life is free,
   my Saviour has my treasure,
   and he will walk with me.

The Bridge

153 In the bleak mid-winter

Christina Georgina Rossetti (1830-1894) Gustav Holst (1874-1934)

CRANHAM Irregular

1. In the bleak mid – win – ter fros – ty wind made
2. Our God, heav'n can – not hold him nor earth sus –
3. E – nough for him, whom che – ru – bim wor – ship night and
4. An – gels and arch – an – gels may have ga – thered
5. What can I give him, poor as I

moan, earth stood hard as ir – on, wa – ter like a
tain; heav'n and earth shall flee a – way when he comes to
day, a breast – ful of milk, and a man – ger – ful of
there, che – ru – bim and se – ra – phim thronged the
am? If I were a shep – herd I would bring a

stone; snow had fal – len, snow on snow, snow on
reign. In the bleak mid – win – ter a sta – ble – place suf –
hay: e – nough for him, whom an – gels fall down be –
air; but on – ly his mo – ther in her mai – den
lamb; if I were a wise man I would do my

snow, in the bleak mid – win – ter, long a – go.
ficed the Lord God al – migh – ty, Je – sus Christ.
fore, the ox and ass and ca – mel which a – dore.
bliss wor – shipped the be – lov – ed with a kiss.
part, yet what I can I give him: give my heart.

154 Into the darkness

Come, Lord Jesus, come

Maggi Dawn

Maggi Dawn

Steadily

1. In-to the dark-ness of this world, in-to the sha-dows of the night; in-to this love-less place you came, light-ened our bur-dens, eased our pain, and made these hearts your home. In-to the dark-ness once

2. Into the longing of our souls,
   into these heavy hearts of stone,
   shine on us now your piercing light,
   order our lives and souls aright,
   by grace and love unknown,
   until in you our hearts unite,
   O come, Lord Jesus, come.

3. O Holy Child, Emmanuel,
   hope of the ages, God with us,
   visit again this broken place,
   till all the earth declares your praise
   and your great mercies own.
   Now let your love be born in us,
   O come, Lord Jesus, come.

Final Refrain
Come in your glory, take your place,
Jesus, the name above all names,
we long to see you face to face,
O come, Lord Jesus, come.

155 Into your courts

Gerrit Gustafson

Gerrit Gustafson

In-to your courts we come, deep in our hearts we
long to be near to the throne of your glo - ry.
As we draw near to you, know that we're here
to do your will, God how we long to be near
to you. May our prayers be like in -

156 I sing praises

Terry MacAlmon

Terry McAlmon

1. I sing prai-ses to your name, O Lord, prai-ses to your name, O Lord, for your name is great and great-ly to be praised. I sing prai-ses to your name, O Lord, prai-ses to your name, O Lord, for your name is great and great-ly to be praised.

2. I give glory to your name, O Lord,
   glory to your name, O Lord,
   for your name is great and greatly to be praised. *(twice)*

157 Isn't he beautiful

John Wimber

John Wimber (b.1933)

2. Yes, you are beautiful,
   beautiful, yes, you are . . .

158 I stand amazed in the presence — *How marvellous*

Charles Homer Gabriel

Charles Homer Gabriel (1856–1932)

MY SAVIOUR'S LOVE 87 87 and Refrain

1. I stand a-mazed in the pre-sence of Je-sus the Na-za-rene, and won-der how he could love me, a sin-ner, con-demned, un-clean.

Refrain

How mar-vel-lous! how won-der-ful, O, how mar-vel-lous! O, how won-der-ful, and my song shall e-ver be:

How mar-vel-lous! how won-der-ful! O, how mar-vel-lous! O, how won-der-ful! is my Sa-viour's love for me!

2. For me it was in the garden
   he prayed – 'Not my will, but thine';
   he had no tears for his own griefs,
   but sweat drops of blood for mine.

3. In pity angels beheld him,
   and came from the world of light,
   to comfort him in the sorrows
   he bore for my soul that night.

4. He took my sins and my sorrows,
   he made them his very own;
   he bore the burden to Calvary,
   and suffered, and died alone.

5. When with the ransomed in glory
   his face I at last shall see,
   'twill be my joy through the ages
   to sing of his love for me.

See over for another arrangement.

Charles Homer Gabriel (1856-1932)
arr. Susie Hare

NEW ARRANGEMENT

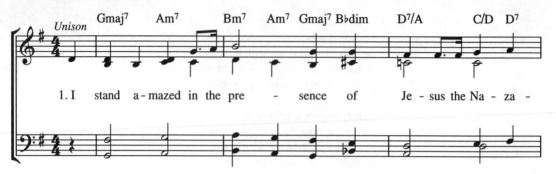

1. I stand a-mazed in the pre - sence of Je - sus the Na - za -

rene, and won-der how he could love me, a

sin - ner, con-demned, un - clean. How mar-vel-lous!

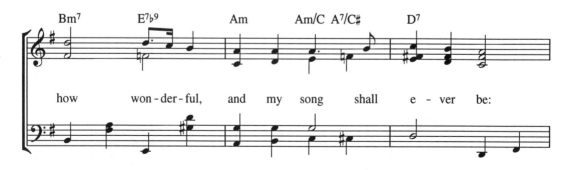

how won-der-ful, and my song shall e - ver be:

How mar - vel - lous! how won - der - ful! is my Sa - viour's love for me!

2. For me it was in the garden
   he prayed – 'Not my will, but thine';
   he had no tears for his own griefs,
   but sweat drops of blood for mine.

3. In pity angels beheld him,
   and came from the world of light,
   to comfort him in the sorrows
   he bore for my soul that night.

4. He took my sins and my sorrows,
   he made them his very own;
   he bore the burden to Calvary,
   and suffered, and died alone.

5. When with the ransomed in glory
   his face I at last shall see,
   'twill be my joy through the ages
   to sing of his love for me.

159 It came upon the midnight clear

Edmund Hamilton Sears (1810-1876) alt.

Traditional English melody
arr. Arthur Seymour Sullivan

NOEL DCM

1. It came up-on the mid-night clear, that glo-rious song of old, from an-gels bend-ing near the earth to touch their harps of gold: 'Peace on the earth, good-will to all, from heav'ns all-gra-cious King!' The world in so-lemn still-ness lay to hear the an-gels sing.

2. Still through the cloven skies they come,
   with peaceful wings unfurled;
   and still their heav'nly music floats
   o'er all the weary world:
   above its sad and lowly plains
   they bend on hov'ring wing;
   and ever o'er its Babel-sounds
   the blessèd angels sing.

3. Yet with the woes of sin and strife
   the world has suffered long;
   beneath the angel-strain have rolled
   two thousand years of wrong;
   and warring humankind hears not
   the love-song which they bring:
   O hush the noise of mortal strife,
   and hear the angels sing!

4. And ye, beneath life's crushing load,
   whose forms are bending low,
   who toil along the climbing way
   with painful steps and slow:
   look now! for glad and golden hours
   come swiftly on the wing;
   O rest beside the weary road,
   and hear the angels sing.

5. For lo, the days are hast'ning on,
   by prophets seen of old,
   when with the ever-circling years
   comes round the age of gold;
   when peace shall over all the earth
   its ancient splendours fling,
   and all the world give back the song
   which now the angels sing.

160 It is a thing most wonderful

William Walsham How (1823-1897)

Thomas Bishop Southgate (1814-1868)

BROOKFIELD LM

1. It is a thing most won - der - ful, al - most too
won - der - ful to be, that God's own Son should
come from heav'n, and die to save a child like me.

2. And yet I know that it is true:
   he chose a poor and humble lot,
   and wept and toiled, and mourned and died,
   for love of those who loved him not.

3. I sometimes think about the cross,
   and shut my eyes, and try to see
   the cruel nails and crown of thorns,
   and Jesus crucified for me.

4. But even could I see him die,
   I could but see a little part
   of that great love which, like a fire,
   is always burning in his heart.

5. I cannot tell how he could love
   a child so weak and full of sin;
   his love must be most wonderful,
   if he could die my love to win.

6. It is most wonderful to know
   his love for me so free and sure;
   but 'tis more wonderful to see
   my love for him so faint and poor.

7. And yet I want to love thee, Lord;
   O light the flame within my heart,
   and I will love thee more and more,
   until I see thee as thou art.

161 It is the Lord

Pete and Cha Wright

Pete and Cha Wright
arr. Susie Hare

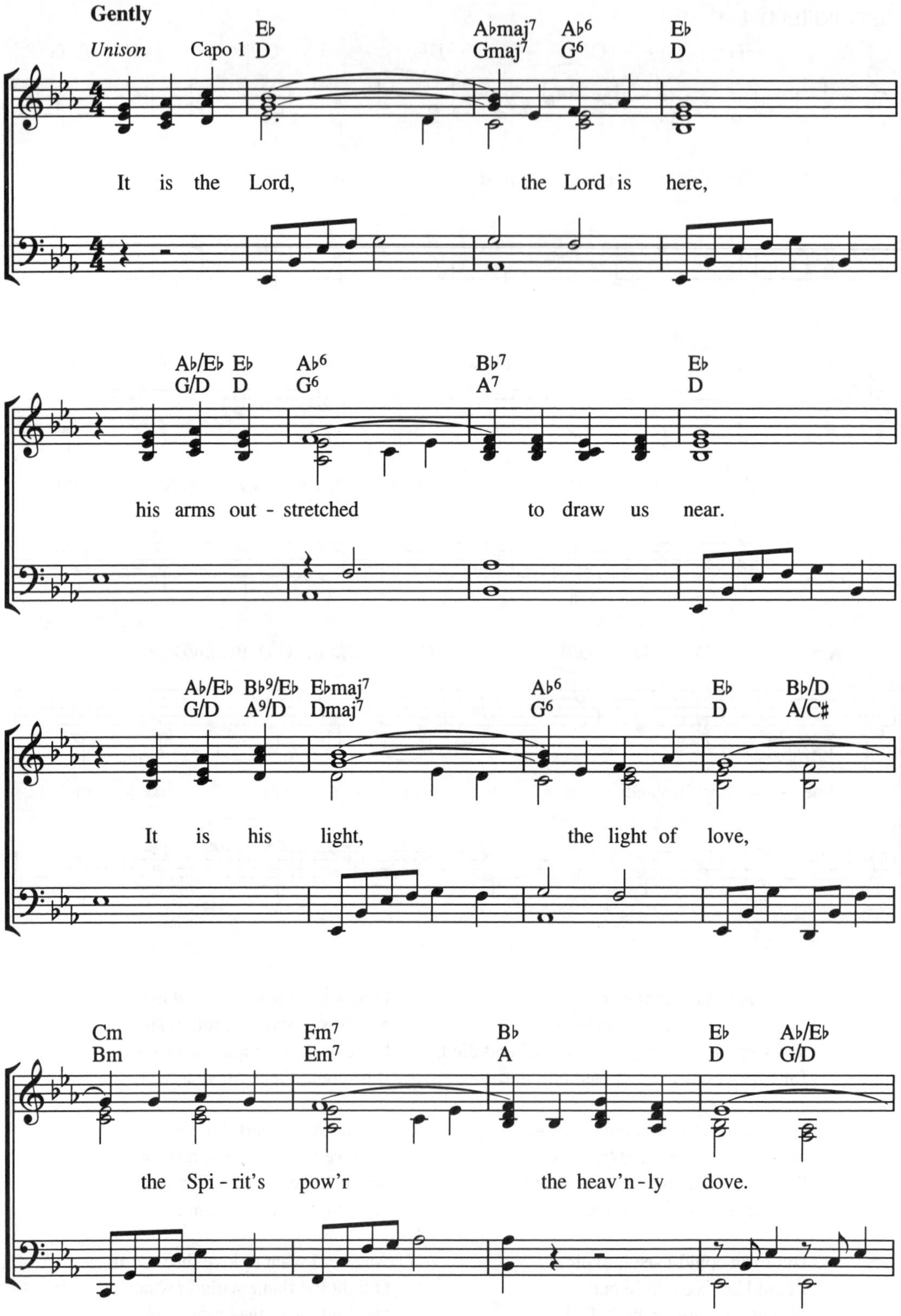

Gently
Unison Capo 1

It is the Lord, the Lord is here,

his arms out - stretched to draw us near.

It is his light, the light of love,

the Spi - rit's pow'r the heav'n - ly dove.

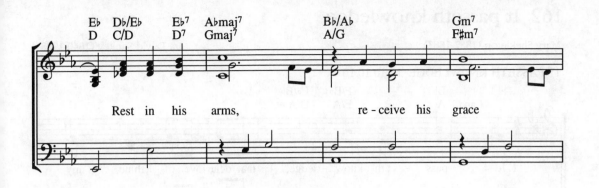

Rest in his arms, re-ceive his grace

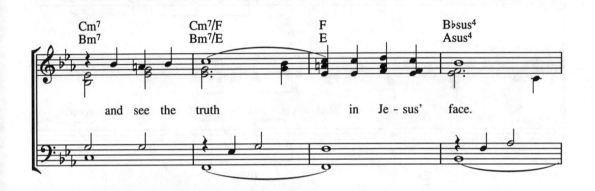

and see the truth in Je-sus' face.

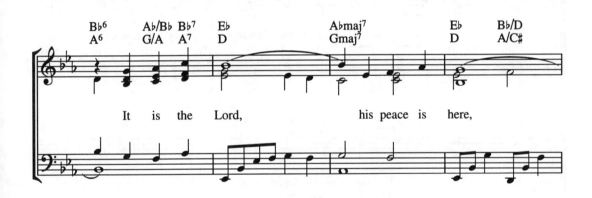

It is the Lord, his peace is here,

his bles-sings fall as we draw near.

162 It passeth knowledge

Mary Shekleton (1827-1883)   Ira David Sankey (1840-1908)

IT PASSETH KNOWLEDGE 10 10 10 10 4

1. It passeth knowledge, that dear love of thine, my Saviour, Jesus! yet this soul of mine would of thy love, in all its breadth and length, its height and depth, and ever-lasting strength, know more and more.

2. It passeth telling, that dear love of thine,
   my Saviour, Jesus! yet these lips of mine
   would fain proclaim, to sinners, far and near,
   a love which can remove all guilty fear,
   and love beget.

3. It passeth praises, that dear love of thine,
   my Saviour, Jesus! yet this heart of mine
   would sing that love, so full, so rich, so free,
   which brings a rebel sinner, such as me,
   nigh unto God.

4. O fill me, Saviour, Jesus, with thy love;
   lead, lead me to the living fount above;
   thither may I, in simple faith, draw nigh,
   and never to another fountain fly,
   but unto thee.

5. And then, when Jesus face to face I see,
   when at his lofty throne I bow the knee,
   then of his love, in all its breadth and length,
   its height and depth, its everlasting strength,
   my soul shall sing.

NEW ARRANGEMENT

With an easy swing

Ira David Sankey (1840-1908)
arr. Susie Hare

1. It pass - eth know - ledge, that dear love of thine, my Sa - viour, Je - sus! yet this soul of mine would of thy love, in all its breadth and length, its height and depth, and e - ver - last - ing strength, know more and more.

163 It's rising up

Matt Redman and Martin Smith

Matt Redman and Martin Smith

1. It's ris-ing up from coast to coast, from
   for-mer things have ta-ken place. Can

north to south, and east to west; the cry of hearts that
this be the new day of praise? A heav'n-ly song that

love your name, which with one voice we will pro-claim.
comes to birth, and reach-es out to all

2. The

the earth. O, let the cry to na-tions ring, that

3. And we have heard the Lion's roar,
   that speaks of heaven's love and pow'r.
   Is this the time, is this the call
   that ushers in your kingdom rule?
   O, let the cry to nations ring,
   that all may come and all may sing:
       'Jesus is alive!' (Ev'ry heart sing:)
       'Jesus is alive!' (With one voice sing:)
       'Jesus is alive!' (All the earth sing:)
       'Jesus is alive!'

The Bridge

164 It's your blood

Michael Christ

Michael Christ

It's your blood that clean - ses me, it's your blood that gives me life, it's your blood that took my place in re - deem - ing sac - ri - fice, and wash - es me whi - ter than the snow, than the snow. My Je - sus, God's pre - cious sac - ri - fice.

165 I want to serve the purpose of God   *In my generation*

Mark Altrogge

Mark Altrogge

Driving

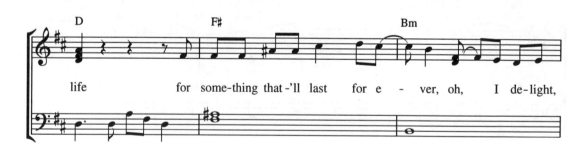

1. I want to serve the pur-pose of God in my ge - ne - ra - tion.
I want to serve the pur-pose of God while I am a - live.
I want to give my life for some-thing that -'ll last for e - ver, oh, I de - light,

I de-light to do your will.

2. I want to build with silver and gold in my generation.
   I want to build with silver and gold while I am alive.
   I want to give my life . . .

3. I want to see the kingdom of God in my generation.
   I want to see the kingdom of God while I am alive.
   I want to give my life . . .

4. I want to see the Lord come again in my generation.
   I want to see the Lord come again while I am alive.
   I want to give my life . . .

166 I will give thanks

Be exalted

Brent Chambers

Brent Chambers
arr. Roland Fudge

Rich and unhurried

I will give thanks to thee, O Lord, a-mong the

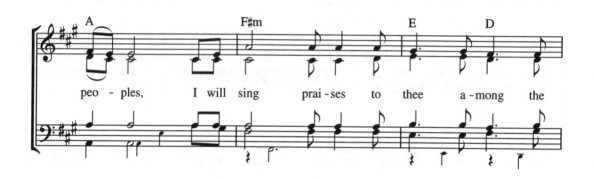

peo - ples, I will sing prai - ses to thee a - mong the

na - tions. For thy stead - fast love is great, is

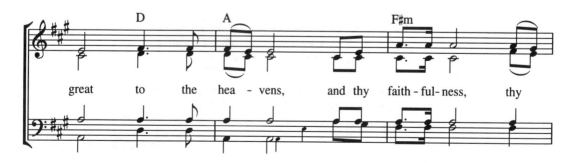

great to the hea - vens, and thy faith - ful - ness, thy

The Bridge

167 I will magnify

Russell L. Lowe

Russell L. Lowe

I will (*echo) mag-ni-fy (echo) your name, O Lord.

I will (echo) ex-alt you, (echo) for e – ver – more.

more. For you are King of kings, and Lord of lords and

you reign in ma – jes-ty. Om – ni – po-tent

Fa – ther, cre – a – tor of all things.

* *Echo on second time only.*

168 I will never be the same again

Geoff Bullock

Geoff Bullock

I will ne-ver be the same a-gain, I can ne-ver re-turn, I've
closed the door. I will walk the path, I'll run the race and I
will ne-ver be the same a-gain. Fall like fire, soak
like rain, flow like migh-ty wa - ters a - gain and a - gain:
sweep a-way the dark - ness, burn a-way the chaff and

169 I will offer up my life

This thankful heart

Matt Redman

Matt Redman

Gently

Unison

1. I will of-fer up my life in spi - rit and truth,

pour -ing out the oil of love as my wor - ship to you.

In sur -ren -der I must give my ev - 'ry part;

Lord, re -ceive the sac -ri - fice of a bro - ken heart.

Refrain

Je-sus, what can I give, what can I bring to so faith-ful a friend,

2. You deserve my ev'ry breath
   for you've paid the great cost;
   giving up your life to death,
   even death on a cross.
   You took all my shame away,
   there defeated my sin,
   opened up the gates of heav'n,
   and have beckoned me in.

170 I will sing of the Lamb

Stuart Townend   Stuart Townend

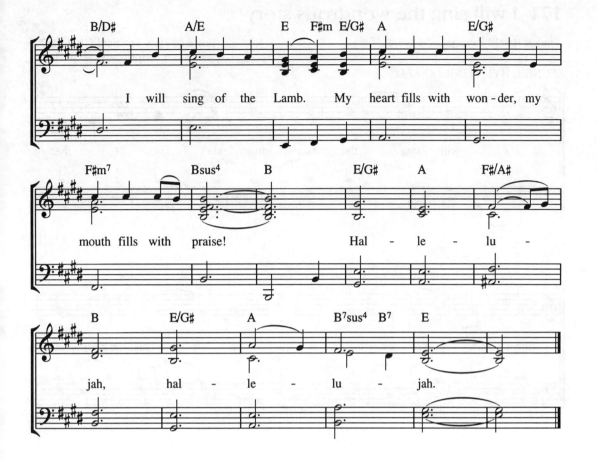

2. Once I was blind, yet believed I saw ev'rything,
   proud in my ways, yet a fool in my part;
   lost and alone in the comp'ny of multitudes,
   life in my body, yet death in my heart.

   Oh, I will sing of the Lamb.
   Oh, I will sing of the Lamb.
   Oh, why should the King save a sinner like me?
   Hallelujah, hallelujah.

3. What shall I give to the man who gave ev'rything,
   humbling himself before all he had made?
   Dare I withhold my own life from his sov'reignty?
   I shall give all for the sake of his name!

   Oh, I will sing of the Lamb.
   Oh, I will sing of the Lamb.
   I'll sing of his love for the rest of my days!
   Hallelujah, hallelujah.

171 I will sing the wondrous story

Francis Harold Rawley (1854-1952)

Rowland Huw Pritchard (1811-1887)
arr. Ralph Vaughan Williams

TUNE 1: HYFRYDOL 87 87 D

1. I will sing the won-drous sto-ry of the Christ who died for me; how he left his home in glo-ry, for the cross on Cal-va-ry. I was lost: but Je-sus found me – found the sheep that

went a-stray; threw his lov-ing arms a-

round me, drew me back in-to his way.

2. I was bruised but Jesus healed me –
   faint was I from many a fall;
   sight was gone, and fears possessed me:
   but he freed me from them all.
   Days of darkness still come o'er me,
   sorrow's paths I often tread:
   but the Saviour still is with me,
   by his hand I'm safely led.

3. He will keep me till the river
   rolls its waters at my feet;
   then he'll bear me safely over,
   where the loved ones I shall meet.
   Yes, I'll sing the wondrous story
   of the Christ who died for me;
   sing it with his saints in glory,
   gathered by the crystal sea.

See over for another tune.

Francis Harold Rawley (1854-1952)

Susie Hare

TUNE 2: QUINTON 87 87 D

1. I will sing the won-drous sto-ry of the Christ who died for me; how he left his home in glo-ry, for the cross on Cal-va-ry. Yes, I'll sing the won-drous sto-ry of the Christ who died for me; sing it with the saints in glo-ry, gath-ered

Verses 1, 2, 3, 4   Verse 5

by   the crys - tal   sea.   2. I   was   sea.

2. I was lost, but Jesus found me –
   found the sheep that went astray;
   threw his loving arms around me,
   drew me back into his way.

3. I was bruised, but Jesus healed me –
   faint was I from many a fall;
   sight was gone, and fears possessed me:
   but he freed me from them all.

4. Days of darkness still come o'er me,
   sorrow's paths I often tread;
   but the Saviour still is with me,
   by his hand I'm safely led.

5. He will keep me till the river
   rolls its waters at my feet;
   then he'll bear me safely over,
   where the loved ones I shall meet.

172 I will worship

You alone are worthy of my praise

David Ruis

David Ruis

Worshipfully, with strength

1. I will wor - ship (I will wor - ship) with
   I will seek you (I will seek you)

all of my heart (with all of my heart).
all of my days (all of my days).

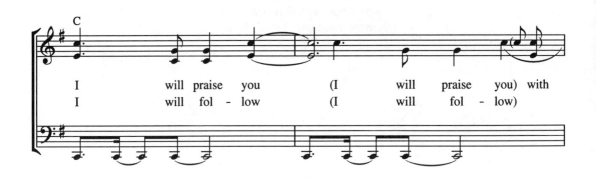

I will praise you (I will praise you) with
I will fol - low (I will fol - low)

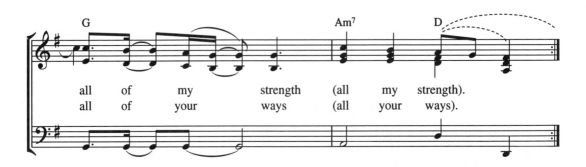

all of my strength (all my strength).
all of your ways (all your ways).

2. I will bow down (I will bow down),
   hail you as King (hail you as King).
   I will serve you (I will serve you),
   give you ev'rything (give you ev'rything).
   I will lift up (I will lift up)
   my eyes to your throne (my eyes to your throne).
   I will trust you (I will trust you),
   I will trust you alone (trust in you alone).

173 Jesus, be the centre

Be the centre

Michael Frye

Michael Frye
arr. Richard Lewis

be my song. Je - sus.
be my guide. Je - sus.

Refrain

Be the fire in my heart, be the wind

in these sails, be the rea - son that I live;

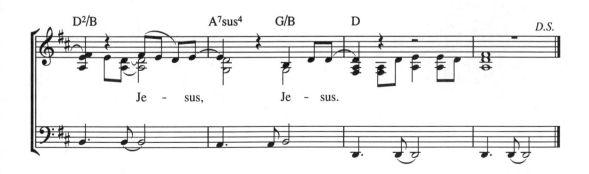

Je - sus, Je - sus.

The Bridge

174 Jesus Christ is risen today

From 'Lyra Davidica'

From 'Lyra Davidica' (1708)

EASTER HYMN 77 77 and Alleluias

1. Je - sus Christ is ris'n to - day, al — le - lu - ia!
our tri - um - phant ho - ly day, al — le - lu - ia!
who did once, up - on the cross, al — le - lu - ia!
suf - fer to re - deem our loss, al — le - lu - ia!

2. Hymns of praise then let us sing, alleluia!
unto Christ, our heav'nly King, alleluia!
who endured the cross and grave, alleluia!
sinners to redeem and save, alleluia!

3. But the pains that he endured, alleluia!
our salvation have procured; alleluia!
now above the sky he's King, alleluia!
where the angels ever sing, alleluia!

175 Jesus Christ, I think upon your sacrifice *Once again*

Matt Redman

Matt Redman

2. Now you are exalted to the highest place,
   King of the heavens, where one day I'll bow.
   But for now, I marvel at this saving grace,
   and I'm full of praise once again.
   I'm full of praise once again.

The Bridge

176 Jesus, come to me

David Barcham

David Barcham

Unhurried

1. Je - sus, come to me now that I need you,

bring your good - ness in, cleanse my heart a - new.

2. Take away my doubt,
   take away my fear,
   cause my heart to know
   that you're ever near.

3. Simply now I cry:
   'Lay your hand on me.'
   Meet, O Master dear,
   ev'ry need in me.

4. Lord, I reach to you,
   though my faith is small,
   trusting that your love
   knows no bounds at all.

5. Jesus, change my ways,
   make me hear and see,
   teach me deeper things,
   show your ways to me.

177 Jesus, God's righteousness revealed *This kingdom*

Geoff Bullock

Geoff Bullock

1. Je - sus, God's right-eous-ness re - vealed, the Son of Man, the Son of God, his king-dom comes. Je - sus, re-demp-tion's sac - ri - fice, now glo-ri - fied, now jus-ti - fied, his king-dom comes. And his

2. Jesus, the expression of God's love,
the grace of God, the word of God, revealed to us;
Jesus, God's holiness displayed,
now glorified, now justified, his kingdom comes.

178 Jesus is King

Wendy Churchill   Wendy Churchill

2. We have a hope that is steadfast and certain,
   gone through the curtain and touching the throne.
   We have a Priest who is there interceding,
   pouring his grace on our lives day by day.

3. We come to him, our Priest and Apostle,
   clothed in his glory and bearing his name,
   laying our lives with gladness before him;
   filled with his Spirit we worship the King.

4. O holy One, our hearts do adore you;
   thrilled with your goodness we give you our praise.
   Angels in light with worship surround him,
   Jesus, our Saviour, for ever the same.

179 Jesus is Lord!

David J. Mansell

David J. Mansell

With majesty

1. Je-sus is Lord! cre-a-tion's voice pro-claims it, for by his pow'r each tree and flow'r was planned and made. Je-sus is Lord! the u-ni-verse de-clares it, sun, moon and stars in hea-ven cry, 'Je-sus is Lord!'

Refrain

Je-sus is Lord! Je-sus is Lord! Praise him with hal-le-lu-jahs for Je-sus is Lord.

2. Jesus is Lord! yet from his throne eternal
in flesh he came to die in pain
on Calv'ry's tree.
Jesus is Lord! from him all life proceeding,
yet gave his life a ransom
thus setting us free.

3. Jesus is Lord! o'er sin the mighty conqu'ror,
from death he rose, and all his foes
shall own his name.
Jesus is Lord! God sent his Holy Spirit
to show by works of power
that Jesus is Lord.

180 Jesus is the name we honour

Jesus is our God

Philip Lawson Johnston

Philip Lawson Johnston

Brightly

1. Je - sus is the name we hon - our; Je - sus is the name we praise. Ma - jes - tic name a - bove all o - ther names, the high - est heav'n and earth pro - claim that Je - sus is our God. We will

2. Jesus is the name we worship;
   Jesus is the name we trust.
   He is the King above all other kings,
   let all creation stand and sing
   that Jesus is our God.

3. Jesus is the Father's splendour;
   Jesus is the Father's joy.
   He will return to reign in majesty,
   and ev'ry eye at last will see
   that Jesus is our God.

The Bridge

181 Jesus, Jesus, healer, Saviour

David Fellingham

David Fellingham

182 Jesus, King of kings

Chris Rolinson

Chris Rolinson

Worshipfully (slow 4)

1. Je - sus, King of kings, we wor - ship and a -

dore you. Je - sus, Lord of heav'n and earth, we

bow down at your feet. Fa - ther, we

bring to you our wor - ship, your sov - 'reign will be

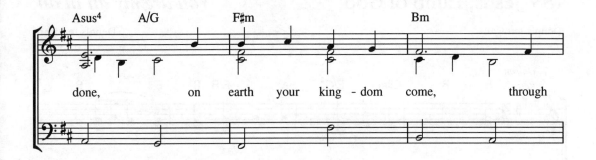

done,   on earth your king - dom come,   through

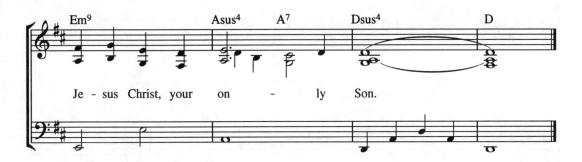

Je - sus Christ, your on - ly Son.

2. Jesus, sov'reign Lord,
   we worship and adore you.
   Jesus, name above all names,
   we bow down at your feet.
   Father, we offer you our worship,
   your sov'reign will be done,
   on earth your kingdom come,
   through Jesus Christ, your only Son.

3. Jesus, light of the world,
   we worship and adore you.
   Jesus, Lord Emmanuel,
   we bow down at your feet.
   Father, for your delight we worship,
   your sov'reign will be done,
   on earth your kingdom come,
   through Jesus Christ, your only Son.

183 Jesus, Lamb of God

You are my all in all

Dennis Jernigan

Dennis Jernigan

Je - sus, Lamb of God, wor - thy is your name.

Je - sus, Lamb of God, wor - thy is your name.

1. You are my strength when I am weak, you are the trea - sure that I

seek, you are my all in all.

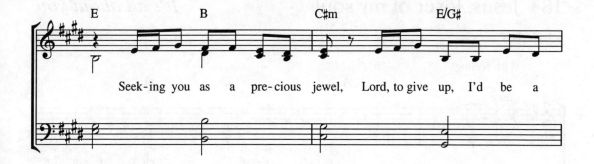

Seek-ing you as a pre-cious jewel, Lord, to give up, I'd be a

fool. You are my all in all.

This can also be sung as a round.

2. Taking my sin, my cross, my shame,
   rising again I bless your name.
   When I fall down, you pick me up,
   when I am dry, you fill my cup.
   You are my all in all.

184 Jesus, lover of my soul

It's all about you

Paul Oakley

Paul Oakley

185 Jesus, restore to us again

Graham Kendrick | Graham Kendrick (b.1950)

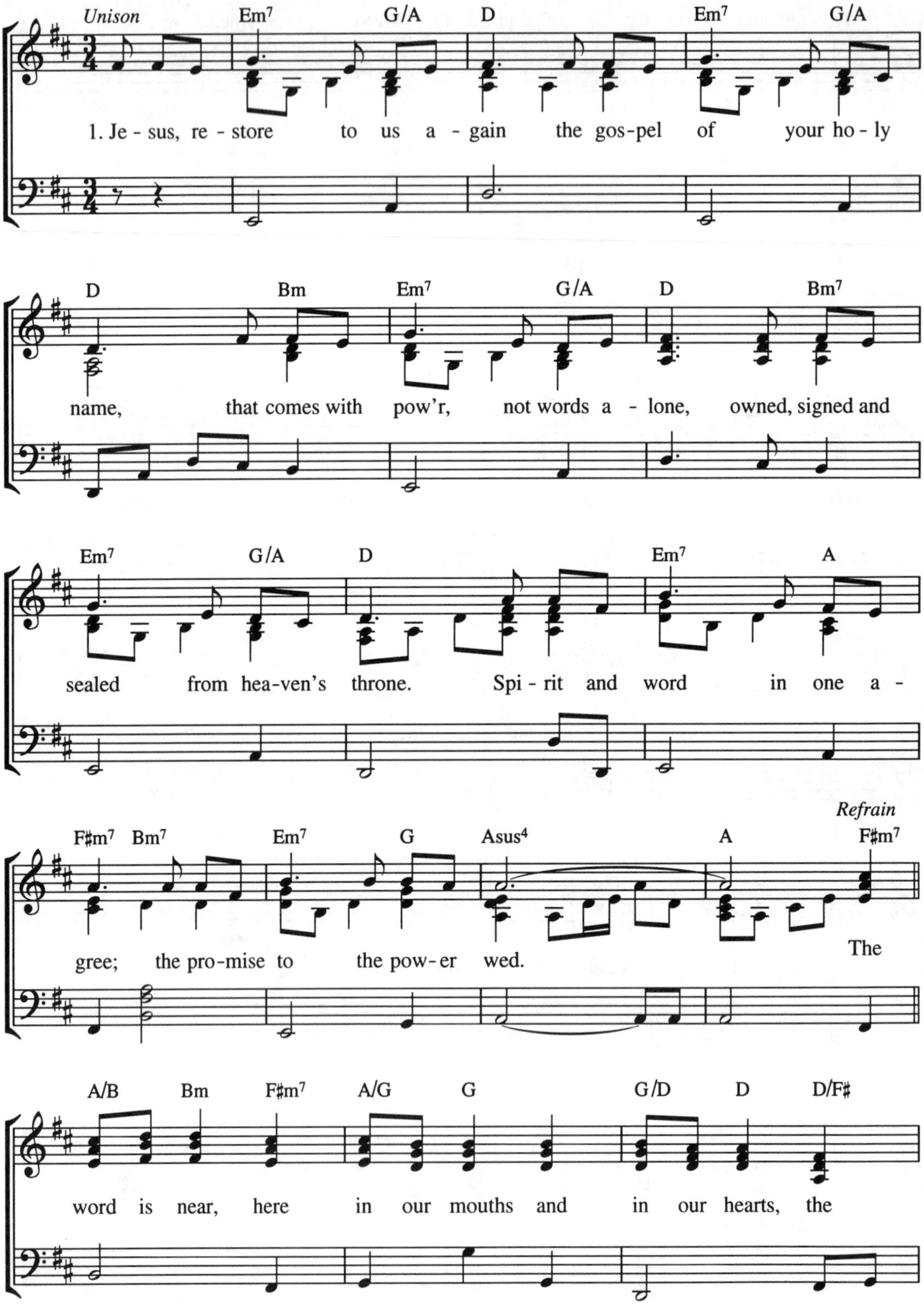
Unison
Em7 G/A D Em7 G/A
1. Je - sus, re - store to us a - gain the gos-pel of your ho - ly
D Bm Em7 G/A D Bm7
name, that comes with pow'r, not words a - lone, owned, signed and
Em7 G/A D Em7 A
sealed from hea-ven's throne. Spi - rit and word in one a -
F♯m7 Bm7 Em7 G Asus4 A
Refrain
F♯m7
gree; the pro-mise to the pow-er wed. The
A/B Bm F♯m7 A/G G G/D D D/F♯
word is near, here in our mouths and in our hearts, the

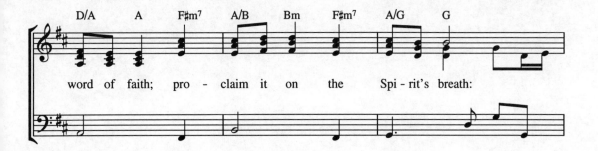

word of faith; pro – claim it on the Spi – rit's breath:

Je – – sus.

2. Your word, O Lord, eternal stands,
   fixed and unchanging in the heav'ns.
   The Word made flesh, to earth came down
   to heal our world with nail-pierced hands.
   Among us here you lived and breathed,
   you are the message we received.

3. Spirit of truth, lead us, we pray,
   into all truth as we obey.
   And as God's will we gladly choose,
   your ancient pow'r again will prove
   Christ's teaching truly comes from God,
   he is indeed the living Word.

4. Upon the heights of this dark land
   with Moses and Elijah stand.
   Reveal your glory once again,
   show us your face, declare your name.
   Prophets and law, in you, complete
   where promises and power meet.

5. Grant us in this decisive hour
   to know the Scriptures and the pow'r;
   the knowledge in experience proved,
   the pow'r that moves and works by love.
   May words and works join hands as one,
   the word go forth, the Spirit come.

The Bridge

186 Jesus shall reign

Isaac Watts (1674-1748) alt.

Melody from Thomas Williams'
'Psalmodia Evangelica' (1789)

TUNE 1: TRURO LM

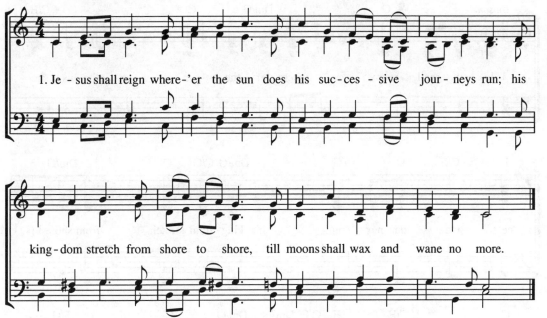

1. Je - sus shall reign where-'er the sun does his suc-ces - sive jour-neys run; his king-dom stretch from shore to shore, till moons shall wax and wane no more.

2. People and realms of ev'ry tongue
   dwell on his love with sweetest song,
   and infant voices shall proclaim
   their early blessings on his name.

3. Blessings abound where'er he reigns:
   the pris'ners leap to lose their chains;
   the weary find eternal rest,
   and all the humble poor are blest.

4. To him shall endless prayer be made,
   and praises throng to crown his head;
   his name like incense shall arise
   with ev'ry morning sacrifice.

5. Let ev'ry creature rise and bring
   peculiar honours to our King;
   angels descend with songs again,
   and earth repeat the loud amen.

See over for another tune.

Isaac Watts (1674-1748) alt.

Susie Hare

TUNE 2: FARRINGDON LM

Steadily

1. Je - sus shall reign where-'er the sun doth his suc - cess - ive jour-neys run; his king-dom stretch from shore to shore, till suns shall rise and set no more. For him shall end - less prayer be made, and prai - ses throng to crown his head; his name like sweet per - fume shall rise with ev - 'ry

Music © Copyright 2001 Kevin Mayhew Ltd.

2. People and realms of ev'ry tongue
   dwell on his love with sweetest song;
   and infant voices shall proclaim
   their young hosannas to his name.
   Blessings abound where'er he reigns;
   the pris'ner leaps to lose his chains;
   the weary find eternal rest
   and all the humble poor are blessed.

3. Where he displays his healing pow'r,
   death and the curse are known no more;
   in him the tribes of Adam boast
   more blessings than their father lost.
   Let ev'ry creature rise and bring
   its grateful honours to our King;
   angels descend with songs again
   and earth repeat the loud 'Amen!'
   Let ev'ry creature rise and bring
   its grateful honours to our King;
   angels descend with songs again
   and earth repeat the loud 'Amen!'

187 Jesus shall take the highest honour

Chris Bowater

Chris Bowater

Je - sus shall take the high — est hon - our,

Je - sus shall take the high - est praise; let all

earth join heav'n in ex - alt - ing the

name which is a - bove all o — ther names. Let's

bow the knee in hum - ble a - do - ra - tion, for

The Bridge

188 Jesus, thank you, Jesus

Fred Chedgey

Fred Chedgey

With simplicity

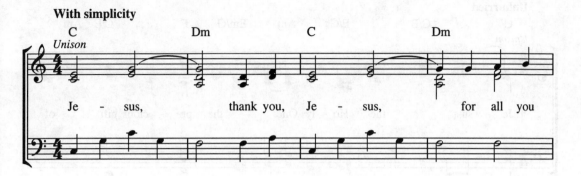

Je - sus, thank you, Je - sus, for all you

are to me, for all the things you do. But I

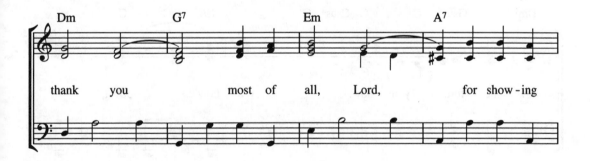

thank you most of all, Lord, for show -ing

me how much I mean to you.

189 Jesus, the Holy One

Susie Hare

Susie Hare

1. Je - sus, the Ho - ly One, the pre - cious gift of

God's own Son. Je - sus, the Ho - ly One, we

bow be - fore you now. We bow down, we

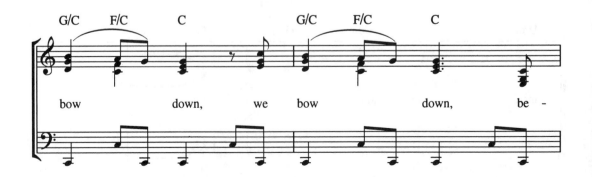

bow down, we bow down, be -

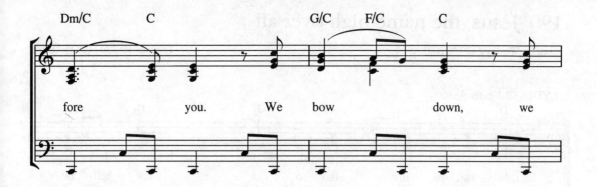

fore you. We bow down, we

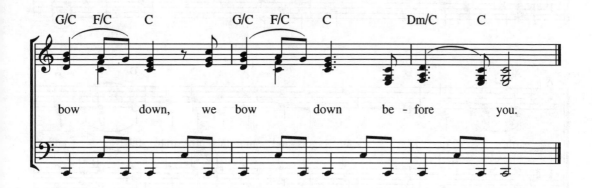

bow down, we bow down be - fore you.

2. Jesus, the Holy Lamb,
   the sacrifice of God for man.
   Jesus, the Holy Lamb,
   we bow before you now.

3. Jesus, the holy name
   that takes our sin, that bears our shame.
   Jesus, the holy name,
   we bow before you now.

190 Jesus, the name high over all

Charles Wesley (1707-1788)

Thomas Phillips (1735-1807)

LYDIA CM extended

1. Je - sus, the name high o - ver all, in hell, or earth, or sky; an - gels and mor-tals pros-trate fall, and de - vils fear and fly, and de - vils fear and fly.

2. Jesus, the name to sinners dear,
   the name to sinners giv'n;
   it scatters all their guilty fear,
   it turns their hell to heav'n.

3. Jesus, the pris'ner's fetters breaks,
   and bruises Satan's head;
   pow'r into strengthless souls he speaks,
   and life into the dead.

4. O, that the world might taste and see
   the riches of his grace!
   The arms of love that compass me,
   hold all the human race.

5. His only righteousness I show,
   his saving grace proclaim:
   'tis all my business here below
   to cry: 'Behold the Lamb!'

6. Happy, if with my latest breath
   I may but gasp his name:
   preach him to all, and cry in death:
   'Behold, behold the Lamb!'

191 Jesus, the very thought of thee

St Bernard of Clairvaux (1091-1153)
trans. Edward Caswall (1814-1878)

John Bacchus Dykes (1823-1876)

ST AGNES (DYKES) CM

1. Je - sus, the ve - ry thought of thee
with sweet - ness fills the breast;
but sweet - er far thy face to see,
and in thy pre - sence rest.

2. No voice can sing, nor heart can frame,
nor can the mind recall
a sweeter sound than thy blest name,
O Saviour of us all!

3. O hope of ev'ry contrite heart,
O joy of all the meek,
to those who ask, how kind thou art!
how good to those who seek!

4. But what to those who find? Ah, this
nor tongue nor pen can show;
the love of Jesus, what it is
none but his loved ones know.

5. Jesus, our only joy be thou,
as thou our prize wilt be;
in thee be all our glory now,
and through eternity.

192 Jesus, thou joy of loving hearts

'Jesu, dulcis memoria' (12th century)
trans. Ray Palmer (1808-1887)

Henry Percy Smith (1825-1898)

MARYTON LM

Worshipfully

1. Je - sus, thou joy of lov - ing hearts,

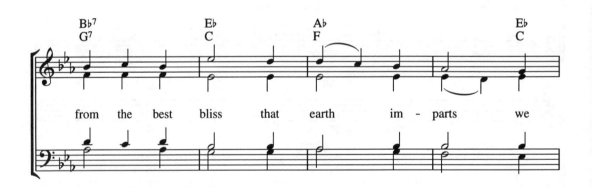

thou fount of life, our lives sus - tain,

from the best bliss that earth im - parts we

turn un - filled to thee a - gain.

2. Thy truth unchanged hath ever stood;
   thou savest those that on thee call;
   to them that seek thee thou art good,
   to them that find thee, all in all.

3. We taste thee, O thou living bread,
   and long to feast upon thee still;
   we drink of thee, the fountain-head,
   and thirst our souls from thee to fill.

4. Our restless spirits yearn for thee,
   where'er our changeful lot is cast;
   glad when thy gracious smile we see,
   blessed when our faith can hold thee fast.

5. O Jesus, ever with us stay;
   make all our moments calm and bright;
   chase the dark night of sin away;
   shed o'er the world thy holy light.

193 Jesus, we have heard your Spirit *Where you lead us*

Martin Leckebusch

Susie Hare

ODIHAM 87 87 D

1. Je-sus, we have heard your Spi-rit say-ing we be-long to you, show-ing us our need for mer-cy, fo-cus-ing our hopes a-new; you have won our hearts' de-vo-tion, now we feel your guid-ing hand: where you

2. As a chosen, pilgrim people
   we are learning day by day
   what it means to be disciples,
   to believe and to obey.
   Word and table show your purpose;
   hearts and lives we gladly bring –
   where you lead us, we will follow,
   suff'ring Saviour, risen King.

3. How we yearn that ev'ry people
   should exalt your matchless name,
   yet so often this world's systems
   countermand your regal claim.
   If we stand for truth and justice
   we, like you, may suffer loss;
   where you lead us, we will follow –
   give us grace to bear our cross.

4. So we journey on together,
   keen to make our calling sure;
   through our joys, our fears, our crises,
   may our faith be made mature.
   Jesus, hope of hearts and nations,
   sov'reign Lord of time and space,
   where you lead us, we will follow
   till we see you face to face.

194 Jesus, what a beautiful name

Tanya Riches

Tanya Riches

195 Jesus, you are changing me

Marilyn Baker   Marilyn Baker

Prayerfully

Je - sus, you are chang - ing me, by your Spi - rit you're ma - king me like you. Je - sus, you're trans - form - ing me, that your love - li - ness may be seen in all I do.

The Bridge

196 Jesus, you are so precious

Nathan Fellingham

Nathan Fellingham

2. Jesus, you are so precious to me,
   your beauty has captured my gaze.
   Now I will come and bow down before you,
   and pour sweet perfume on your feet.

197 Join all the glorious names

Isaac Watts (1674-1748)

John Bacchus Dykes (1823-1876)

ST GODRIC 66 66 88

2. Great prophet of my God,
   my tongue would bless thy name:
   by thee the joyful news
   of our salvation came:
   the joyful news of sins forgiv'n,
   of hell subdued and peace with heav'n.

3. Jesus, my great high priest,
   offered his blood, and died;
   my guilty conscience seeks
   no sacrifice beside:
   his pow'rful blood did once atone,
   and now it pleads before the throne.

4. My Saviour and my Lord,
   my conqu'ror and my King,
   thy sceptre and thy sword,
   thy reigning grace I sing:
   thine is the pow'r; behold, I sit
   in willing bonds beneath thy feet.

5. Now let my soul arise,
   and tread the tempter down:
   my captain leads me forth
   to conquest and a crown:
   march on, nor fear to win the day,
   though death and hell obstruct the way.

6. Should all the hosts of death,
   and pow'rs of hell unknown,
   put their most dreadful forms
   of rage and malice on,
   I shall be safe; for Christ displays
   superior pow'r and guardian grace.

The Bridge

198 Joy to the world!

Isaac Watts (1674-1748) alt.

George Frideric Handel (1685-1759)

ANTIOCH CM

1. Joy to the world! The Lord is come; let earth re-ceive her King; let ev-'ry heart pre-pare him room and heav'n and na-ture sing, and heav'n and na-ture sing, and and heav'n and na-ture sing, and heav'n and na-ture heav'n, and heav'n and na-ture sing! sing,

2. Joy to the earth! The Saviour reigns;
   let us our songs employ;
   while fields and floods, rocks, hills and plains
   repeat the sounding joy,
   repeat the sounding joy,
   repeat, repeat the sounding joy.

3. He rules the world with truth and grace,
   and makes the nations prove
   the glories of his righteousness,
   and wonders of his love,
   and wonders of his love,
   and wonders, wonders of his love.

199 Just as I am

Charlotte Elliott (1789-1871)

W. B. Bradbury (1816-1868)

TUNE 1: WOODWORTH 88 86 extended

1. Just as I am, with-out one plea but that thy
blood was shed for me, and that thou bid'st me come to
thee, O Lamb of God, I come, I come.

2. Just as I am, though tossed about
   with many a conflict, many a doubt,
   fightings and fears within, without,
   O Lamb of God, I come, I come.

3. Just as I am, poor, wretched, blind;
   sight, riches, healing of the mind,
   yea, all I need, in thee to find,
   O Lamb of God, I come, I come.

4. Just as I am, thou wilt receive,
   wilt welcome, pardon, cleanse, relieve:
   because thy promise I believe,
   O Lamb of God, I come, I come.

5. Just as I am, thy love unknown
   has broken ev'ry barrier down,
   now to be thine, yea, thine alone,
   O Lamb of God, I come, I come.

6. Just as I am, of that free love
   the breadth, length, depth and height to prove,
   here for a season, then above,
   O Lamb of God, I come, I come.

Charlotte Elliott (1789-1871)   Arthur Henry Brown (1830-1926)

TUNE 2: SAFFRON WALDEN 88 86

1. Just as I am, with-out one plea but that thy blood was shed for me, and that thou bid'st me come to thee, O Lamb of God, I come.

2. Just as I am, though tossed about
   with many a conflict, many a doubt,
   fightings and fears within, without,
   O Lamb of God, I come.

3. Just as I am, poor, wretched, blind;
   sight, riches, healing of the mind,
   yea, all I need, in thee to find,
   O Lamb of God, I come.

4. Just as I am, thou wilt receive,
   wilt welcome, pardon, cleanse, relieve:
   because thy promise I believe,
   O Lamb of God, I come.

5. Just as I am, thy love unknown
   has broken ev'ry barrier down,
   now to be thine, yea, thine alone,
   O Lamb of God, I come.

6. Just as I am, of that free love
   the breadth, length, depth and height to prove,
   here for a season, then above,
   O Lamb of God, I come.

200 Lamb of God

Chris Bowater   Chris Bowater

Worshipfully

Lamb of God, Ho-ly One, Je-sus Christ,

Son of God, lift-ed up wil-ling-ly to

die; that I the guil - ty one may

know the blood once shed still free-ly flow - ing, still

The Bridge

201 Lead us, heavenly Father, lead us

James Edmeston (1791-1867)　　　　　　　　　　　Friedrich Filitz (1804-1876)

MANNHEIM 87 87 87

1. Lead us, heav'n-ly Fa-ther, lead us o'er the world's tem-
pes-tuous sea; guard us, guide us, keep us, feed us,
for we have no help but thee; yet pos-ses-sing
ev-'ry bles-sing if our God our Fa-ther be.

2. Saviour, breathe forgiveness o'er us:
   all our weakness thou dost know;
   thou didst tread this earth before us,
   thou didst feel its keenest woe;
   lone and dreary, faint and weary,
   through the desert thou didst go.

3. Spirit of our God, descending,
   fill our hearts with heav'nly joy,
   love with ev'ry passion blending,
   pleasure that can never cloy:
   thus provided, pardoned, guided,
   nothing can our peace destroy.

202 Let everything that has breath

Matt Redman | Matt Redman

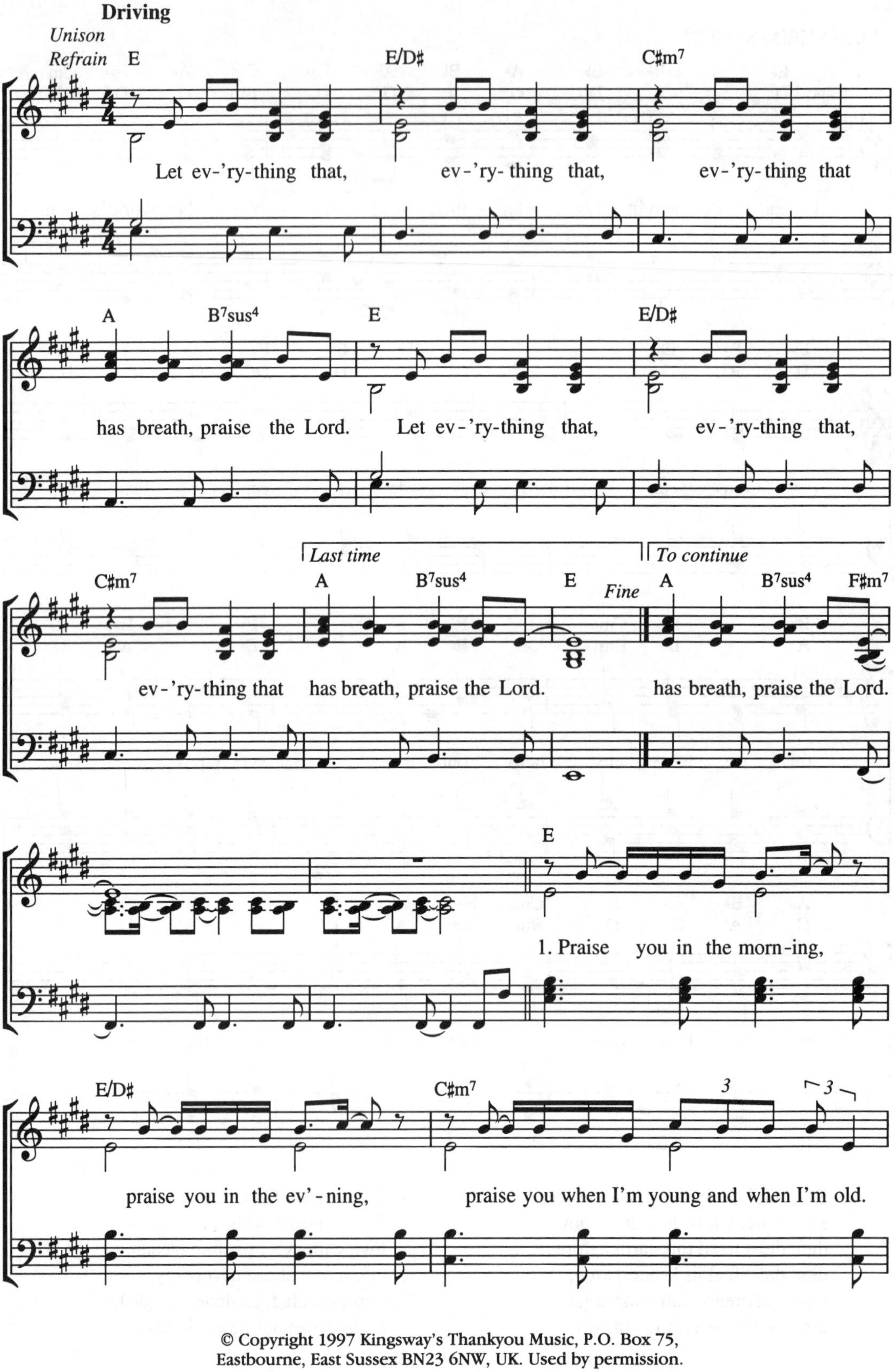

Driving
Unison
Refrain
E
E/D♯
C♯m7
Let ev-'ry-thing that, ev-'ry-thing that, ev-'ry-thing that
A
B7sus4
E
E/D♯
has breath, praise the Lord. Let ev-'ry-thing that, ev-'ry-thing that,
Last time
To continue
C♯m7
A
B7sus4
E
Fine
A
B7sus4
F♯m7
ev-'ry-thing that has breath, praise the Lord. has breath, praise the Lord.
E
1. Praise you in the morn-ing,
E/D♯
C♯m7
3
3
praise you in the ev'-ning, praise you when I'm young and when I'm old.

2. Praise you in the heavens,
   joining with the angels,
   joining you for ever and a day.
   Praise you on the earth now,
   joining with creation,
   calling all the nations to your praise.
   If they could see...

203 Let every tribe and every tongue — *We give you praise*

Debbye Graafsma

Debbye Graafsma

With strength

Unison

Let ev-'ry tribe and ev-'ry tongue bring praise to the Lamb, for he has tri-umphed o - ver all, he has tri - umphed. With his blood he has re-deemed us for e - ver to reign with him in glo-ry, a - men. We sing glo - ry, glo - ry to the Lamb; Son of God, the great I Am.

204 Let praises ring

Mike and Claire McIntosh

Mike and Claire McIntosh

Lively and majestically

1. Let prai - ses ring, let prai - ses ring, lift voi - ces up to love him, lift hearts and hands to touch him, O let prai - ses ring. And fill the skies with an - thems high that tell his ex - cel - len - cies, as priests and kings who rule with

2. Let praises ring, let praises ring,
   bow down in adoration,
   cry out his exaltation,
   O let praises ring.
   And lift the name above all names
   till ev'ry nation knows
   the love of God has come to men,
   his mercies overflow.

The Bridge

205 Let us, with a gladsome mind

John Milton (1608-1674)
based on Psalm 136

From 'Hymn Tunes of the United Brethren'
adapt. by John Bernard Wilkes (1785-1869)

MONKLAND 77 77

1. Let us, with a glad - some mind, praise the Lord, for he is kind;

Refrain

for his mer - cies ay en - dure, e - ver faith - ful, e - ver sure.

2. Let us blaze his name abroad,
   for of gods he is the God;

3. He, with all-commanding might,
   filled the new-made world with light;

4. He the golden-tressèd sun
   caused all day his course to run;

5. And the moon to shine at night,
   'mid her starry sisters bright;

6. All things living he doth feed,
   his full hand supplies their need;

7. Let us, with a gladsome mind,
   praise the Lord, for he is kind;

206 Let your living water flow

Living water

John Watson

John Watson

With a strong beat

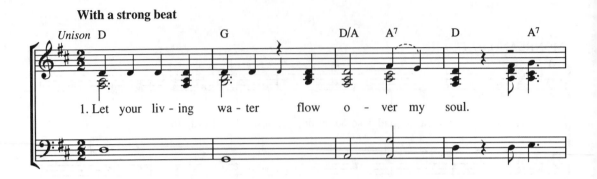

1. Let your liv-ing wa-ter flow o-ver my soul.

Let your Ho-ly Spi-rit come and take con-trol of

ev-'ry si-tu-a-tion that has trou-bled my mind.

All my cares and bur-dens on to you I roll. roll.

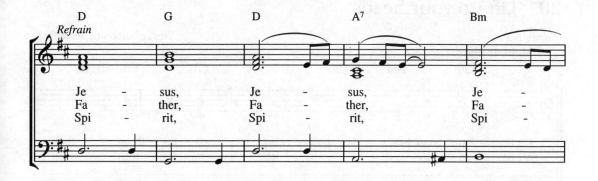

Refrain

| D | G | D | A⁷ | Bm |

Je - sus,   Je - sus,   Je -
Fa - ther,   Fa - ther,   Fa -
Spi - rit,   Spi - rit,   Spi -

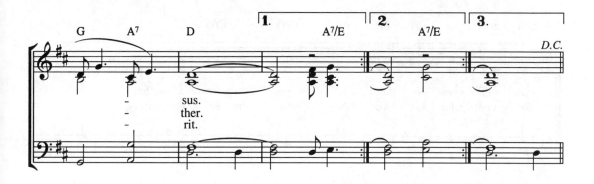

| G | A⁷ | D | **1.** A⁷/E | **2.** A⁷/E | **3.** |

D.C.

- sus.
- ther.
- rit.

2. Come now, Holy Spirit, and take control.
   Hold me in your loving arms and make me whole.
   Wipe away all doubt and fear and take my pride.
   Draw me to your love and keep me by your side.

3. Give your life to Jesus, let him fill your soul.
   Let him take you in his arms and make you whole.
   As you give your life to him, he'll set you free.
   You will live and reign with him eternally.

4. Let your living water flow over my soul.
   Let your Holy Spirit come and take control
   of ev'ry situation that has troubled my mind.
   All my cares and burdens on to you I roll.

207 Lift up your heads

Trevor Burch

Trevor Burch arr. Susie Hare

Majestically

1. Lift up your heads, your king is on his throne; look
2. Lift up your voice and let your prai - ses ring; your

with the eyes of faith, he reigns su-preme a - lone.
Sa - viour who is wor - thy, give him ev - 'ry - thing.

Lift up your hearts and in his pre - sence stand. He
Lift up your hands, made ho - ly by the cross, in

is the King of glo - ry, Sa - viour of man - kind.
joy - ful, liv - ing wor - ship to the King of kings.

3. Je - sus, we are yours, by your blood made whole;

208 Light has dawned

Graham Kendrick

Graham Kendrick (b.1950)

1. Light has dawned that e - ver shall blaze, dark - ness flees a - way. Christ the light has shone in our hearts, turn - ing night to day. We pro - claim him King of kings, we lift high his name.

Heav'n and earth shall bow at his feet, when he comes to

reign.

reign.

reign.

Women

2. Saviour of the world is he,
   heaven's King come down.
   Judgement, love and mercy meet
   at his thorny crown.

Men

3. Life has sprung from hearts of stone,
   by the Spirit's breath.
   Hell shall let its captives go,
   life has conquered death.

All

4. Blood has flowed that cleanses from sin,
   God his love has proved.
   Men may mock and demons may rage,
   we shall not be moved!

Refrain twice to end.

209 Lo, he comes with clouds descending

Charles Wesley (1707-1788),
John Cennick (1718-1755)
and Martin Madan (1726-1790), alt.

From Charles Wesley's
'Select Hymns with Tunes Annext'

HELMSLEY 87 87 47

1. Lo, he comes with clouds des - cend - ing,

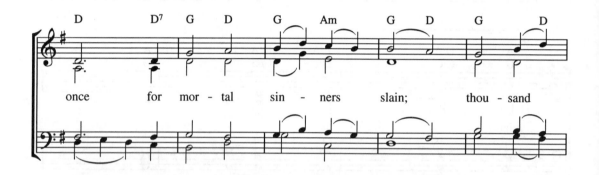

once for mor - tal sin - ners slain; thou - sand

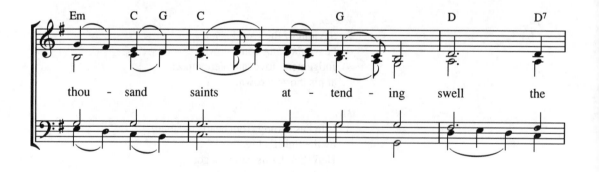

thou - sand saints at - tend - ing swell the

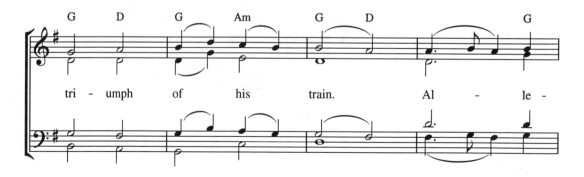

tri - umph of his train. Al - le -

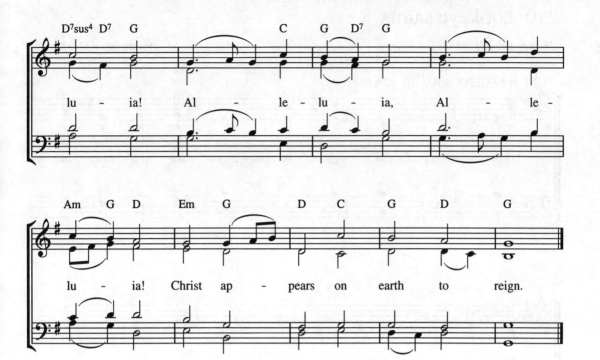

lu - ia! Al - le - lu - ia, Al - le -

lu - ia! Christ ap - pears on earth to reign.

2. Ev'ry eye shall now behold him
   robed in glorious majesty;
   we who set at naught and sold him,
   pierced and nailed him to the tree,
   deeply wailing, deeply wailing, deeply wailing,
   shall the true Messiah see.

3. Those dear tokens of his passion
   still his dazzling body bears,
   cause of endless exultation
   to his ransomed worshippers:
   with what rapture, with what rapture, with what rapture
   gaze we on those glorious scars!

4. Yea, amen, let all adore thee,
   high on thine eternal throne;
   Saviour, take the pow'r and glory,
   claim the kingdom for thine own.
   Alleluia! Alleluia! Alleluia!
   Thou shalt reign, and thou alone.

210 Look, ye saints

Thomas Kelly (1769-1854)   Henry Smart (1813-1879)

TUNE 1: REGENT SQUARE 87 87 87

1. Look, ye saints, the sight is glo-rious: see the Man of
Sor-rows now; from the fight re-turned vic-to-rious,
ev-'ry knee to him shall bow: Crown him, crown him!
Crown him, crown him! Crowns be-come the Vic-tor's brow.

2. Crown the Saviour! angels, crown him!
   Rich the trophies Jesus brings;
   in the seat of pow'r enthrone him,
   while the vault of heaven rings:
   Crown him, crown him!
   Crown him, crown him!
   Crown the Saviour King of kings!

3. Sinners in derision crowned him,
   mocking thus the Saviour's claim;
   saints and angels crowd around him,
   own his title, praise his name:
   Crown him, crown him!
   Crown him, crown him!
   Spread abroad the Victor's fame.

4. Hark, those bursts of acclamation!
   Hark those loud triumphant chords!
   Jesus takes the highest station:
   O what joy the sight affords!
   Crown him, crown him!
   Crown him, crown him!
   King of kings and Lord of lords!

See over for another tune

Thomas Kelly (1769-1854)   Susie Hare

TUNE 2: BENTLEY 87 87 D

1. Look, ye saints, the sight is glo-rious: see the Man of
Sor-rows now; from the fight re-turned vic-to-rious,
ev-'ry knee to him shall bow: Crown him, crown him!
(Women) Crown him, crown him! *(All)* Crowns be-come the vic-tor's brow.

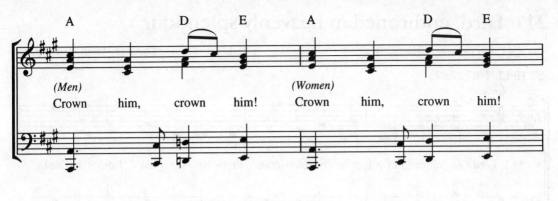

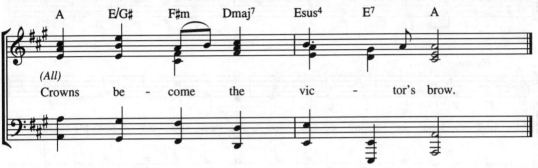

2. Crown the Saviour! angels, crown him!
   Rich the trophies Jesus brings;
   in the seat of pow'r enthrone him,
   while the vault of heaven rings:
   Crown him, crown him!
   Crown him, crown him!
   Crown the Saviour King of kings!

3. Sinners in derision crowned him,
   mocking thus the Saviour's claim;
   saints and angels crowd around him,
   own his title, praise his name:
   Crown him, crown him!
   Crown him, crown him!
   Spread abroad the Victor's fame.

4. Hark, those bursts of acclamation!
   Hark those loud triumphant chords!
   Jesus takes the highest station:
   O what joy the sight affords!
   Crown him, crown him!
   Crown him, crown him!
   King of kings and Lord of lords!

211 Lord, enthroned in heavenly splendour

George Hugh Bourne (1840-1925)

George Clement Martin (1844-1916)

ST HELEN 87 87 87

1. Lord, en-throned in heav'n-ly splen-dour, first-be-got-ten from the dead, thou a-lone, our strong de-fen-der, lift-est up thy peo-ple's head. Al-le-lu-ia, al-le-lu-ia, Je-su, true and liv-ing bread.

* Optional notes for accompanist

2. Here our humblest homage pay we,
here in loving rev'rence bow;
here for faith's discernment pray we,
lest we fail to know thee now.
Alleluia, alleluia,
thou art here, we ask not how.

3. Though the lowliest form doth veil thee
as of old in Bethlehem,
here as there thine angels hail thee,
Branch and Flow'r of Jesse's Stem.
Alleluia, alleluia,
we in worship join with them.

4. Paschal Lamb, thine off'ring, finished
once for all when thou wast slain,
in its fullness undiminished
shall for evermore remain.
Alleluia, alleluia,
cleansing souls from ev'ry stain.

5. Life-imparting heav'nly manna,
stricken rock with streaming side,
heav'n and earth with loud hosanna
worship thee, the Lamb who died.
Alleluia, alleluia,
ris'n, ascended, glorified!

212 Lord, for the years

Lord of the years

Timothy Dudley-Smith (b.1926)

Michael Baughen (b.1930)
arr. David Iliff

LORD OF THE YEARS 11 10 11 10

1. Lord, for the years your love has kept and guid - ed, urged and in - spired us, cheered us on our way, sought us and saved us, par-don'd and pro - vi - ded, Lord of the years, we bring our thanks to - day.

2. Lord, for that word, the word of life which fires us,
   speaks to our hearts and sets our souls ablaze,
   teaches and trains, rebukes us and inspires us,
   Lord of the word, receive your people's praise.

3. Lord, for our land, in this our generation,
   spirits oppressed by pleasure, wealth and care;
   for young and old, for commonwealth and nation,
   Lord of our land, be pleased to hear our prayer.

4. Lord, for our world; when we disown and doubt him,
   loveless in strength, and comfortless in pain;
   hungry and helpless, lost indeed without him,
   Lord of the world, we pray that Christ may reign.

5. Lord, for ourselves; in living pow'r remake us,
   self on the cross and Christ upon the throne;
   past put behind us, for the future take us,
   Lord of our lives, to live for Christ alone.

213 Lord, how majestic you are

You are my everything

Stuart Townend

Stuart Townend

Smoothly

Unison

1. Lord, how ma-jes-tic you are, my eyes meet your gaze and my bur-den is lift - ed. Your word is a lamp to my feet, your hand swift to bless and your ban-ner a shield. You are my ev - 'ry - thing, you who made earth and sky and sea, all that you've placed in - side of me calls out your

2. Lord, how resplendent you are,
when I think of your heavens,
the work of your fingers –
what is man, that you are mindful of him,
yet you've crowned him with glory
and caused him to reign!

214 Lord, I come before your throne of grace

What a faithful God

Robert and Dawn Critchley

Robert and Dawn Critchley

1. Lord, I come be-fore your throne of grace; I find
2. Lord of mer-cy you have heard my cry; through the

rest in your pre-sence and full - ness of joy. In
storm you're the bea-con, my song in the night. In the

wor - ship and won-der I be - hold your face, sing-ing:
shel - ter of your wings, hear my heart's re - ply, sing-ing:

'What a faith - ful God have I'. What a faith - ful

God have I, what a faith - ful

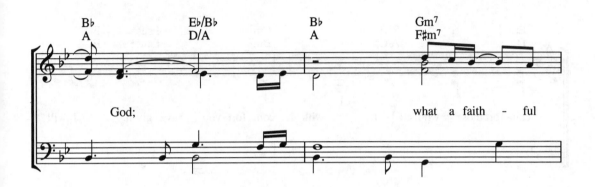

God; what a faith - ful

God have I, faith - ful in ev - 'ry

way.

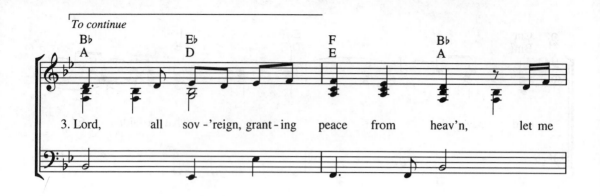

To continue

Bb / A   Eb / D   F / E   Bb / A

3. Lord, all sov-'reign, grant-ing peace from heav'n, let me

Eb / D   Bb/D / A/C#   Cm⁷ / Bm⁷   Fsus⁴ / Esus⁴   F / E

com-fort those who suf - fer with the com-fort you have giv'n. I will

Bb / A   Eb / D   F / E   Gsus⁴ / F#sus⁴   G / F#

tell of your great love for as long as I live, sing-ing:

Cm⁷ / Bm   Fsus⁴ / Esus⁴   F / E   Bb / A   *Refrain*   *D.S. al Fine*

'What a faith - ful God have I'. What a faith - ful

215 Lord, I come to you

Power of your love

Geoff Bullock

Geoff Bullock

the weak-nes-ses I see in me
as your will un-folds in my life,

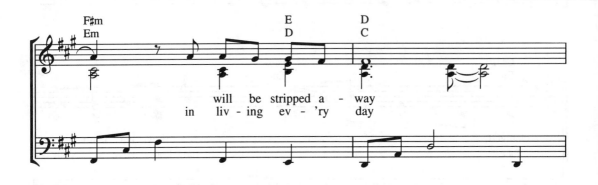

will be stripped a-way
in liv-ing ev-'ry day

by the pow'r of your love.
in the pow'r of your love.

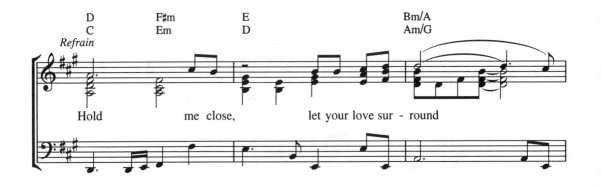

Refrain

Hold me close, let your love sur-round

216 Lord, I lift your name on high

You came from heaven to earth

Rick Founds

Rick Founds

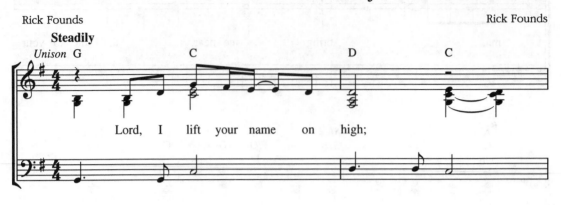

Lord, I lift your name on high;

Lord, I love to sing your prai - ses.

I'm so glad you're in my life;

I'm so glad you came to save us.

You came from hea - ven to earth to show the way,

from the earth to the cross, my debt to pay,

from the cross to the grave, from the grave to the sky,

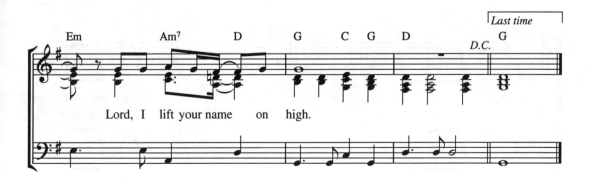

Lord, I lift your name on high.

217 Lord, I stand in the midst — *Hallelujah to the Lamb*

Don Moen and Debbye Graafsma

Don Moen and Debbye Graafsma

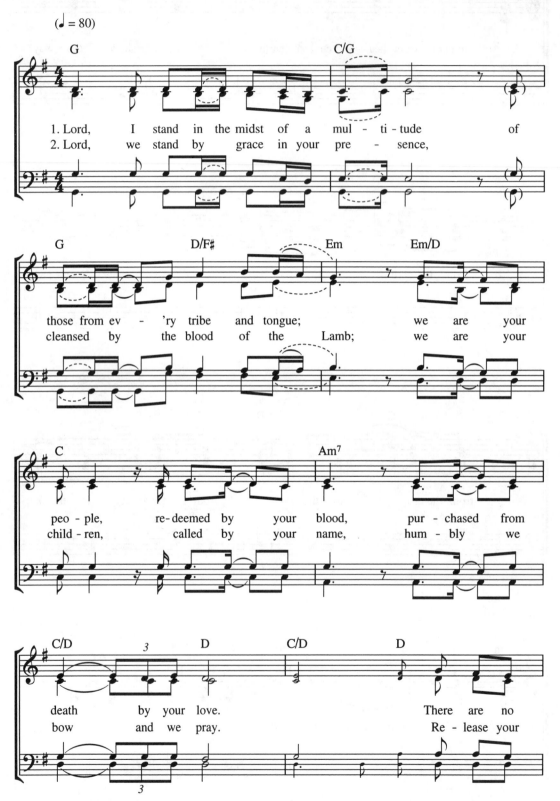

1. Lord, I stand in the midst of a mul-ti-tude of those from ev-'ry tribe and tongue; we are your peo-ple, re-deemed by your blood, pur-chased from death by your love. There are no
2. Lord, we stand by grace in your pre-sence, cleansed by the blood of the Lamb; we are your child-ren, called by your name, hum-bly we bow and we pray. Re-lease your

The Bridge

218 Lord, I want to tell you

Overflow of worship

Marilyn Baker

Marilyn Baker

Slow and gentle

Unison

1. Lord, I want to tell you how much I love you; your ten - der - ness and mer - cy have o - ver - whelmed my heart. Let my whole life be, an o - ver - flow of wor - ship, all I have and all I am I give back, Lord, to you.

2. Lord, I want to tell you my heart's desire;
   the love you've put within me will burn with holy fire.
   Let my actions spring from an overflow of worship;
   all I have and all I am I gladly give back to you.

219 Lord Jesus Christ

Living Lord

Patrick Appleford

Patrick Appleford (b.1925)

LIVING LORD 9 8 88 83

1. Lord Je - sus Christ, you have come to us,

you are one with us, Ma - ry's Son. Cleans-ing our souls from

all their sin, pour-ing your love and good-ness in, Je - sus, our love for

you we sing, liv - ing Lord. Lord.

2. Lord Jesus Christ,
   now and ev'ry day
   teach us how to pray,
   Son of God.
   You have commanded us to do
   this in remembrance, Lord, of you.
   Into our lives your pow'r breaks through,
   living Lord.

3. Lord Jesus Christ,
   you have come to us,
   born as one of us,
   Mary's Son.
   Led out to die on Calvary,
   risen from death to set us free,
   living Lord Jesus, help us see
   you are Lord.

4. Lord Jesus Christ,
   I would come to you,
   live my life for you,
   Son of God.
   All your commands I know are true,
   your many gifts will make me new,
   into my life your pow'r breaks through,
   living Lord.

220 Lord of lords

Jessy Dixon, Randy Scruggs
and John Thompson

Jessy Dixon, Randy Scruggs
and John Thompson

221 Lord of the Church

Timothy Dudley-Smith (b.1926)

Traditional Irish melody
arr. John Barnard

LONDONDERRY AIR 11 10 11 10 D

1. Lord of the Church, we pray for our re - new - ing: Christ o - ver all, our un - di - vi - ded aim. Fire of the Spi - rit, burn for our en - du - ing, wind of the Spi - rit, fan the liv - ing flame! We turn to Christ a - mid our fear and fail - ing, the will that

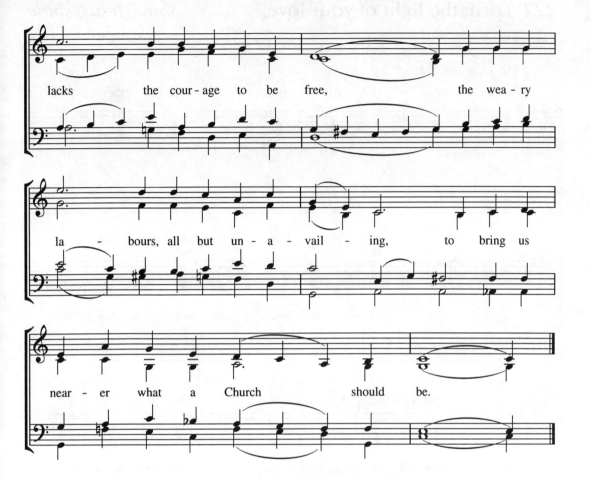

lacks the cour-age to be free, the wea-ry
la - bours, all but un - a - vail - ing, to bring us
near - er what a Church should be.

2. Lord of the Church, we seek a Father's blessing,
   a true repentance and a faith restored,
   a swift obedience and a new possessing,
   filled with the Holy Spirit of the Lord!
   We turn to Christ from all our restless striving,
   unnumbered voices with a single prayer:
   the living water for our souls' reviving,
   in Christ to live, and love and serve and care.

3. Lord of the Church, we long for our uniting,
   true to one calling, by one vision stirred;
   one cross proclaiming and one creed reciting,
   one in the truth of Jesus and his word!
   So lead us on; till toil and trouble ended,
   one Church triumphant one new song shall sing,
   to praise his glory, risen and ascended,
   Christ over all, the everlasting King!

222 Lord, the light of your love

Shine, Jesus, shine

Graham Kendrick

Graham Kendrick (b.1950)

Majestic and steady

1. Lord, the light of your love is shin - ing, in the midst of the dark - ness, shin - ing; Je - sus, Light of the World, shine up - on us, set us free by the truth you now bring us. Shine on me, shine on me.

2. Lord, I come to your awesome presence,
   from the shadows into your radiance;
   by the blood I may enter your brightness,
   search me, try me, consume all my darkness.
   Shine on me, shine on me.

3. As we gaze on your kingly brightness,
   so our faces display your likeness,
   ever changing from glory to glory;
   mirrored here may our lives tell your story.
   Shine on me, shine on me.

   (Refrain twice to end)

223 Lord, what a sacrifice I see

The greatest love

Susie Hare

Susie Hare

Steadily

Ab2
Capo 1 G2

Db/Ab
C/G

Unison

1. Lord, what a sac-ri-fice I see as I
2. Lord, what a pro-mise of your grace as I
3. Lord, what a pri-vi-lege I own to

Cm7   Fm7   Bbm7   Ebsus4   Eb
Bm7   Em7   Am7   Dsus4   D

turn my eyes to Cal - va - ry;
turn my eyes to seek your face;
free - ly come be - fore your throne;

Ab   Eb/G   Fm   Ab/Eb
G   D/F#   Em   G/D

there, my sins nailed to a tree, a King stands
clothed in right-eous-ness, I place my sin-ful-
there, to know and to be known, sur-ren-dered

Bbm7   Db/Eb Eb7   **1.** Ab2   Db/Ab   **2, 3.** Ab   Db/F   Eb/G
Am7   C/D D7   G2   C/G   Gb   C/E   D/F#

D.C.   *Refrain*

in in-stead of me.
ness in your em- brace. The
now to you a- lone.

224 Lord, you are the author of my life *Author of my life*

Judy Pruett

Judy Pruett

Flowing

Lord, you are the au - thor of my life, you have be - gun
a work in me, you have pre - des - tined me to
do your per - fect will. And Lord, you are the Lord
of all my days, you are the Lord of all my nights,
you have cho - sen me to car - ry forth your word.

225 Lord, you have my heart

Martin Smith

Martin Smith

Lord, you have my heart, and I will search for yours;
Je - sus, take my life and lead me on.
Lord, you have my heart, and I will search for yours; let me be to you a sac - ri - fice.
(Men) And

226 Lord, your love will always find me

Susie Hare

Susie Hare

1. Lord, your love will al - ways find me, e - ven in the deep - est place; e - ven there your hand will lift me up in - to your heart of grace. You have planned and you can see all that I will e - ver be; Lord, it is too won - der-ful for me. You are the one

2. Lord, your love will always find me,
   even on the highest hill;
   on the far side of the ocean,
   there your hand will guide me still.
   You have planned and you can see
   all that I will ever be;
   Lord, it is too wonderful for me.

3. Lord, your love will always find me,
   I cannot escape your gaze;
   you know ev'rything about me,
   all my words and all my ways.
   You have planned and you can see
   all that I will ever be;
   Lord, it is too wonderful for me.

4. Search me Lord and know me fully,
   know my heart and know my mind;
   test the anxious thoughts within me,
   purify the things you find.
   You have planned and you can see
   all that I will ever be;
   Lord, it is too wonderful for me.

227 Lord, you were rich beyond all splendour

Frank Houghton and,
in this version, Jubilate Hymns.

Traditional French carol
arr. David Iliff

BERGERS 98 98 98

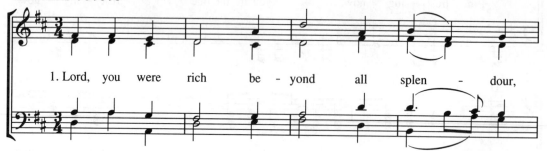

1. Lord, you were rich be-yond all splen-dour,

yet, for love's sake, be-came so poor;

leav-ing your throne in glad sur-ren-der,

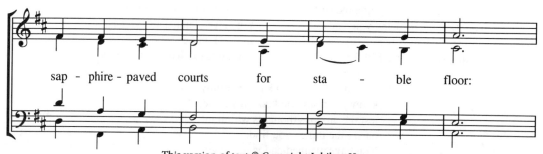

sap-phire-paved courts for sta-ble floor:

Lord, you were rich be - yond all splen - dour,

yet, for love's sake, be - came so poor.

2. You are our God beyond all praising,
   yet, for love's sake, became a man;
   stooping so low, but sinners raising
   heav'nwards by your eternal plan:
   you are our God, beyond all praising,
   yet, for love's sake, became a man.

3. Lord, you are love beyond all telling,
   Saviour and King, we worship you;
   Emmanuel, within us dwelling,
   make us and keep us pure and true:
   Lord, you are love beyond all telling,
   Saviour and King, we worship you.

228 Love divine, all loves excelling

Charles Wesley (1707-1788) alt.   John Stainer (1840-1901)

TUNE 1: LOVE DIVINE 87 87

1. Love divine, all loves excelling, joy of
heav'n, to earth come down, fix in us thy humble
dwelling, all thy faithful mercies crown.

2. Jesu, thou art all compassion,
   pure unbounded love thou art;
   visit us with thy salvation,
   enter ev'ry trembling heart.

3. Breathe, O breathe thy loving Spirit
   into ev'ry troubled breast;
   let us all in thee inherit,
   let us find thy promised rest.

4. Take away the love of sinning,
   Alpha and Omega be;
   end of faith, as its beginning,
   set our hearts at liberty.

5. Come, Almighty to deliver,
   let us all thy grace receive;
   suddenly return, and never,
   never more thy temples leave.

6. Thee we would be always blessing,
   serve thee as thy hosts above;
   pray, and praise thee without ceasing,
   glory in thy perfect love.

7. Finish then thy new creation,
   pure and spotless let us be;
   let us see thy great salvation
   perfectly restored in thee.

8. Changed from glory into glory,
   till in heav'n we take our place,
   till we cast our crowns before thee,
   lost in wonder, love, and praise.

(Sung as four eight-line verses when using Tune 2.)

Charles Wesley (1707-1788) alt.

William Penfro Rowlands (1860-1937)

TUNE 2: BLAENWERN 87 87 D

229 Love songs from heaven

Noel and Tricia Richards

Noel and Tricia Richards

1. Love songs from hea-ven are fill-ing the earth, bring-ing great hope to all na - tions; e - vil has pros-pered, but truth is a - live, in this dark world the light still shines.

Refrain

For you we live, and for you we may die,

through us may Je - sus be seen;
for you a - lone we will of - fer our lives,
in this dark world our light will shine.

2. Nothing has silenced this gospel of Christ;
   it echoes down through the ages.
   Blood of the martyrs has made your church strong,
   in this dark world the light still shines.

3. Let ev'ry nation be filled with your song;
   this is the cry of your people,
   'We will not settle for anything less,
   in this dark world, our light must shine.'

230 Majesty

Jack W. Hayford

Jack W. Hayford (b.1934)

Triumphantly

See over for another arrangement

Jack W. Hayford (b.1934)
arr. Susie Hare

NEW ARRANGEMENT

Building

Ma - jes-ty, wor-ship his ma - jes-ty,

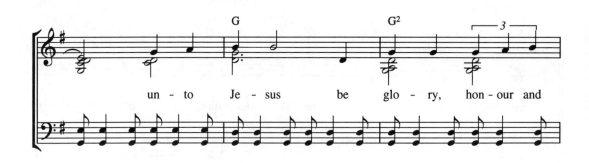

un - to Je - sus be glo - ry, hon - our and

praise. Ma - jes-ty,

231 Make me a channel of your peace

Sebastian Temple,
based on the Prayer of St Francis

Sebastian Temple (1928-1997)

2. Make me a channel of your peace.
   Where there's despair in life, let me bring hope.
   Where there is darkness, only light,
   and where there's sadness, ever joy.

3. Make me a channel of your peace.
   It is in pardoning that we are pardoned,
   in giving of ourselves that we receive,
   and in dying that we're born to eternal life.

232 Make way, make way

Graham Kendrick

Graham Kendrick (b.1950)

1. Make way, make way, for Christ the King in splen - dour ar - rives; fling wide the gates and wel - come him in - to your lives. *(Men)* Make

(Women) (make way,) (make way,) (for the King of kings;)
(Men) way, make way, for the King of kings; make
(make way,) (make way,)
way, make way, *(All)* and let his king - dom in!

2. He comes the broken hearts to heal,
   the pris'ners to free;
   the deaf shall hear, the lame shall dance,
   the blind shall see.

3. And those who mourn with heavy hearts,
   who weep and sigh,
   with laughter, joy and royal crown
   he'll beautify.

4. We call you now to worship him
   as Lord of all,
   to have no gods before him,
   their thrones must fall.

233 Man of sorrows!

Philipp Bliss, alt.

Philipp Bliss (1838-1876)

GETHSEMANE 777 8

2. Bearing shame and scoffing rude,
   in my place condemned he stood;
   sealed my pardon with his blood:
   Alleluia! What a Saviour!

3. Guilty, vile and helpless we;
   spotless Lamb of God was he:
   full atonement – can it be?
   Alleluia! What a Saviour!

4. Lifted up was he to die:
   'It is finished!' was his cry;
   now in heav'n exalted high:
   Alleluia! What a Saviour!

5. When he comes, our glorious King,
   all his ransomned home to bring,
   then anew this song we'll sing:
   Alleluia! What a Saviour!

234 Master, speak! Thy servant heareth

Frances Ridley Havergal (1836-1879)

Lowell Mason (1792-1872)

TUNE 1: OTTAWA 87 87 77

1. Mas - ter, speak! Thy ser - vant hear - eth, wait - ing for thy gra - cious word, long - ing for thy voice that cheer - eth; Mas - ter, let it now be heard. I am list - 'ning, Lord, for thee; what hast thou to say to me?

2. Speak to me by name, O Master,
   let me know it is to me;
   speak, that I may follow faster,
   with a step more firm and free,
   where the Shepherd leads the flock
   in the shadow of the Rock.

3. Master, speak! Though least and lowest,
   let me not unheard depart;
   Master, speak! For, O, thou knowest
   all the yearning of my heart,
   knowest all its truest need;
   speak, and make me blest indeed.

4. Master, speak: and make me ready,
   when thy voice is truly heard,
   with obedience glad and steady
   still to follow ev'ry word.
   I am list'ning, Lord, for thee;
   Master, speak! O speak to me!

Frances Ridley Havergal (1836-1879)

John Evans arr. Susie Hare

TUNE 2: BROCKWELL 87 87 77 77

235 May the fragrance

Graham Kendrick

Graham Kendrick (b.1950)

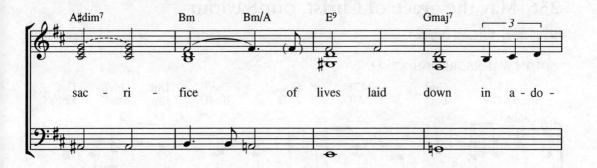

sac - ri - fice of lives laid down in a - do -

verse 3 D.S. | *Last time*

ra - tion.

2. *(Men)*   May the glory of Jesus fill his church.
   (Women) May the glory of Jesus fill his church.
   (Men)   May the glory of Jesus fill his church.
   (Women) Radiant glory of Jesus,
   (All)   shining from our faces
           as we gaze in adoration.

3. *(Men)*   May the beauty of Jesus fill my life.
   (Women) May the beauty of Jesus fill my life.
   (Men)   May the beauty of Jesus fill my life.
   (Women) Perfect beauty of Jesus,
   (All)   fill my thoughts, my words, my deeds;
           may I give in adoration.
           Fill my thoughts, my words, my deeds;
           may I give in adoration.

236 May the grace of Christ, our Saviour

Martin E. Leckebusch (b.1962)

Susie Hare

SOUTH WARNBOROUGH 87 87 D

1. May the grace of Christ, our Saviour, be our guide in all we do, for his willing self-abasement shows the pathway to pursue; as we give to other people may he make us rich indeed, bringing

to our hu-man frail-ty all the strength he knows we need.

2. May the love of God our Father
   clothe and fill us day by day;
   may compassion be our watchword
   and forgiveness chart our way –
   for to holiness he called us,
   to reflect his purity:
   in our actions may his kindness
   be a light for all to see.

3. May the friendship of God's Spirit
   be a joy for ever near;
   in our times of doubt and trouble
   may his presence banish fear.
   As his comfort makes us stronger,
   glorious freedom may we know;
   by the life of God he brings us,
   more like Jesus may we grow.

*(This text can also be sung in the second
person rather than the first:*

   *May the grace of Christ, your Saviour,
   be your guide in all you do . . .*

*Such usage may be suitable for a
commissioning service.)*

The Bridge

237 May the mind of Christ my Saviour

Kate Barclay Wilkinson (1859-1928)　　　　　　　Arthur Cyril Barham Gould (1891-1953)

ST LEONARD'S 87 85

1. May the mind of Christ my Sa-viour live in me from day to day,
by his love and pow'r con-trol-ling all I do and say.

2. May the word of God dwell richly
in my heart from hour to hour,
so that all may see I triumph
only through his pow'r.

3. May the peace of God my Father
rule my life in ev'rything,
that I may be calm to comfort
sick and sorrowing.

4. May the love of Jesus fill me,
as the waters fill the sea;
him exalting, self abasing,
this is victory.

5. May I run the race before me,
strong and brave to face the foe,
looking only unto Jesus
as I onward go.

6. May his beauty rest upon me
as I seek the lost to win,
and may they forget the channel,
seeing only him.

238 Meekness and majesty

This is your God

Graham Kendrick

Graham Kendrick (b.1950)

THIS IS YOUR GOD 66 65 D and Refrain

1. Meek-ness and ma-jes-ty, man-hood and de-i-ty, in per-fect

har-mo-ny, the Man who is God. Lord of e-ter-ni-ty

dwells in hu-ma-ni-ty, kneels in hu-mi-li-ty and wash-es our

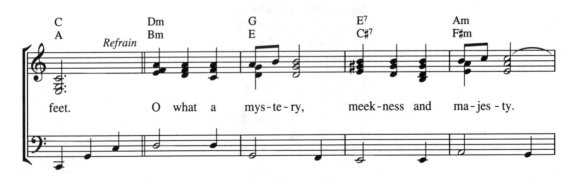

feet. O what a mys-te-ry, meek-ness and ma-jes-ty.

Bow down and wor-ship for this is your God, this is your God.

God,

this is your God.

2. Father's pure radiance,
   perfect in innocence,
   yet learns obedience
   to death on a cross.
   Suffering to give us life,
   conquering through sacrifice,
   and as they crucify
   prays: 'Father forgive.'

3. Wisdom unsearchable,
   God the invisible,
   love indestructible
   in frailty appears.
   Lord of infinity,
   stooping so tenderly,
   lifts our humanity
   to the heights of his throne.

239 Men of faith

Martin Smith

Shout to the north

Martin Smith

Unison

1. Men of faith, rise up and sing of the great and glo - rious King. You are strong when you feel weak, in your bro - ken-ness com-plete.

Refrain

Shout to the north and the south, sing to the east and the west. Je - sus is Sa - viour to all, Lord of hea - ven and earth.

Last time to Coda

1st and 3rd times

2nd time

2. Rise up,
3. Rise up,

2. Rise up, women of the truth,
   stand and sing to broken hearts.
   Who can know the healing pow'r
   of our awesome King of love?

3. Rise up, church with broken wings,
   fill this place with songs again
   of our God who reigns on high,
   by his grace again we'll fly.

240 Most holy judge

I'm justified

Steve and Vikki Cook

Steve and Vikki Cook

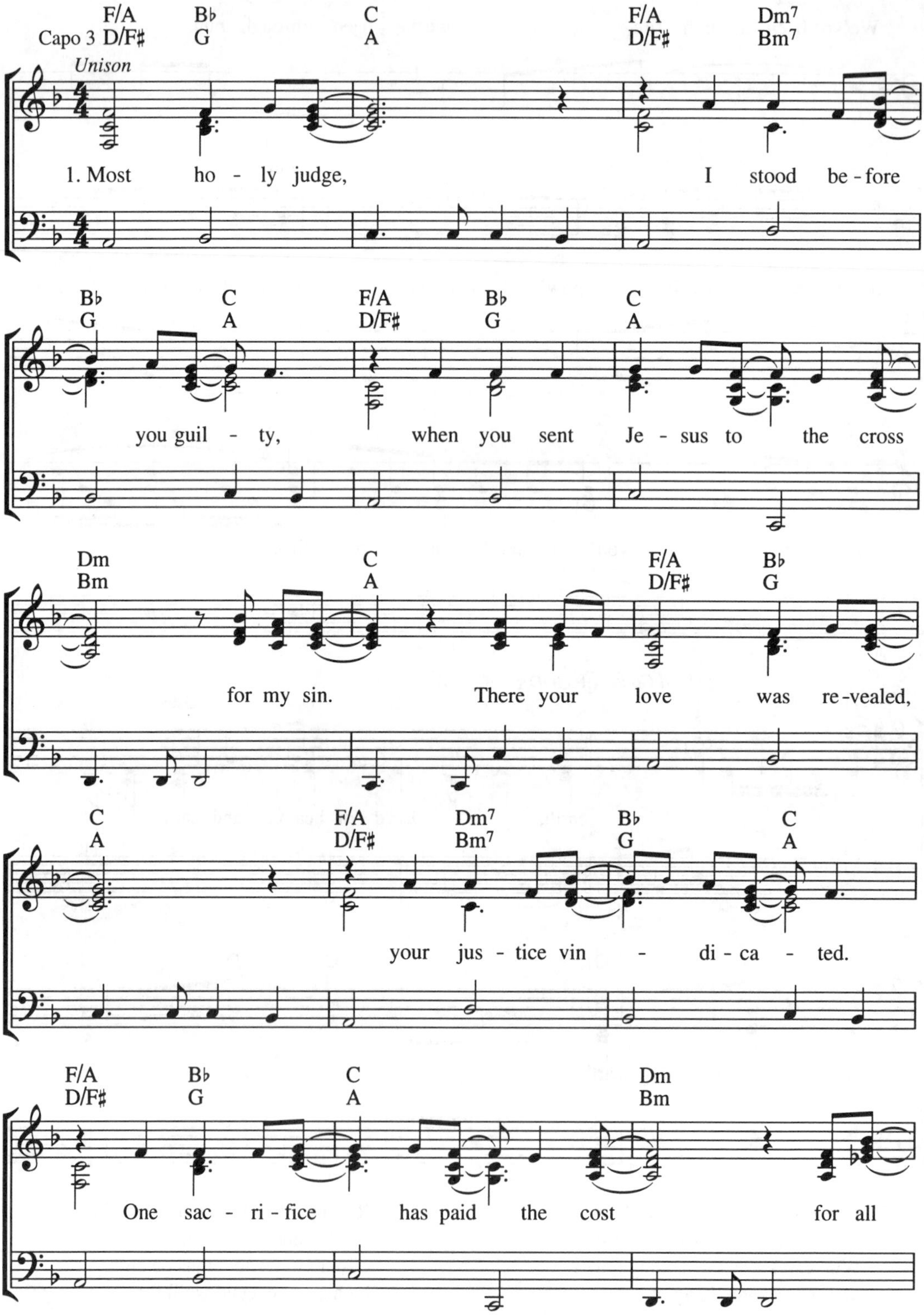
F/A Bb C F/A Dm7
Capo 3 D/F# G A D/F# Bm7
Unison
1. Most ho - ly judge, I stood be - fore
Bb C F/A Bb C
G A D/F# G A
you guil - ty, when you sent Je - sus to the cross
Dm C F/A Bb
Bm A D/F# G
for my sin. There your love was re - vealed,
C F/A Dm7 Bb C
A D/F# Bm7 G A
your jus - tice vin - di - ca - ted.
F/A Bb C Dm
D/F# G A Bm
One sac - ri - fice has paid the cost for all

2. I come to you and I can call you 'Father',
   there is no fear, there is no shame before you.
   For by your gift of grace now I am one of your children,
   an heir with those who bear your name and share the hope of glory.

241 Most worthy Lord

Cha Wright

Cha Wright arr. Susie Hare

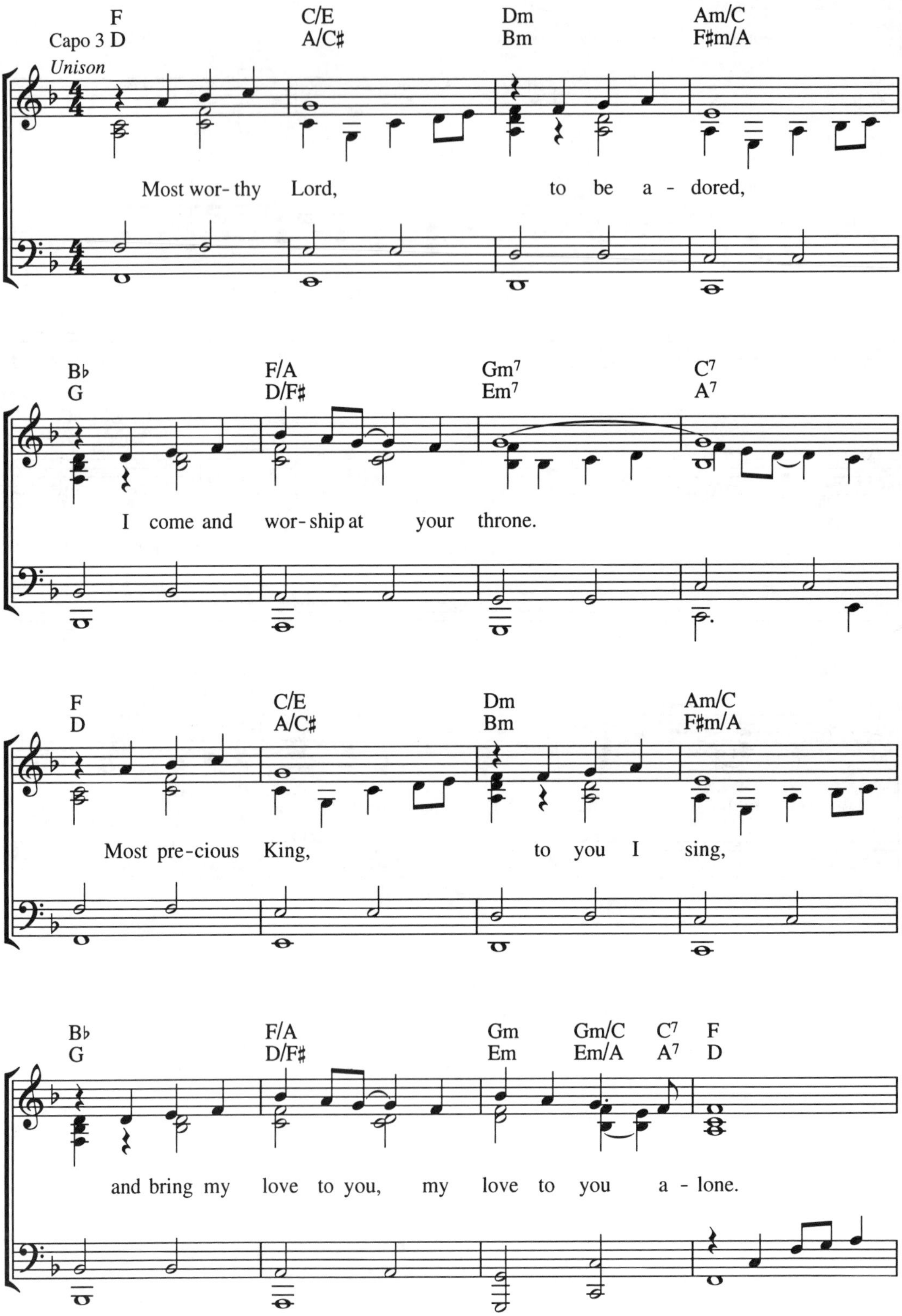

F C/E Dm Am/C
Capo 3 D A/C♯ Bm F♯m/A
Unison
Most wor- thy Lord, to be a - dored,
B♭ F/A Gm7 C7
G D/F♯ Em7 A7
I come and wor- ship at your throne.
F C/E Dm Am/C
D A/C♯ Bm F♯m/A
Most pre-cious King, to you I sing,
B♭ F/A Gm Gm/C C7 F
G D/F♯ Em Em/A A7 D
and bring my love to you, my love to you a - lone.

The Bridge

242 My God, how wonderful thou art

Frederick William Faber (1814-1863)

James Turle (1802-1882)

WESTMINSTER CM

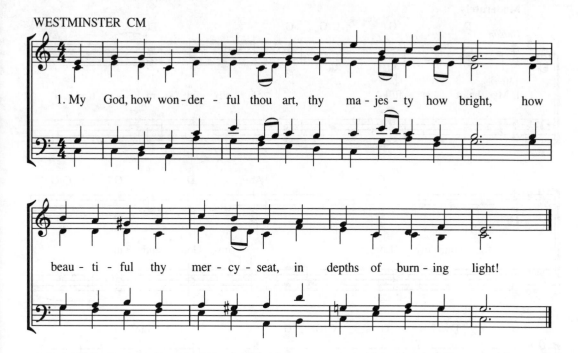

1. My God, how won-der-ful thou art, thy ma-jes-ty how bright, how
beau-ti-ful thy mer-cy-seat, in depths of burn-ing light!

2. How dread are thine eternal years,
O everlasting Lord,
by prostrate spirits day and night
incessantly adored!

3. How wonderful, how beautiful,
the sight of thee must be,
thine endless wisdom, boundless pow'r,
and aweful purity!

4. O how I fear thee, living God,
with deepest, tend'rest fears,
and worship thee with trembling hope,
and penitential tears!

5. Yet I may love thee too, O Lord,
almighty as thou art,
for thou hast stooped to ask of me
the love of my poor heart.

6. No earthly father loves like thee,
no mother, e'er so mild,
bears and forbears as thou hast done
with me thy sinful child.

7. Father of Jesus, love's reward,
what rapture will it be,
prostrate before thy throne to lie,
and gaze and gaze on thee!

243 My heart is full

All the glory

Graham Kendrick

Graham Kendrick (b.1950)

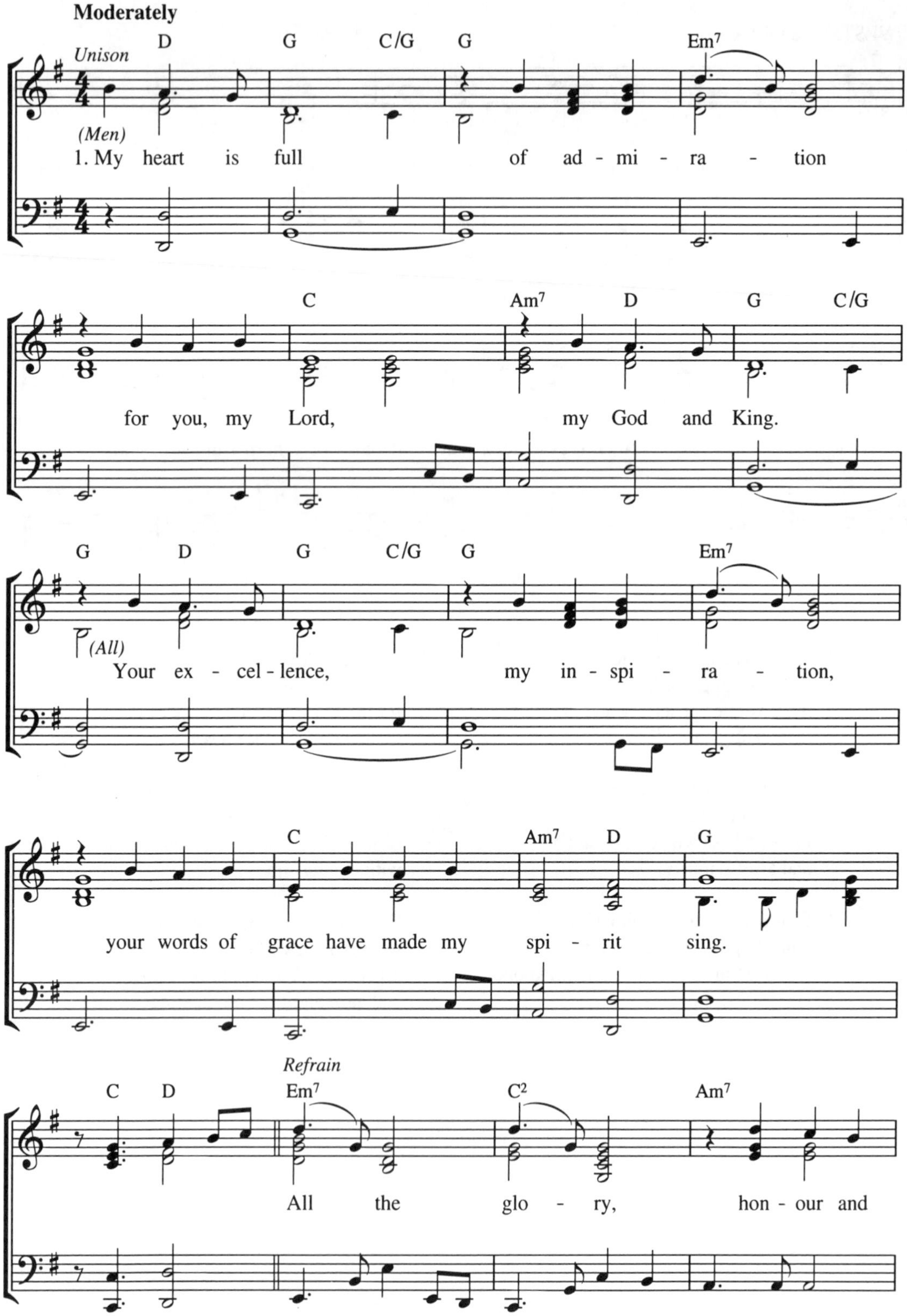
Moderately
Unison
(Men)
D G C/G G Em7
1. My heart is full of ad - mi - ra - tion
C Am7 D G C/G
for you, my Lord, my God and King.
G D G C/G G Em7
(All)
Your ex - cel - lence, my in - spi - ra - tion,
C Am7 D G
your words of grace have made my spi - rit sing.
Refrain
C D Em7 C2 Am7
All the glo - ry, hon - our and

pow'r be - long to you, be - long to you.

Je - sus, Sa - viour, a - noint - ed

One, I wor - ship you, I wor - ship you.

2. *(Men)* You love what's right and hate what's evil,
therefore your God sets you on high,
(Women) and on your head pours oil of gladness,
while fragrance fills your royal palaces.

3. *(All)* Your throne, O God, will last for ever,
justice will be your royal decree.
In majesty, ride out victorious,
for righteousness, truth and humility.

244 My hope is built on nothing less

Edward Mote and,
in this version, Jubilate Hymns

Henri Hémi
adapted by James Walton

ST CATHERINE 88 88 88

1. My hope is built on no - thing less than Je - sus' blood and

right - eous - ness; no me - rit of my own I claim,

but whol - ly trust in Je - sus' name. On Christ, the so - lid

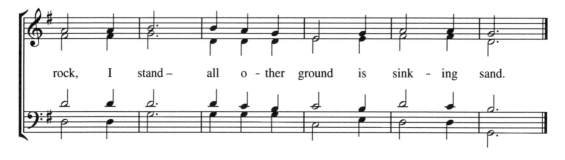

rock, I stand – all o - ther ground is sink - ing sand.

2. When weary in this earthly race,
   I rest on his unchanging grace;
   in ev'ry wild and stormy gale
   my anchor holds and will not fail.
   On Christ, the solid rock, I stand –
   all other ground is sinking sand.

3. His vow, his covenant and blood
   are my defence against the flood;
   when earthly hopes are swept away
   he will uphold me on that day.
   On Christ, the solid rock, I stand –
   all other ground is sinking sand.

4. When the last trumpet's voice shall sound,
   O may I then in him be found!
   Clothed in his righteousness alone,
   faultless to stand before his throne.
   On Christ, the solid rock, I stand –
   all other ground is sinking sand.

245 My Jesus, I love thee

William R. Featherston and
Adoniram J. Gordon

William R. Featherston and
Adorinam J. Gordon

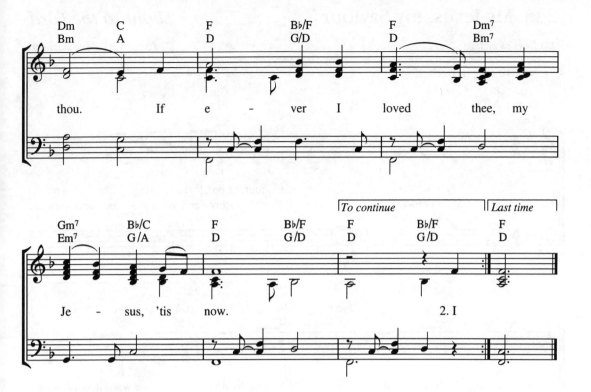

thou. If e - ver I loved thee, my

Je - sus, 'tis now. 2. I

To continue   *Last time*

2. I love thee because thou has first lovèd me,
   and purchased my pardon on Calvary's tree.
   I love thee for wearing the thorns on thy brow.
   If ever I loved thee, my Jesus, 'tis now.

3. In mansions of glory and endless delight,
   I'll ever adore thee in heaven so bright.
   I'll sing with a glittering crown on my brow.
   If ever I loved thee, my Jesus, 'tis now.

246 My Jesus, my Saviour

Shout to the Lord

Darlene Zschech

Darlene Zschech

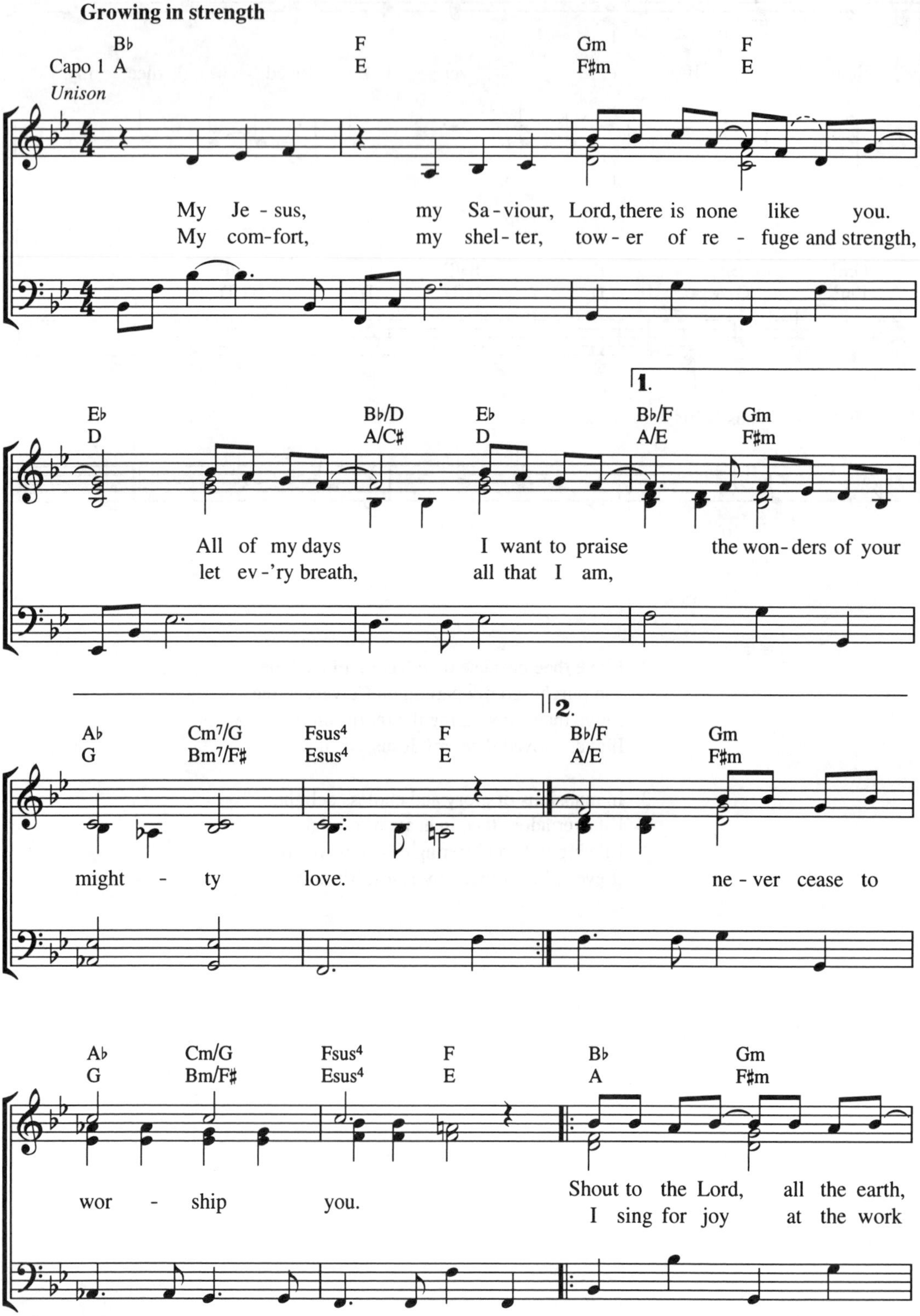

Growing in strength
Capo 1
Unison
B♭ A F E Gm F♯m F E
My Je - sus, my Sa - viour, Lord, there is none like you.
My com - fort, my shel - ter, tow - er of re - fuge and strength,
E♭ D B♭/D A/C♯ E♭ D
1. B♭/F A/E Gm F♯m
All of my days I want to praise the won - ders of your
let ev - 'ry breath, all that I am,
A♭ G Cm7/G Bm7/F♯ Fsus4 Esus4 F E
might - ty love.
2. B♭/F A/E Gm F♯m
ne - ver cease to
A♭ G Cm/G Bm/F♯ Fsus4 Esus4 F E
wor - ship you.
B♭ A Gm F♯m
Shout to the Lord, all the earth,
I sing for joy at the work

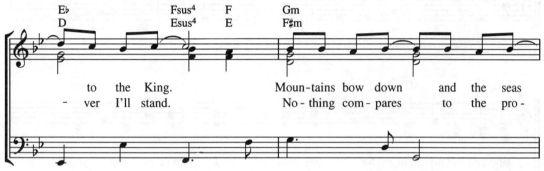

247 My Jesus, nothing I withhold

Susie Hare

Susie Hare

Gently

1. My Jesus, nothing I withhold from you now; take my silver and my gold, for all that I have belongs to you, all that I am and all I do. My Jesus, nothing I withhold from you. 2. My you.

2. My Jesus, ev'rything I yield to you now,
   all my selfish pride revealed,
   for nothing compares with knowing you,
   your love alone can make me new.
   My Jesus, ev'rything I yield to you.

3. My Jesus, let your will be done and in me
   finish what you have begun,
   that my life is purposed now to be
   all that your heart desires to see.
   My Jesus, let your will be done in me.

4. My Jesus, nothing I withhold from you now;
   take my silver and my gold,
   for all that I have belongs to you,
   all that I am and all I do.
   My Jesus, nothing I withhold from you.

248 My life is in you, Lord

Daniel Gardner

Daniel Gardner

My life is in you, Lord, my strength is in you, Lord, my

hope is in you, Lord, in you, it's in you. My

life is in you, Lord, my strength is in you, Lord, my

Last time to Coda

hope is in you, Lord, in you, it's in you. I will

249 My lips shall praise you

Restorer of my soul

Noel and Tricia Richards

Noel and Tricia Richards

My lips shall praise you, my great Re-deem-er; my heart will wor-ship, Al-migh-ty Sa-viour. Sa-viour.

1. You take all my guilt a-way, turn the dark-est

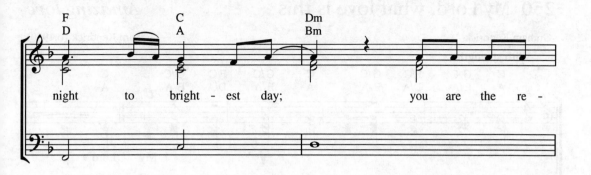

night   to   bright - est day;   you   are   the   re -

sto - rer   of   my   soul.

2. Love that conquers ev'ry fear,
   in the midst of trouble you draw near;
   you are the restorer of my soul.

3. You're the source of happiness,
   bringing peace when I am in distress;
   you are the restorer of my soul.

250 My Lord, what love is this

Amazing love

Graham Kendrick

Graham Kendrick (b.1950)

With strength

1. My Lord, what love is this, that pays so dear-ly, that I, the guil-ty one, may go free! A-maz-ing love, O what sac-ri-fice, the

2. And so they watched him die,
   despised, rejected;
   but O, the blood he shed
   flowed for me!

3. And now this love of Christ
   shall flow like rivers;
   come, wash your guilt away,
   live again!

251 My song is love unknown

Samuel Crossman (c.1624-1683)

John Ireland (1879-1962)

LOVE UNKNOWN 66 66 88

Unison

1. My song is love un - known, my Sa - viour's love to me; love to the love - less shown, that they might love - ly be. O who am I that for my sake my Lord should take frail flesh, and die?

2. He came from his blest throne
   salvation to bestow;
   but they made strange, and none
   the longed-for Christ would know.
   But O, my friend, my friend indeed,
   who at my need his life did spend!

3. Sometimes they strew his way,
   and his sweet praises sing;
   resounding all the day
   hosannas to their King;
   then 'Crucify!' is all their breath,
   and for his death they thirst and cry.

4. Why, what hath my Lord done?
   What makes this rage and spite?
   He made the lame to run,
   he gave the blind their sight.
   Sweet injuries! Yet they at these
   themselves displease, and 'gainst him rise.

5. They rise, and needs will have
   my dear Lord made away;
   a murderer they save,
   the Prince of Life they slay.
   Yet cheerful he to suff'ring goes,
   that he his foes from thence might free.

6. Here might I stay and sing,
   no story so divine;
   never was love, dear King,
   never was grief like thine.
   This is my friend in whose sweet praise
   I all my days could gladly spend.

See over for another arrangement.

John Ireland (1879-1962)
arr. Susie Hare

NEW ARRANGEMENT

Gently

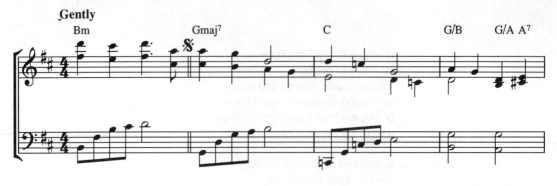

1. My song is love un - known, my Sa - viour's love to

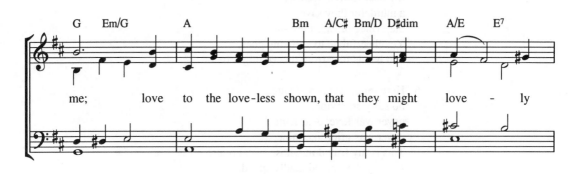

me; love to the love-less shown, that they might love - ly

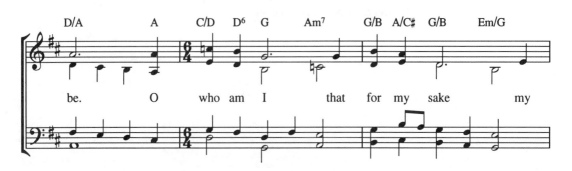

be. O who am I that for my sake my

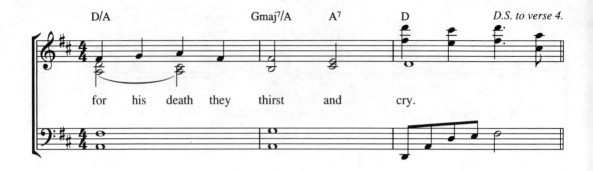

D.S. to verse 4.

for his death they thirst and cry.

2. He came from his blest throne
   salvation to bestow;
   but they made strange, and none
   the longed-for Christ would know.
   But O, my friend, my friend indeed,
   who at my need his life did spend!

3. Sometimes they strew his way,
   and his sweet praises sing;
   resounding all the day
   hosannas to their King;
   then 'Crucify!' is all their breath,
   and for his death they thirst and cry.

4. Why, what hath my Lord done?
   What makes this rage and spite?
   He made the lame to run,
   he gave the blind their sight.
   Sweet injuries! Yet they at these
   themselves displease, and 'gainst him rise.

5. They rise, and needs will have
   my dear Lord made away;
   a murderer they save,
   the Prince of Life they slay.
   Yet cheerful he to suff'ring goes,
   that he his foes from thence might free.

6. Here might I stay and sing,
   no story so divine;
   never was love, dear King,
   never was grief like thine.
   This is my friend in whose sweet praise
   I all my days could gladly spend.

252 Name of all majesty

Timothy Dudley-Smith (b.1926)

Malcolm Archer (b.1952)

NAME OF ALL MAJESTY 66 64 D

1. Name of all ma-jes-ty, fa-thom-less mys-te-ry, King of the a - ges by an-gels a - dored; pow'r and au - tho - ri-ty, splen-dour and dig - ni-ty, bow to his mas-te-ry, Je - sus is Lord!

2. Child of our destiny,
God from eternity,
love of the Father
on sinners outpoured;
see now what God has done
sending his only Son,
Christ the beloved one,
Jesus is Lord!

3. Saviour of Calvary,
costliest victory,
darkness defeated
and Eden restored;
born as a man to die,
nailed to a cross on high,
cold in the grave to lie,
Jesus is Lord!

4. Source of all sov'reignty,
light, immortality,
life everlasting
and heaven assured;
so with the ransomed, we
praise him eternally,
Christ in his majesty,
Jesus is Lord!

253 No eye has seen

How high and how wide

Mark Altrogge

Mark Altrogge

With power

1. No eye has seen and no ear has heard and no mind has e - ver con - ceived the glo - ri - ous things that you have pre - pared for ev - 'ry one who has be - lieved. You brought us near and you called us your own, and

made us joint heirs with your Son. How

high and how wide, how deep and how long, how sweet and how

strong is your love. How lav-ish your grace, how

faith-ful your ways, how great is your love, O Lord.

2. Objects of mercy who should have known wrath,
   we're filled with unspeakable joy,
   riches of wisdom, unsearchable wealth
   and the wonder of knowing your voice.
   You are our treasure and our great reward,
   our hope and our glorious King.

254 No gift so wonderful

Have we any room for Jesus?

Susie Hare

Susie Hare

Unhurried

Unison

1. No gift so won - der - ful, no love so beau - ti -
2. No gift so won - der - ful, no love so beau - ti -

ful, in just a hum - ble birth, hea-ven came down to earth.
ful; what are we meant to see – is it just his - to - ry?

And in the still of night,
And is he still, we find,

the world was gi - ven light, as in - to sin and
a ba - by in our mind, and is the sta - ble

shame, the love of hea - ven came.
scene all it will e - ver mean?

The Bridge

255 No one but you, Lord

Only you

Andy Park

Andy Park

Slowly, with strength

1. No one but you, Lord, can sat-is-fy the long-ing in my heart. No-thing I do, Lord, can take the place of draw-ing near to you. On-ly you can fill my deep-est long-ing, on-ly you can breathe in me new life; on-ly you can fill my heart with laugh-ter, on-ly you can ans-wer my heart's cry.

2. Father, I love you,
   come satisfy the longing in my heart.
   Fill me, overwhelm me,
   until I know your love deep in my heart.

256 No other name

Robert Gay

Robert Gay

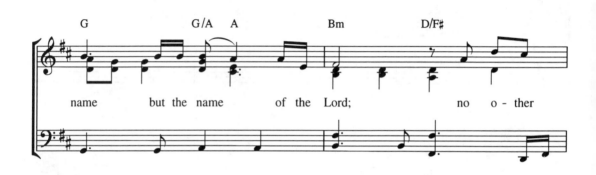

No o-ther name but the name of Je-sus, no o-ther

name but the name of the Lord; no o-ther

name but the name of Je - sus is wor - thy of glo-ry, and

Last time to Coda

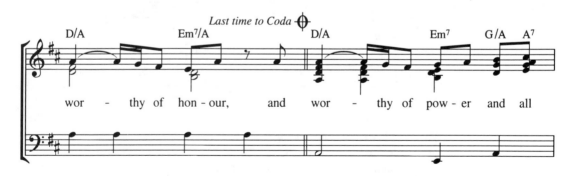

wor - thy of hon-our, and wor - thy of pow - er and all

257 No scenes of stately majesty

Graham Kendrick

Graham Kendrick (b.1950)

1. No scenes of state-ly ma-jes-ty for the King of kings. No nights a-glow with can-dle flame for the King of love. No flags of em-pire hung in shame for Cal-va-ry. No flow'rs per-fumed the lone-ly way

that led him to a bor-rowed tomb for Eas-ter

Day.

2. No wreaths upon the ground were laid
for the King of kings.
Only a crown of thorns remained
where he gave his love.
A message scrawled in irony –
King of the Jews –
lay trampled where they turned away,
and no one knew
that it was the first Easter Day.

3. Yet nature's finest colours blaze
for the King of kings.
And stars in jewelled clusters say,
'Worship heaven's King.'
Two thousand springtimes more have bloomed –
is that enough?
Oh, how can I be satisfied
until he hears
the whole world sing of Easter love.

4. My prayers shall be a fragrance sweet
for the King of kings.
My love the flowers at his feet
for the King of love.
My vigil is to watch and pray
until he comes.
My highest tribute to obey
and live to know
the pow'r of that first Easter Day.

5. I long for scenes of majesty
for the risen King.
For nights aglow with candle flame
for the King of love.
A nation hushed upon its knees
at Calvary,
where all our sins and griefs were nailed
and hope was born
of everlasting Easter Day.

258 Nothing shall separate us

Noel and Tricia Richards   Noel and Tricia Richards

Strong and bright

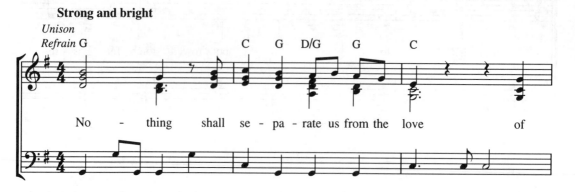

No - thing shall se - pa - rate us from the love of

God. No - thing shall se - pa - rate us from the

love of God. God.

1. God did not spare his on - ly Son, gave

him to save us all.
Sin's price was met

by Je - sus' death
and hea - ven's mer - cy falls.

2. Up from the grave Jesus was raised
   to sit at God's right hand;
   pleading our cause in heaven's courts,
   forgiven we can stand.

3. Now by God's grace we have embraced
   a life set free from sin;
   we shall deny all that destroys
   our union with him.

259 Nothing we have ever done

Susie Hare   Susie Hare

1. No-thing we have e-ver done, no-thing we have said,
2. No-thing we can e-ver be, no-thing we can give,
3. We have works pre-pared for us, not for our own pride,

could have raised us up to life; sins had made us dead.
can re-deem us from the life that we used to live.
but that he who works in us should be glo-ri-fied.

No-thing we have e-ver earned brings us to this place, but
Fu-tures of e-ter-nal wrath we de-serve to face, but
Ways of sin and self-ish-ness melt in his em-brace and

now God's throne of judge-ment has be-come his throne of

grace. And he has raised us up to the

The Bridge

260 No wonder that we sing

Lex Loizides

Lex Loizides

1. No won-der that we sing, he's o-pened up the joys of hea-ven; we're trust-ing in his per-fect right-eous-ness.
2. No won-der that we serve, he's teach-ing us to love our neigh-bour; we're go-ing with the grace of God to all.

No won-der that we give, we've stum-bled on the great-est trea-sure; and all our lives are his, for he has bought us with his blood.
No won-der that we pray, be-liev-ing God will save the seek-er; to all the world we say that we are not a-shamed of him.

261 Now thank we all our God

'Nun danket alle Gott'
by Martin Rinkart (1586-1649)
trans. Catherine Winkworth (1827-1878)

Melody by Johann Crüger (1598-1662)
harm. William Henry Monk (1823-1889)

TUNE 1: NUN DANKET 67 67 66 66

1. Now thank we all our God, with hearts and hands and voices, who won-drous things hath done, in whom his world re-joices; who from our mo-ther's arms hath blessed us on our way with count-less gifts of love, and still is ours to-day.

2. O may this bounteous God
   through all our life be near us,
   with ever joyful hearts
   and blessèd peace to cheer us;
   and keep us in his grace,
   and guide us when perplexed,
   and free us from all ills
   in this world and the next.

3. All praise and thanks to God
   the Father now be given,
   the Son and him who reigns
   with them in highest heaven,
   the one eternal God,
   whom earth and heav'n adore;
   for thus it was, is now,
   and shall be evermore.

'Nun danket alle Gott'
by Martin Rinkart (1586-1649)
trans. Catherine Winkworth (1827-1878)

Geoffrey Beaumont (1903-1970)

TUNE 2: GRACIAS 67 67 66 66

262 Now unto the King

Unto the King

Joey Holder

Joey Holder

The Bridge

263 O Breath of Life

Elizabeth Ann Porter Head (1850-1936)

Mary Jane Hammond (1878-1964)

SPIRITUS VITAE 98 98

1. O Breath of Life, come sweep-ing through us, re - vive your Church with life and pow'r; O Breath of Life, come cleanse, re - new us, and fit your Church to meet this hour.

2. O Breath of Love, come breathe within us,
   renewing thought and will and heart;
   come, love of Christ, afresh to win us,
   revive your Church in ev'ry part!

3. O Wind of God, come bend us, break us,
   till humbly we confess our need;
   then, in your tenderness remake us,
   revive, restore – for this we plead.

4. Revive us, Lord; is zeal abating
   while harvest fields are vast and white?
   Revive us, Lord, the world is waiting –
   equip your Church to spread the light.

264 O come, all ye faithful

Original Latin attributed to John Francis Wade
trans. Frederick Oakeley (1802-1880)

John Francis Wade's MS Book (1751)

ADESTE FIDELES Irregular and Refrain

1. O come, all ye faithful, joyful and triumphant,
come ye, O come ye to Bethlehem;
come and behold him, born the King of angels:

Refrain

O come, let us adore him, O come, let us adore him, O
come, let us adore him, Christ the Lord.

2. True God of true God,
   Light of Light eternal,
   lo! he abhors not the Virgin's womb;
   Son of the Father,
   begotten, not created:

3. Sing, choirs of angels,
   sing in exultation,
   sing, all ye citizens of heav'n above;
   glory to God
   in the highest:

4. Yea, Lord, we greet thee,
   born this happy morning,
   Jesus, to thee be glory giv'n;
   Word of the Father,
   now in flesh appearing:

265 O Father of the fatherless

Father me

Graham Kendrick

Graham Kendrick (b.1950)

1. O Father of the fatherless, in whom all families are blessed, I love the way you father me. You gave me life, forgave the past, now in your arms I'm safe at last; I love the way you father me. Father me,

for e - ver you'll fa - ther me, and in your em-brace I'll be for e - ver se-cure; I love the way you fa - ther me.

To verses

I love the way you fa - ther me.

Last time

2. When

2. When bruised and broken I draw near,
   you hold me close and dry my tears;
   I love the way you father me.
   At last my fearful heart is still,
   surrendered to your perfect will;
   I love the way you father me.

3. If in my foolishness I stray,
   returning empty and ashamed,
   I love the way you father me.
   Exchanging for my wretchedness
   your radiant robes of righteousness,
   I love the way you father me.

4. And when I look into your eyes,
   from deep within my spirit cries,
   I love the way you father me.
   Before such love I stand amazed
   and ever will through endless days;
   I love the way you father me.

266 O for a closer walk with God

William W. Cowper (1731-1800) alt.   William Gardiner (1770-1853)

BELMONT CM

1. O for a clo - ser walk with God, the

calm of sins for - giv'n, a light to shine up -

on the road that leads at last to heav'n.

2. O gentle messenger, return –
   return, O holy Dove;
   I hate the sins that made you mourn
   and grieved your heart of love.

3. Restore the happiness I knew
   when first I saw the Lord;
   refresh me with the radiant view
   of Jesus and his word!

4. From ev'ry idol I have known
   now set my spirit free;
   O make me worship you alone,
   and reign supreme in me.

5. So shall my walk be close with God,
   my wand'rings be forgiv'n;
   so shall his light mark out the road
   that leads at last to heav'n.

267 O for a heart to praise my God

Charles Wesley (1707-1788)   James Walch (1837-1901)

SAWLEY CM

Joyfully

1. O for a heart to praise my God, a heart from sin set free; a heart that al - ways feels thy blood so free - ly shed for me.

2. A heart resigned, submissive, meek,
   my great Redeemer's throne;
   where only Christ is heard to speak,
   where Jesus reigns alone.

3. A humble, lowly, contrite heart,
   believing, true and clean;
   which neither life nor death can part
   from him who dwells within.

4. A heart in ev'ry thought renewed,
   and full of love divine;
   perfect and right and pure and good:
   a copy, Lord, of thine.

5. Thy nature, gracious Lord, impart,
   come quickly from above;
   write thy new name upon my heart,
   thy new best name of love.

268 O for a thousand tongues to sing

Charles Wesley (1707-1788)

Thomas Jarman (1776-1861)

LYNGHAM 86 86 extended

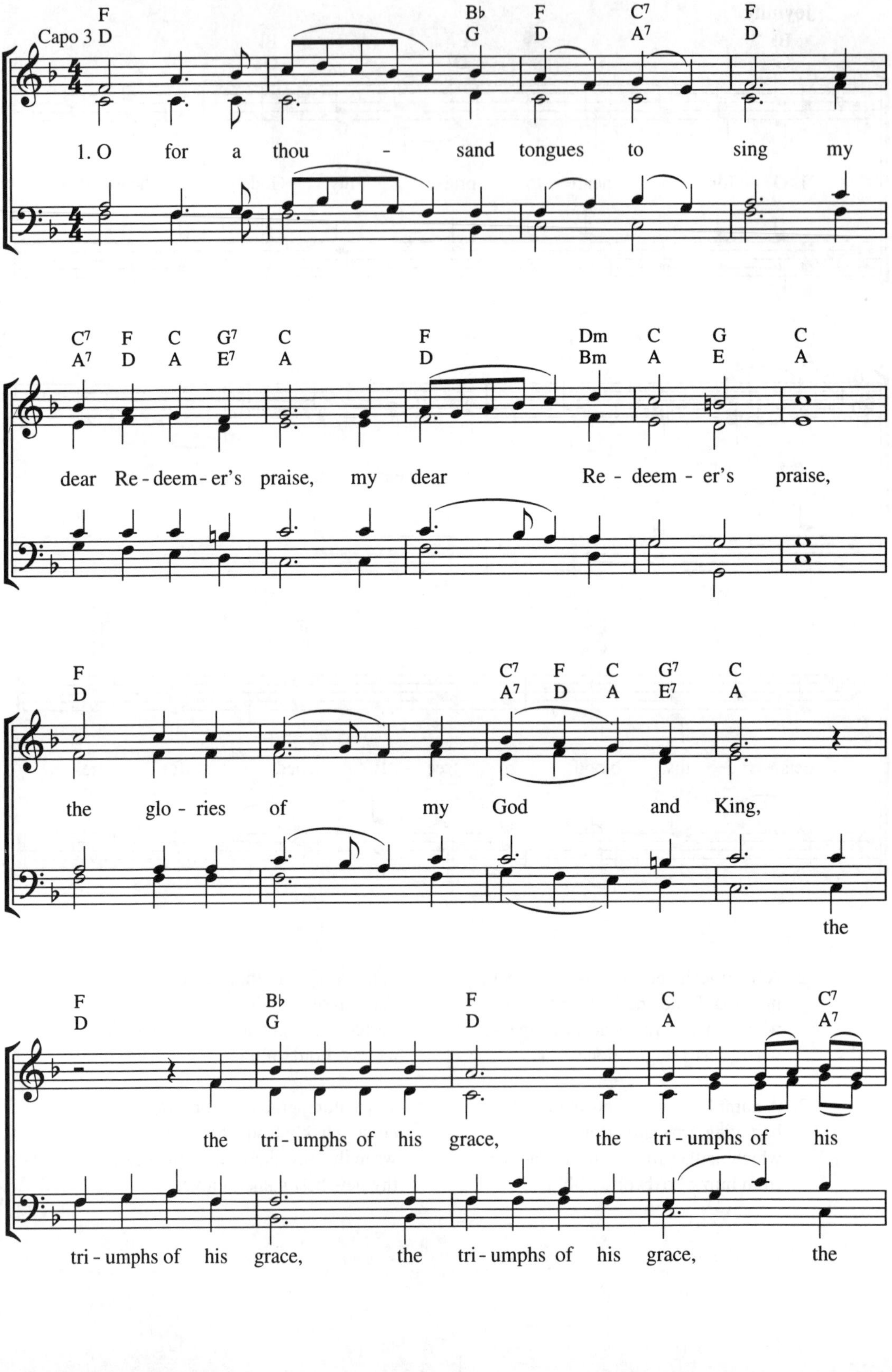

Capo 3
F D
B♭ G
F D
C7 A7
F D
1. O for a thou - sand tongues to sing my
C7 A7
F D
C A
G7 E7
C A
F D
Dm Bm
C A
G E
C A
dear Re - deem - er's praise, my dear Re - deem - er's praise,
F D
C7 A7
F D
C A
G7 E7
C A
the glo - ries of my God and King,
the
F D
B♭ G
F D
C A
C7 A7
the tri - umphs of his grace, the tri - umphs of his
tri - umphs of his grace, the tri - umphs of his grace, the

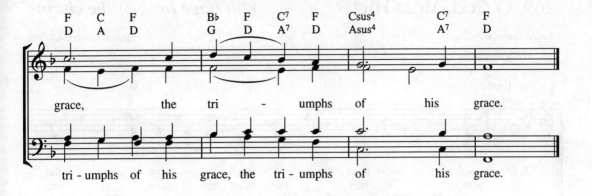

grace, the tri - umphs of his grace.

tri - umphs of his grace, the tri - umphs of his grace.

2. Jesus! the name that charms our fears,
   that bids our sorrows cease,
   that bids our sorrows cease;
   'tis music in the sinner's ears,
   'tis life and health and peace. *(x3)*

3. He breaks the pow'r of cancelled sin,
   he sets the pris'ner free,
   he sets the pris'ner free;
   his blood can make the foulest clean;
   his blood availed for me. *(x3)*

4. He speaks; and list'ning to his voice,
   new life the dead receive,
   new life the dead receive,
   the mournful broken hearts rejoice,
   the humble poor believe. *(x3)*

5. Hear him, ye deaf; his praise, ye dumb,
   your loosened tongues employ,
   your loosened tongues employ;
   ye blind, behold your Saviour come;
   and leap, ye lame, for joy! *(x3)*

6. My gracious Master and my God,
   assist me to proclaim,
   assist me to proclaim
   and spread through all the earth abroad
   the honours of thy name. *(x3)*

269 O God, Most High

You have broken the chains

Jamie Owens-Collins

Jamie Owens-Collins

With strength

1. O God, Most High, Almighty King, the champion of heaven, Lord of everything; you've fought, you've won, death's lost its sting, and standing in your victory we sing.

pow'r of hell has been undone, the captivity held captive by the risen One, and in the name of God's great Son, we claim the mighty victory you've won.

Refrain

You have broken the chains that held our captive souls.

You have broken the chains and used them on

270 O God of burning, cleansing flame

Send the fire

William Booth

Lex Loizides

1. O God of burn-ing, cleans-ing flame: send the fi-re! Your blood-bought gift to-day we claim: send the fire to-day! Look down and see this wait-ing host, and send the pro-mised Ho-ly Ghost; we need a-no-ther Pen-te-cost! Send the fire to-

2. God of Elijah, hear our cry: send the fire!
   and make us fit to live or die: send the fire today!
   To burn up ev'ry trace of sin,
   to bring the light and glory in,
   the revolution now begin!
   Send the fire today! Send the fire today!

3. It's fire we want, for fire we plead: send the fire!
   The fire will meet our ev'ry need: send the fire today!
   For strength to always do what's right,
   for grace to conquer in the fight,
   for pow'r to walk the world in white.
   Send the fire today! Send the fire today!

4. To make our weak heart strong and brave: send the fire!
   To live, a dying world to save: send the fire today!
   O, see us on your altar lay,
   we give our lives to you today,
   so crown the off'ring now we pray:
   Send the fire today! Send the fire today! Send the fire today!

271 O happy day

Philip Doddridge (1702-1751)

Ron Jones

TUNE 1: LIVERPOOL LM and Refrain

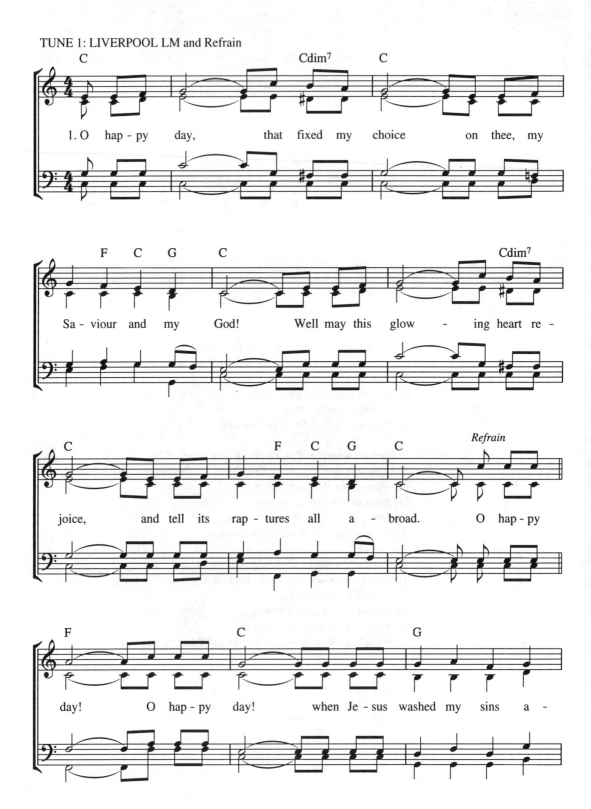

1. O hap-py day, that fixed my choice on thee, my Sa-viour and my God! Well may this glow - ing heart re-joice, and tell its rap-tures all a-broad. O hap-py day! O hap-py day! when Je-sus washed my sins a-

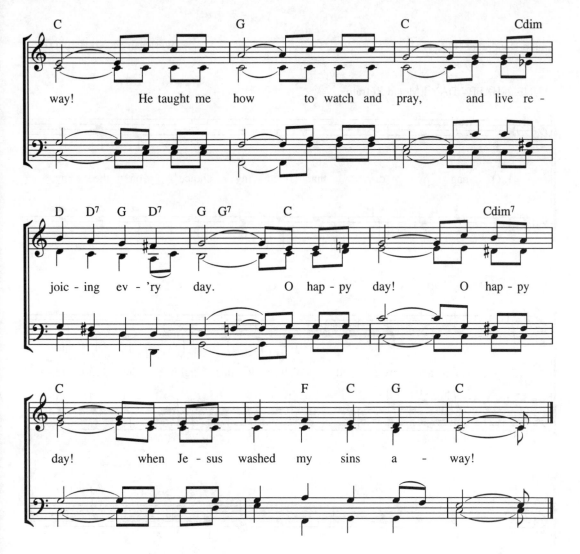

2. 'Tis done, the great transaction's done!
   I am my Lord's, and he is mine;
   he drew me, and I followed on,
   charmed to confess the voice divine.

3. Now rest, my long-divided heart,
   fixed on this blissful centre, rest;
   nor ever from thy Lord depart,
   with him of ev'ry good possessed.

4. High heav'n, that heard the solemn vow,
   that vow renewed shall daily hear,
   till in life's latest hour I bow,
   and bless in death a bond so dear.

See over for another tune.

Philip Doddridge (1702-1751)

'Wesleyan Sacred Harp' (1855)

TUNE 2: HAPPY DAY LM and Refrain

1. O hap-py day, that fixed my choice on thee, my

Sa - viour and my God! Well may this glow - ing heart re -

Refrain

joice, and tell its rap - tures all a - broad. Hap - py

day, hap - py day! when Je - sus washed my sins a -

way! He taught me how to watch and pray, and live re-

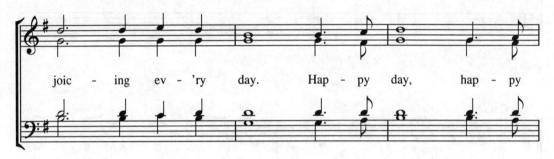

joic - ing ev - 'ry day. Hap - py day, hap - py

day, when Je - sus washed my sins a - way.

2. 'Tis done, the great transaction's done!
   I am my Lord's, and he is mine;
   he drew me, and I followed on,
   charmed to confess the voice divine.

3. Now rest, my long-divided heart,
   fixed on this blissful centre, rest;
   nor ever from thy Lord depart,
   with him of ev'ry good possessed.

4. High heav'n, that heard the solemn vow,
   that vow renewed shall daily hear,
   till in life's latest hour I bow,
   and bless in death a bond so dear.

See over for another arrangement.

'Wesleyan Sacred Harp' (1855)
arr. Susie Hare

NEW ARRANGEMENT

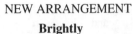

2. 'Tis done, the great transaction's done!
   I am my Lord's, and he is mine;
   he drew me, and I followed on,
   charmed to confess the voice divine.

3. Now rest, my long-divided heart,
   fixed on this blissful centre, rest;
   nor ever from thy Lord depart,
   with him of ev'ry good possessed.

4. High heav'n, that heard the solemn vow,
   that vow renewed shall daily hear,
   till in life's latest hour I bow,
   and bless in death a bond so dear.

272 O how I love thy law

Gerrit Gustafson

Gerrit Gustafson

1. O how I love thy law, it is my
2. You are the truth and life, and I will

me - di - ta - tion all of the day;
cling to ev - 'ry word that you say; your

fill - ing my mind and heart, with its
wis - dom is my de - light, I will

light I will know the way.
walk in your truth each day.

Thy

273 O Jesus, I have promised

John Ernest Bode (1816-1874)

Basil Harwood (1859-1949)

TUNE 1: THORNBURY 76 76 D

wan - der from the path - way if thou wilt be my Guide.

2. O let me feel thee near me:
   the world is ever near;
   I see the sights that dazzle,
   the tempting sounds I hear;
   my foes are ever near me,
   around me and within;
   but, Jesus, draw thou nearer,
   and shield my soul from sin.

3. O let me hear thee speaking
   in accents clear and still,
   above the storms of passion,
   the murmurs of self-will;
   O speak to reassure me,
   to hasten or control;
   O speak, and make me listen,
   thou Guardian of my soul.

4. O Jesus, thou hast promised,
   to all who follow thee,
   that where thou art in glory
   there shall thy servants be;
   and, Jesus, I have promised
   to serve thee to the end;
   O give me grace to follow
   my Master and my Friend.

5. O let me see thy footmarks,
   and in them plant mine own;
   my hope to follow duly
   is in thy strength alone.
   O guide me, call me, draw me,
   uphold me to the end;
   and then in heav'n receive me,
   my Saviour and my Friend.

See over for another tune.

John Ernest Bode (1816-1874)

James William Elliott (1833-1915)

TUNE 2: DAY OF REST 76 76 D

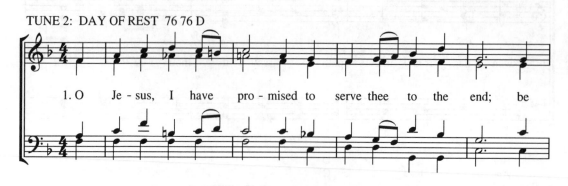

1. O Je - sus, I have pro - mised to serve thee to the end; be

thou for e - ver near me, my Mas - ter and my Friend; I

shall not fear the bat - tle if thou art by my side, nor

wan - der from the path - way if thou wilt be my Guide.

2. O let me feel thee near me:
   the world is ever near;
   I see the sights that dazzle,
   the tempting sounds I hear;
   my foes are ever near me,
   around me and within;
   but, Jesus, draw thou nearer,
   and shield my soul from sin.

3. O let me hear thee speaking
   in accents clear and still,
   above the storms of passion,
   the murmurs of self-will;
   O speak to reassure me,
   to hasten or control;
   O speak, and make me listen,
   thou Guardian of my soul.

4. O Jesus, thou hast promised,
   to all who follow thee,
   that where thou art in glory
   there shall thy servants be;
   and, Jesus, I have promised
   to serve thee to the end;
   O give me grace to follow
   my Master and my Friend.

5. O let me see thy footmarks,
   and in them plant mine own;
   my hope to follow duly
   is in thy strength alone.
   O guide me, call me, draw me,
   uphold me to the end;
   and then in heav'n receive me,
   my Saviour and my Friend.

274 O kneel me down again

Humble King

Brenton Brown

Brenton Brown
arr. Richard Lewis

275 O let the Son of God enfold you

Spirit song

John Wimber

John Wimber

1. O let the Son of God en-fold you with his Spi-rit and his love, let him fill your heart and sa-tis-fy your soul. O let him have the things that hold you, and his Spi-rit like a dove will des-cend up-on your life and make you whole. Je -

2. O come and sing this song with gladness
   as your hearts are filled with joy,
   lift your hands in sweet surrender to his name.
   O give him all your tears and sadness,
   give him all your years of pain,
   and you'll enter into life in Jesus' name.

276 O little town of Bethlehem

Phillips Brooks (1835-1893) alt.

Traditional English melody collected and
arr. Ralph Vaughan Williams (1872-1958)

TUNE 1: FOREST GREEN DCM

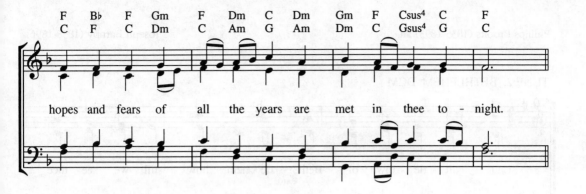

| F | B♭ | F | Gm | F | Dm | C | Dm | Gm | F | Csus⁴ | C | F |
| C | F | C | Dm | C | Am | G | Am | Dm | C | Gsus⁴ | G | C |

hopes and fears of all the years are met in thee to - night.

2. O morning stars, together
   proclaim the holy birth,
   and praises sing to God the King,
   and peace upon the earth.
   For Christ is born of Mary;
   and, gathered all above,
   while mortals sleep, the angels keep
   their watch of wond'ring love.

3. How silently, how silently,
   the wondrous gift is giv'n!
   So God imparts to human hearts
   the blessings of his heav'n.
   No ear may hear his coming;
   but in this world of sin,
   where meek souls will receive him, still
   the dear Christ enters in.

4. O holy child of Bethlehem,
   descend to us, we pray;
   cast out our sin, and enter in,
   be born in us today.
   We hear the Christmas angels
   the great glad tidings tell:
   O come to us, abide with us,
   our Lord Emmanuel.

See over for another tune.

Phillips Brooks (1835-1893) alt.

Joseph Barnby (1838-1896)

TUNE 2: BETHLEHEM DCM

1. O lit - tle town of Beth - le - hem, how still we see thee

lie! A - bove thy deep and dream - less sleep the

si - lent stars go by. Yet in thy dark streets shi - neth the

e - ver - last - ing light; the hopes and fears of

all the years are met in thee to - night.

2. O morning stars, together
   proclaim the holy birth,
   and praises sing to God the King,
   and peace upon the earth.
   For Christ is born of Mary;
   and, gathered all above,
   while mortals sleep, the angels keep
   their watch of wond'ring love.

3. How silently, how silently,
   the wondrous gift is giv'n!
   So God imparts to human hearts
   the blessings of his heav'n.
   No ear may hear his coming;
   but in this world of sin,
   where meek souls will receive him, still
   the dear Christ enters in.

4. O holy child of Bethlehem,
   descend to us, we pray;
   cast out our sin, and enter in,
   be born in us today.
   We hear the Christmas angels
   the great glad tidings tell:
   O come to us, abide with us,
   our Lord Emmanuel.

The Bridge

277 O Lord, hear my prayer

From Scripture

Jacques Berthier (1923-1994)

278 O Lord, my God

How great thou art

'O Støre Gud' by Karl Boberg (1859-1940)
trans. Stuart K. Hine (1899-1989)

Swedish folk melody
arr. Stuart K. Hine

HOW GREAT THOU ART 11 10 11 10 and Refrain

1. O Lord, my God, when I, in awe-some won-der, con-si-der all the works thy hand has made, I see the stars, I hear the roll-ing thun-der, thy pow'r through-out the u-ni-verse dis-played. Then sings my soul, my Sa-viour God, to thee: how great thou

2. When through the woods and forest glades I wander,
   and hear the birds sing sweetly in the trees;
   when I look down from lofty mountain grandeur,
   and hear the brook, and feel the gentle breeze.

3. And when I think that God, his Son not sparing,
   sent him to die, I scarce can take it in
   that on the cross, my burden gladly bearing,
   he bled and died to take away my sin.

4. When Christ shall come with shout of acclamation,
   and take me home, what joy shall fill my heart;
   then I shall bow in humble adoration,
   and there proclaim: my God, how great thou art.

279 O Lord our God

We will magnify

Philip Lawson Johnston

Philip Lawson Johnston

1. O Lord our God, how ma-jes - tic is your name; the earth is filled with your glo - ry. O Lord our God, you are robed in ma-jes - ty; you've set your glo-ry a-bove the hea -

2. O Lord our God, you have established a throne,
   you reign in righteousness and splendour.
   O Lord our God, the skies are ringing with your praise;
   soon those on earth will come to worship.

3. O Lord our God, the world was made at your command,
   in you all things now hold together.
   Now to him who sits on the throne and to the Lamb
   be praise and glory and pow'r for ever.

280 O Lord, you have been good

You have been good

Twila Paris

Twila Paris

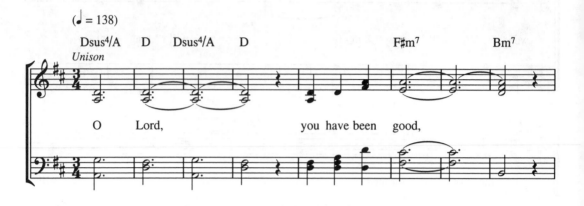

O Lord, you have been good,

you have been faith - ful to all ge - ne - ra -

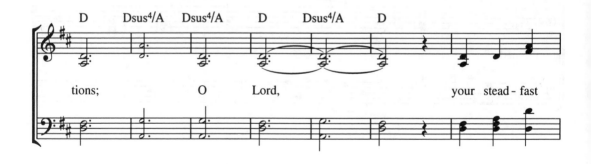

tions; O Lord, your stead - fast

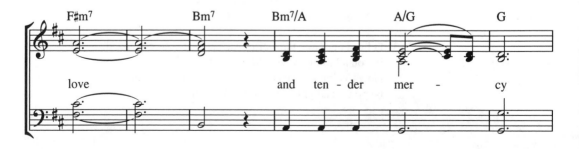

love and ten - der mer - cy

The Bridge

281 O Lord, your tenderness

Graham Kendrick

Graham Kendrick (b.1950)

With feeling

O Lord, your ten-der-ness, melt-ing all my

bit-ter-ness, O Lord, I re-ceive your

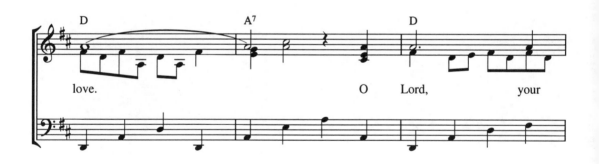

love. O Lord, your

love-li-ness, chang-ing all my ug-li-ness, O

Lord, I re - ceive your love.

O Lord, I re - ceive your

love, O Lord, I re -

ceive your love.

282 O Love that searches all my soul

Susie Hare,
based on Psalm 51 vs. 10-12

Susie Hare

POWNTLEY 86 86 86 866

Unhurried

1. O Love that search - es all my soul, cre -

ate in me a - new, a pu - ri - fied and

con - trite heart that search - es af - ter you. Je -

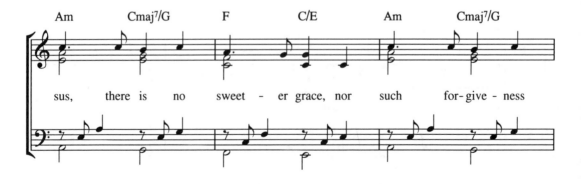

sus, there is no sweet - er grace, nor such for - give - ness

known   as   in   the hum - ble   hearts   of   those   where -

in   your love   is   sown,   where - in   your love   is   sown.

2. O Love that washes all my sins,
   create in me anew,
   salvation's joy and peace restored
   as I abide in you.
   Jesus, there is no sweeter joy
   than that which grace revives,
   nor greater peace within my heart
   than heaven's love provides,
   than heaven's love provides.

3. O Love that lifts my voice to sing,
   create in me anew,
   a song that always fills my heart
   with thankfulness to you.
   Jesus, there is no sweeter song
   than that which breathes your name,
   and through eternity my praise
   will always be the same,
   will always be the same.

The Bridge

283 O Love that wilt not let me go

George Matheson (1842-1906)

Albert Lister Peace (1844-1912)

ST MARGARET 88 88 6

1. O Love that wilt not let me go, I rest my wea-ry soul in thee; I give thee back the life I owe, that in thine o-cean depths its flow may rich - er, full - er be.

2. O Light that follow'st all my way,
   I yield my flick'ring torch to thee;
   my heart restores its borrowed ray,
   that in thy sunshine's blaze its day
   may brighter, fairer be.

3. O Joy that seekest me through pain,
   I cannot close my heart to thee;
   I trace the rainbow through the rain,
   and feel the promise is not vain
   that morn shall tearless be.

4. O Cross that liftest up my head,
   I dare not ask to fly from thee:
   I lay in dust life's glory dead,
   and from the ground there blossoms red
   life that shall endless be.

284 On a hill far away

The old rugged cross

George Bennard

George Bennard (1873-1958)

THE OLD RUGGED CROSS 66 8 D and Refrain

1. On a hill far a-way stood an old rug-ged cross, the em-blem of suff-'ring and shame; and I loved that old cross where the dear-est and best for a world of lost sin-ners was slain. So I'll cher-ish the old rug-ged cross, till my tro-phies at last I lay

down; I will cling to the old rug - ged cross

and ex - change it some day for a crown.

2. O that old rugged cross,
   so despised by the world,
   has a wondrous attraction for me:
   for the dear Lamb of God
   left his glory above
   to bear it to dark Calvary.

3. In the old rugged cross,
   stained with blood so divine,
   a wondrous beauty I see.
   For 'twas on that old cross
   Jesus suffered and died
   to pardon and sanctify me.

4. To the old rugged cross
   I will ever be true,
   its shame and reproach gladly bear.
   Then he'll call me some day
   to my home far away;
   there his glory for ever I'll share.

See over for another arrangement.

George Bennard (1873-1958)
arr. Susie Hare

NEW ARRANGEMENT

Blues style

1. On a hill far a-way stood an old rug-ged cross, the em-blem of suff-'ring and shame; and I loved that old cross where the dear-est and best for a world of lost sin-ners was slain. So I'll che-rish the old rug-ged cross, till my

tro - phies at last I lay down; I will
cling to the old rug - ged cross and ex-
change it some day for a crown.

2. O that old rugged cross,
   so despised by the world,
   has a wondrous attraction for me:
   for the dear Lamb of God
   left his glory above
   to bear it to dark Calvary.

3. In the old rugged cross,
   stained with blood so divine,
   a wondrous beauty I see.
   For 'twas on that old cross
   Jesus suffered and died
   to pardon and sanctify me.

4. To the old rugged cross
   I will ever be true,
   its shame and reproach gladly bear.
   Then he'll call me some day
   to my home far away;
   there his glory for ever I'll share.

The Bridge

285 Once in royal David's city

Cecil Frances Alexander (1818-1895)   Henry John Gauntlett (1805-1876)

IRBY 87 87 77

1. Once in roy-al Da-vid's ci-ty stood a low-ly cat-tle shed, where a
mo-ther laid her ba-by in a man-ger for his bed. Ma-ry
was that mo-ther mild, Je-sus Christ her lit-tle child.

2. He came down to earth from heaven
   who is God and Lord of all,
   and his shelter was a stable,
   and his cradle was a stall.
   With the poor, and mean, and lowly
   lived on earth our Saviour holy.

3. And through all his wondrous childhood
   he would honour and obey,
   love, and watch the lowly maiden
   in whose gentle arms he lay.
   Christian children all must be
   mild, obedient, good as he.

4. For he is our childhood's pattern:
   day by day like us he grew;
   he was little, weak, and helpless;
   tears and smiles like us he knew;
   and he feeleth for our sadness,
   and he shareth in our gladness.

5. And our eyes at last shall see him,
   through his own redeeming love;
   for that child so dear and gentle
   is our Lord in heav'n above;
   and he leads his children on
   to the place where he is gone.

286 One thing I ask

Andy Park

Andy Park

Prayerfully

One thing I ask, one thing I
Hear me, O Lord, hear me when I

seek, that I may dwell in your
cry; Lord, do not hide your

house, O Lord. All of my
face from me. You have been my

days, all of my life,
strength, you have been my shield,

287 Only by grace

Gerrit Gustafson

Gerrit Gustafson

Gently

Unison

On - ly by grace can we en - ter,

on - ly by grace can we stand; not by our hu - man en - dea -

- vour, but by the blood of the Lamb.

In - to your pre - sence you call us, you call us to come.

In - to your pre - sence you draw us, and

288 On the blood-stained ground

I kneel down

Graham Kendrick

Graham Kendrick (b.1950)

1. On the blood-stained ground, where the sha-dow falls, of a cross and a crown of thorns, I kneel down, I kneel down, I lift my eyes to a tear-stained face; who is this dy-ing in my place? I kneel down, I kneel down.

2. As you wash the stains of my guilty heart,
   'til I'm clean in ev'ry part,
   I kneel down, I kneel down.
   Wash away my shame, my pain, my pride,
   ev'ry sin that I once denied,
   I kneel down, I kneel down.

289 O praise ye the Lord!

Henry Williams Baker (1821-1877)
based on Psalms 148 and 150, alt.

Charles Hubert Hastings Parry (1848-1918)

LAUDATE DOMINUM (PARRY) 10 10 11 11

1. O praise ye the Lord! praise him in the height; re-
joice in his word, ye an-gels of light; ye
hea-vens, a-dore him, by whom ye were made, and
wor-ship be-fore him, in bright-ness ar-rayed.

2. O praise ye the Lord! praise him upon earth,
   in tuneful accord, all you of new birth;
   praise him who hath brought you his grace from above,
   praise him who hath taught you to sing of his love.

3. O praise ye the Lord! all thins that give sound;
   each jubilant chord re-echo around;
   loud organs his glory forth tell in deep tone,
   and, sweet harp, the story of what he hath done.

4. O praise ye the Lord! Thanksgiving and song
   to him be outpoured all ages along:
   for love in creation, for heaven restored,
   for grace of salvation, O praise ye the Lord!

290 O righteous God

Mal Pope

Mal Pope

With awe

Unison

1. O right-eous God who search-es minds and hearts, bring to an end the vio-lence of my foes, and make the right-eous more se-cure, O right - eous God. Sing praise to the name of the Lord most high. Sing

praise to the name of the Lord most high. Give

thanks to the Lord who res - cues me, O

right - eous God.

2. O Lord my God, I take refuge in you;
   save and deliver me from all my foes.
   My shield is God the Lord most high,
   O Lord my God.

291 O sacred King

Matt Redman

Matt Redman

O sa-cred King, O ho-ly King, how can I ho-nour you right-ly, ho-nour that's fit for your name? O sa-cred friend, O ho-ly friend, I don't take what you give light-ly; friend-ship in-stead of dis-grace. For it's the mys-t'ry of the u-ni-verse;

292 O, that you would bless me

Phil Rogers

Phil Rogers

1. O, that you would bless me, and en-large my bor - ders, that your hand would be with me, O Lord, O Lord. O, that you would keep me, keep me from all e - vil, so that I may not be a-shamed O Lord, O Lord. May your

king-dom come, may your will be done on earth as it is in hea-

-ven; may your king-dom come, may your will be done, through

me, O Lord, O Lord.

2. O, that you would fill me,
   fill me with your Spirit,
   so that I may know your pow'r,
   O Lord, O Lord.
   O, that you would use me
   to fulfil your purposes,
   that through me your glory would shine,
   O Lord, O Lord.

293 O the deep, deep love of Jesus!

Samuel Trevor Francis (1834-1925)

From an anthem by
Thomas Williams (1869-1944)

EBENEZER (TON -Y- BOTEL) 87 87 D

1. O the deep, deep love of Je - sus!
Vast, un - mea - sured, bound - less, free; roll - ing as a
migh - ty o - cean in its full - ness
o - ver me. Un - der - neath me, all a - round me,

is the cur - rent of thy love; lead - ing on - ward,

lead - ing home - ward, to my glo - rious rest a - bove.

2. O the deep, deep love of Jesus!
   Spread his praise from shore to shore,
   how he loveth, ever loveth,
   changeth never, nevermore;
   how he watches o'er his loved ones,
   died to call them all his own;
   how for them he intercedeth,
   watcheth o'er them from the throne.

3. O the deep, deep love of Jesus!
   Love of ev'ry love the best;
   'tis an ocean vast of blessing,
   'tis a haven sweet of rest.
   O the deep, deep love of Jesus!
   'Tis a heav'n of heav'ns to me;
   and it lifts me up to glory,
   for it lifts me up to thee.

294 O the valleys shall ring

Dave Bilbrough

Dave Bilbrough
arr. Andy Silver and Christopher Norton

O the val - leys shall ring with the sound of praise, and the li - on shall lie with the lamb. Of his gov - ern - ment there shall be no end, and his glo - ry shall fill the earth.

May your will be done, may your king - dom

come! Let it rule, let it reign in our lives.

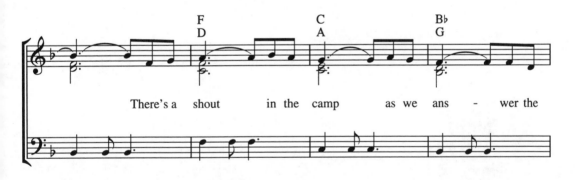

There's a shout in the camp as we ans - wer the

call: Hail the King! Hail the Lord of lords!

The Bridge

295 O thou who camest from above

Charles Wesley (1707-1788),
based on Leviticus 6:13

Samuel Sebastian Wesley (1810-1876)

HEREFORD LM

1. O thou who cam-est from a-bove the pure ce-les-tial fire to im-part, kin-dle a flame of sa-cred love on the mean al-tar of my heart.

2. There let it for thy glory burn
   with inextinguishable blaze,
   and trembling to its source return
   in humble prayer and fervent praise.

3. Jesus, confirm my heart's desire
   to work and speak and think for thee;
   still let me guard the holy fire
   and still stir up thy gift in me.

4. Ready for all thy perfect will,
   my acts of faith and love repeat,
   till death thy endless mercies seal,
   and make the sacrifice complete.

296 Our Father in heaven

Susie Hare

Susie Hare

Calypso

Unison

Our Fa - ther in hea - ven, hal - low-ed be your name,

your king - dom come, your will be done on

earth as in hea - ven. Give us to - day our

dai - ly bread. For-give us our sins as we for-give

297 Over all the earth

Lord, reign in me

Brenton Brown

Brenton Brown

1. O-ver all the earth, you reign on high, ev-'ry moun-tain stream
2. O-ver ev-'ry thought, o-ver ev-'ry word, may my life re-flect

ev-'ry sun-set sky. But my one re-quest, Lord, my on-ly aim
the beau-ty of my Lord; 'cause you mean more to me than a-ny earth-ly thing,

is that you'd reign in me a-gain.
so won't you reign in me a-gain. Lord, reign in me,

reign in your pow'r; o-ver all my dreams, in my dark-est hour.

You are the Lord of all I am, so won't you

reign in me a-gain.

298 Over the mountains and the sea

I could sing of your love for ever

Martin Smith

Martin Smith

O-ver the moun-tains and the sea your ri-ver runs with love for me,

and I will o-pen up my heart and let the Heal-er set me free.

I'm hap-py to be in the truth, and I will dai-ly lift my hands,

for I will al-ways sing of when your love came down.

I could sing of your love for e-ver, I could sing of your love

299 Overwhelmed by love

Noel Richards

Noel Richards

1. O - ver - whelmed by love, deep-er than o - ceans,
2. All my sin was laid on your dear Son,

high as the hea - vens. E - ver - liv - ing God, your love has
your pre-cious One. All my debt he paid, great is your

res - cued me.
love for me.

No one could e - ver earn your

love, your grace and mer-cy is free. Lord,

these words are true, so is my love for you.

300 O worship the King

Robert Grant (1779-1838),
based on Psalm 104

Melody and bass by William Croft (1678-1727)
in 'A Supplement to the New Version' (1708)

HANOVER 10 10 11 11

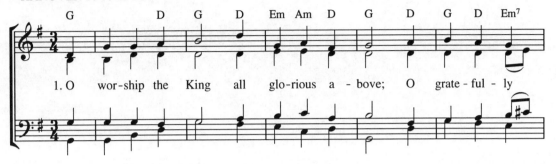

1. O wor-ship the King all glo-rious a - bove; O grate-ful - ly

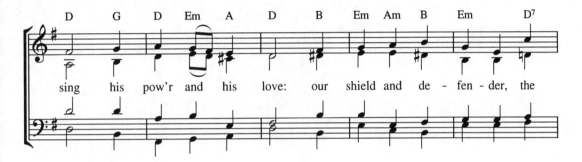

sing his pow'r and his love: our shield and de - fen - der, the

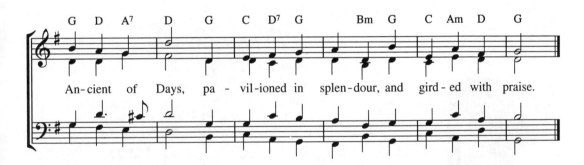

An-cient of Days, pa - vil-ioned in splen-dour, and gird - ed with praise.

2. O tell of his might, O sing of his grace,
   whose robe is the light, whose canopy space;
   his chariots of wrath the deep thunder-clouds form,
   and dark is his path on the wings of the storm.

3. This earth with its store of wonders untold,
   almighty, thy pow'r hath founded of old:
   hath stablished it fast by a changeless decree,
   and round it hath cast, like a mantle, the sea.

4. Thy bountiful care what tongue can recite?
   It breathes in the air, it shines in the light;
   it streams from the hills, it descends to the plain,
   and sweetly distils in the dew and the rain.

5. Frail children of dust, and feeble as frail,
   in thee do we trust, nor find thee to fail;
   thy mercies how tender, how firm to the end!
   Our maker, defender, redeemer, and friend.

6. O measureless might, ineffable love,
   while angels delight to hymn thee above,
   thy humbler creation, though feeble their lays,
   with true adoration shall sing to thy praise.

The Bridge

301 O worship the Lord in the beauty of holiness

John Samuel Bewley Monsell (1811-1875)

Melody from the 'Rheinhardt MS',
Üttingen (1754)

WAS LEBET 13 10 13 10

2. Low at his feet lay thy burden of carefulness:
high on his heart he will bear it for thee,
comfort thy sorrows, and answer thy prayerfulness,
guiding thy steps as may best for thee be.

3. Fear not to enter his courts in the slenderness
of the poor wealth thou wouldst reckon as thine:
truth in its beauty, and love in its tenderness,
these are the off'rings to lay on his shrine.

4. These, though we bring them in trembling and fearfulness,
he will accept for the name that is dear;
mornings of joy give for evenings of tearfulness,
trust for our trembling and hope for our fear.

5. O worship the Lord in the beauty of holiness;
bow down before him, his glory proclaim;
with gold of obedience, and incense of lowliness,
kneel and adore him: the Lord is his name.

302 Pass me not, O gentle Saviour

Frances Jane van Alstyne
(Fanny J. Crosby) (1820-1915)

William Howard Doane (1832-1916)

PASS ME NOT 85 85 and Refrain

1. Pass me not, O gentle Saviour, hear my humble cry;
while on others thou art calling, do not pass me by.

Refrain

Saviour! Saviour! Hear my humble cry,
and while others thou art calling, do not pass me by.

2. Let me at a throne of mercy
   find a sweet relief;
   kneeling there in deep contrition,
   help my unbelief.

3. Trusting only in thy merit,
   would I seek thy face;
   heal my wounded, broken spirit,
   save me by thy grace.

4. Thou the spring of all my comfort,
   more than life to me,
   whom have I on earth beside thee?
   whom in heav'n but thee?

William Howard Doane (1832-1916)
arr. Susie Hare

NEW ARRANGEMENT

Relaxed

1. Pass me not, O gen-tle Sa - viour, hear my hum-ble cry; while on o-thers thou art call - ing, do not pass me by.

Refrain

Sa - viour! Sa - viour! Hear my hum-ble cry, and while o-thers thou art call - ing, do not pass me by.

303 Peace I leave with you

Fred Chedgey

Fred Chedgey
arr. Susie Hare

304 People awaken, open your eyes *Light of the world*

Trevor Burch

Trevor Burch
arr. Susie Hare

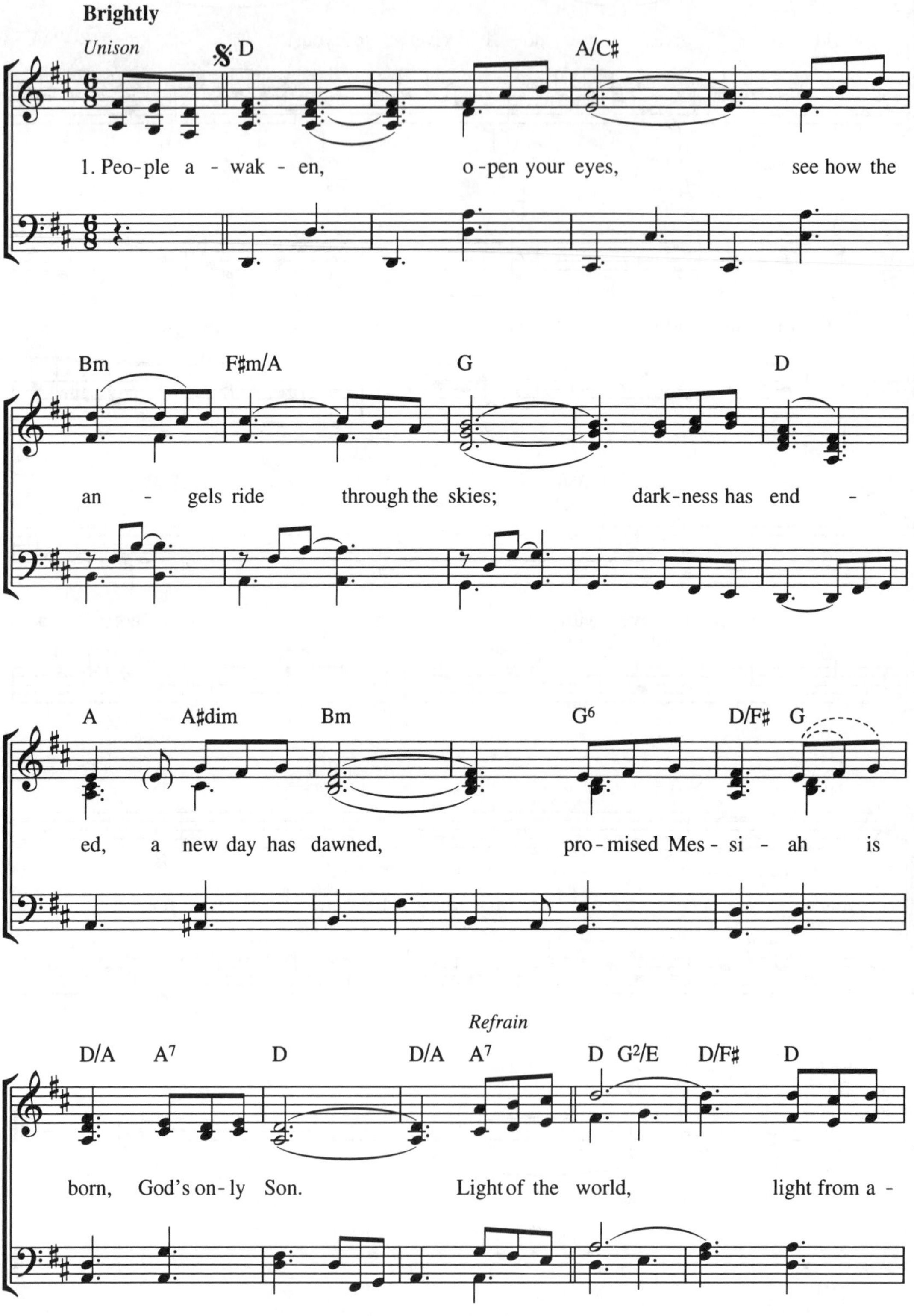
Brightly
Unison
D A/C♯
1. Peo-ple a - wak - en, o-pen your eyes, see how the
Bm F♯m/A G D
an - gels ride through the skies; dark-ness has end -
A A♯dim Bm G6 D/F♯ G
ed, a new day has dawned, pro-mised Mes - si - ah is
Refrain
D/A A7 D D/A A7 D G2/E D/F♯ D
born, God's on-ly Son. Light of the world, light from a -

bove, God's re-ve-la - tion and gift of his love;

re-new your birth - place here in my heart, e-ver reign

in me, ne-ver de - part. 2. Child of the
3. The zeal of the

2. Child of the Father, bringer of peace
   to ev'ry soul that longs for release,
   bring us the liberty won on the tree,
   taking our sin, making us whole, setting us free.

3. The zeal of the Father has done great things –
   Jesus is risen with healing wings!
   Daystar eternal, rule from your throne,
   loving your people and leading them on.

305 Praise God from whom all blessings flow

Andy Piercy and Dave Clifton

Andy Piercy and Dave Clifton
arr. Alison Berry

Steady rock feel

Praise God from whom all bless-ings flow, praise him, all crea-tures here

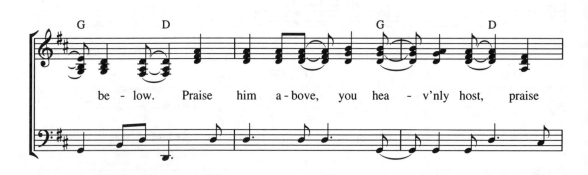

be - low. Praise him a-bove, you hea - v'nly host, praise

Fa - ther, Son and Ho - ly Ghost. Praise - ly Ghost. Give

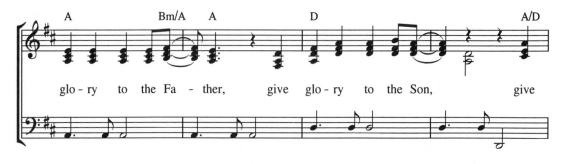

glo - ry to the Fa - ther, give glo - ry to the Son, give

306 Praise him, praise him!

Frances Jane van Alstyne (Fanny J. Crosby) (1820-1915)

Chester G. Allen (1838-1878)

PRAISE HIM 12 10 12 10 11 10 12 10

1. Praise him, praise him! Jesus, our blessèd Redeemer!

Sing, O earth, his wonderful love proclaim!

Hail him, hail him! highest archangels in glory;

strength and honour give to his holy name!

Like a shepherd, Jesus will guard his children,

in his arms he car- ries them all day long.

Praise him, praise him! tell of his ex- cel- lent great - ness;

praise him, praise him e - ver in joy - ful song!

2. Praise him, praise him! Jesus, our blessèd Redeemer!
   For our sins he suffered, and bled, and died!
   He – our rock, our hope of eternal salvation,
   hail him, hail him! Jesus the crucified!
   Sound his praises – Jesus who bore our sorrows,
   love unbounded, wonderful, deep and strong.

3. Praise him, praise him! Jesus, our blessèd Redeemer!
   Heav'nly portals, loud with hosannas ring!
   Jesus, Saviour, reigneth for ever and ever:
   crown him, crown him! Prophet, and Priest, and King!
   Christ is coming, over the world victorious,
   pow'r and glory unto the Lord belong.

307 Praise, my soul, the King of heaven!

Henry Francis Lyte (1793-1847)
based on Psalm 103

John Goss (1800-1880)

PRAISE, MY SOUL 87 87 87

Unison

1. Praise, my soul, the King of hea - ven! To his feet thy tri - bute bring; ran - somed, healed, re - stored, for - giv - en, who like me his praise should sing? Praise him! Praise him! Praise him! Praise him! Praise the e - ver - last - ing King!

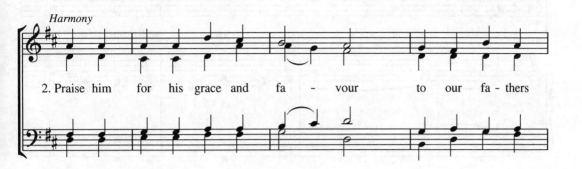

Harmony

2. Praise him for his grace and fa - vour to our fa - thers

in dis - tress; praise him still the same as e - ver,

slow to chide and swift to bless. Praise him! Praise him!

Praise him! Praise him! Glo - rious in his faith - ful - ness!

3. Fa - ther - like, he tends and spares us; well our fee - ble frame he knows; in his hands he gen - tly bears us, res - cues us from all our foes. Praise him! Praise him! Praise him! Praise him! Wide - ly as his mer - cy flows!

4. An-gels, help us to a-dore him; ye be-hold him face to face; sun and moon, bow down be-fore him, dwell-ers all in time and space. Praise him! Praise him! Praise him! Praise him! Praise with us the God of grace!

See over for another arrangement

John Goss (1800-1880)
arr. Susie Hare

NEW ARRANGEMENT

1. Praise, my soul, the King of hea - ven!
2. Praise him for his grace and fa - vour

To his feet thy tri - bute bring; ran - somed,
to our fa - thers in dis - tress; praise him

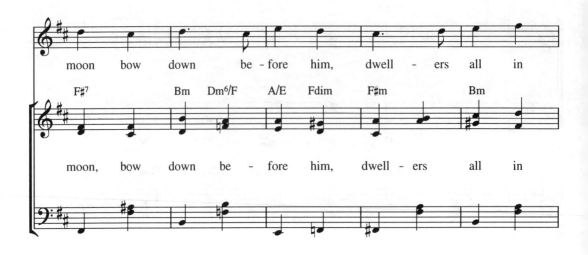

moon bow down be-fore him, dwell-ers all in

F#⁷　　　Bm　Dm⁶/F　A/E　Fdim　F#m　　Bm

moon, bow down be-fore him, dwell-ers all in

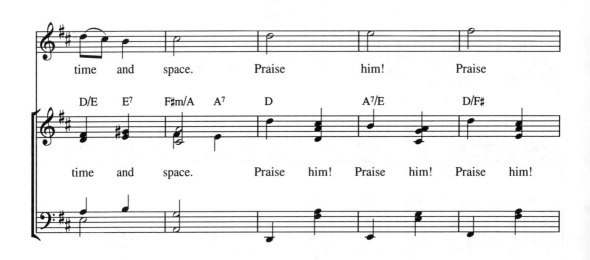

time and space. Praise him! Praise

D/E　E⁷　F#m/A　A⁷　　D　　　A⁷/E　　D/F#

time and space. Praise him! Praise him! Praise him!

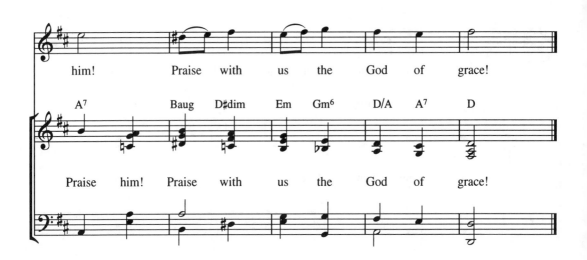

him! Praise with us the God of grace!

A⁷　　　Baug　D#dim　Em　Gm⁶　D/A　A⁷　　D

Praise him! Praise with us the God of grace!

308 Praise the name of Jesus

Roy Hicks

Roy Hicks

Worshipfully

Unison

Capo 3

Praise the name of Je - sus, praise the name of Je - sus, he's my rock, he's my for - tress, he's my de - li - ve - rer, in him will I trust. Praise the name of Je - sus.

309 Praise to the Holiest

John Henry Newman (1801-1890)

John Bacchus Dykes (1823-1876)
arr. Susie Hare

GERONTIUS CM

1. Praise to the Holiest in the height,
and in the depth be praise;
in all his words most wonderful,
most sure in all his ways.

2. O loving wisdom of our God!
   When all was sin and shame,
   a second Adam to the fight
   and to the rescue came.

3. O wisest love! that flesh and blood,
   which did in Adam fail,
   should strive afresh against the foe,
   should strive and should prevail;

4. And that a higher gift than grace
   should flesh and blood refine,
   God's presence and his very self,
   and essence all divine.

5. And in the garden secretly,
   and on the cross on high,
   should teach his brethren, and inspire
   to suffer and to die.

6. Praise to the Ho - liest in the height, and in the

6. Praise to the Ho - liest in the height, and in the

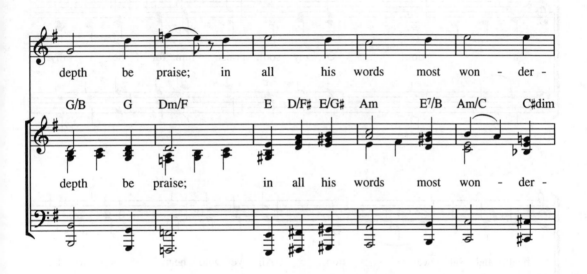

depth be praise; in all his words most won - der -

depth be praise; in all his words most won - der -

ful, most sure in all his ways.

ful, most sure in all his ways.

310 Praise to the Lord, the Almighty

Joachim Neander (1650-1680)
trans. Catherine Winkworth (1827-1878)

From 'Praxis Pietatis Melica' (1668)

LOBE DEN HERREN 14 14 4 7 8

1. Praise to the Lord, the Al - migh - ty, the King of cre - a - tion! O my soul, praise him, for he is thy health and sal - va - tion. All ye who hear, now to his

tem - ple draw near; join - ing in glad a - do - ra - tion.

2. Praise to the Lord, who o'er all things so wondrously reigneth,
   shieldeth thee gently from harm, or when fainting sustaineth:
   hast thou not seen
   how thy heart's wishes have been
   granted in what he ordaineth?

3. Praise to the Lord, who doth prosper thy work and defend thee,
   surely his goodness and mercy shall daily attend thee:
   ponder anew
   what the Almighty can do,
   if to the end he befriend thee.

4. Praise to the Lord, O let all that is in us adore him!
   All that hath life and breath, come now with praises before him.
   Let the 'Amen'
   sound from his people again,
   gladly for ay we adore him.

311 Praise you, Lord

Nettie Rose

Nettie Rose
arr. Christopher Norton

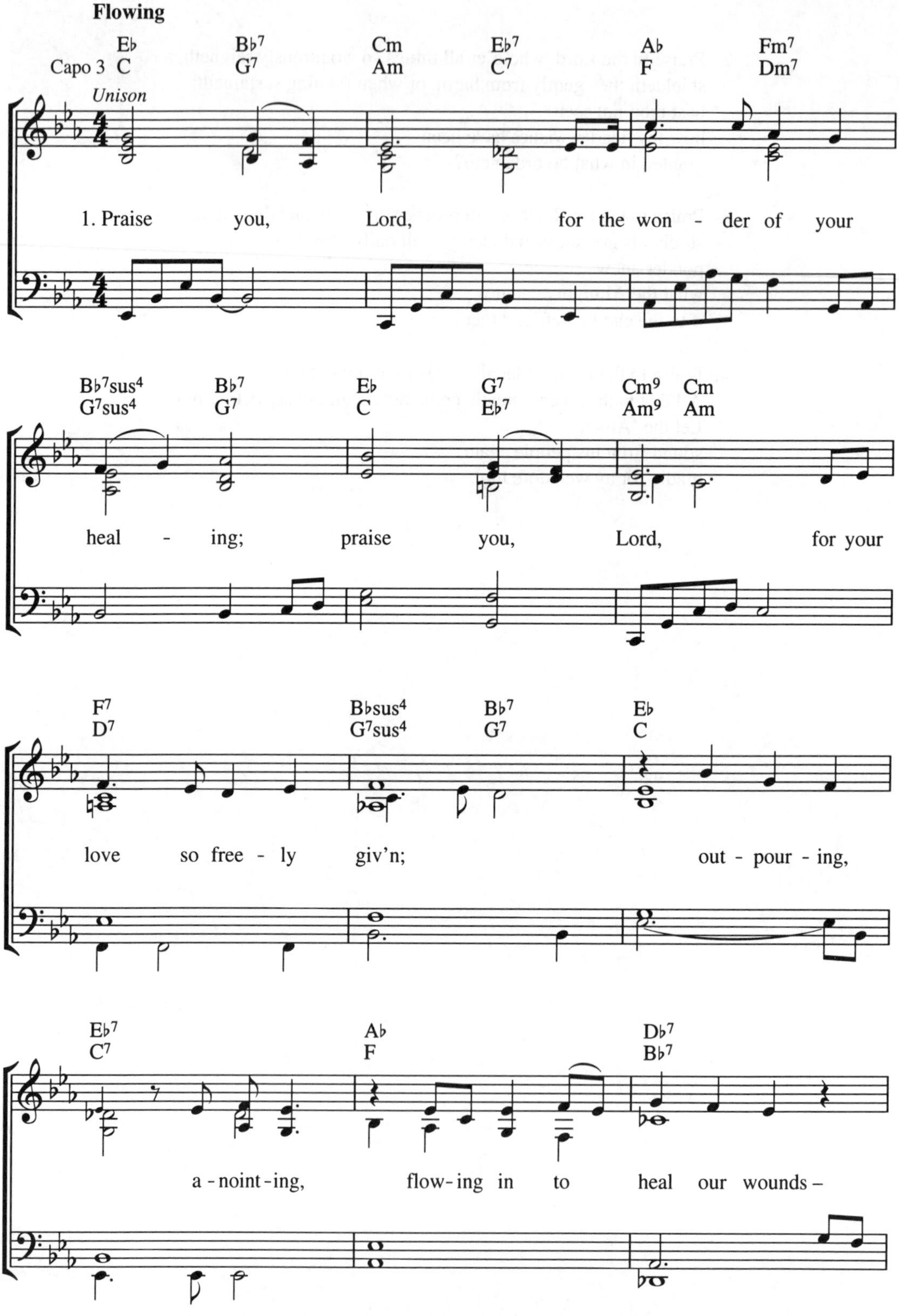

Flowing
Capo 3
Eb Bb7 Cm Eb7 Ab Fm7
C G7 Am C7 F Dm7
Unison
1. Praise you, Lord, for the won - der of your
Bb7sus4 Bb7 Eb G7 Cm9 Cm
G7sus4 G7 C Eb7 Am9 Am
heal - ing; praise you, Lord, for your
F7 Bbsus4 Bb7 Eb
D7 G7sus4 G7 C
love so free - ly giv'n; out - pour - ing,
Eb7 Ab Db7
C7 F Bb7
a - noint - ing, flow - ing in to heal our wounds –

praise you, Lord, for your love for me.

2. Praise you, Lord,
   for your gift of liberation;
   praise you, Lord,
   you have set the captives free;
   the chains that bind are broken
   by the sharpness of your sword –
   praise you, Lord,
   you gave your life for me.

3. Praise you, Lord,
   you have borne the depths of sorrow;
   praise you, Lord,
   for your anguish on the tree;
   the nails that tore your body
   and the pain that tore your soul –
   praise you, Lord,
   your tears, they fell for me.

4. Praise you, Lord,
   you have turned our thorns to roses;
   glory, Lord, as they bloom upon your brow;
   the path of pain is hallowed,
   for your love has made it sweet –
   praise you, Lord,
   and may I love you now.

312 Purify my heart

Refiner's fire

Brian Doerksen

Brian Doerksen

1. Pu - ri - fy my heart, let me be as gold and pre-cious sil-ver. Pu - ri - fy my heart, let me be as gold, pure gold. Re - fin - er's fire, my heart's one de-sire is to be ho - ly,

2. Purify my heart,
   cleanse me from within and make me holy.
   Purify my heart,
   cleanse me from my sin, deep within.

The Bridge

313 Reign in me

Chris Bowater

Chris Bowater

314 Rejoice!

Graham Kendrick

Graham Kendrick (b.1950)

1. Now is the time for us to march up-on the land, in-to our hands he will give the ground we claim.

He rides in ma-jes-ty to lead us in-to vic-to-ry, the world shall see that Christ is Lord! Re-

2. God is at work in us
   his purpose to perform,
   building a kingdom
   of power not of words,
   where things impossible
   by faith shall be made possible;
   let's give the glory to him now.

3. Though we are weak, his grace
   is ev'rything we need;
   we're made of clay
   but this treasure is within.
   He turns our weaknesses
   into his opportunities,
   so that the glory goes to him.

315 Rejoice, the Lord is King!

Charles Wesley (1707-1788)

George Frideric Handel (1685-1759)

GOPSAL 66 66 and Refrain

1. Re-joice, the Lord is King! Your Lord and King a-dore; mor-tals, give thanks and sing, and tri-umph e-ver-more.

Refrain

Lift up your heart, lift up your voice; re-joice, a-gain I say, re-joice.

2. Jesus the Saviour reigns,
   the God of truth and love;
   when he had purged our stains,
   he took his seat above.

3. His kingdom cannot fail;
   he rules o'er earth and heav'n;
   the keys of death and hell
   are to our Jesus giv'n.

4. He sits at God's right hand
   till all his foes submit,
   and bow to his command,
   and fall beneath his feet.

316 Restore, O Lord

Graham Kendrick
and Chris Rolinson

Graham Kendrick (b.1950)
and Chris Rolinson

Steadily, with feeling

1. Re - store, O Lord, the hon-our of your name, in works of sov-'reign pow - er come shake the earth a - gain, that all may see, and come with rev-'rent fear to the liv-ing God, whose king-dom shall out - last the years.

2. Restore, O Lord,
   in all the earth your fame,
   and in our time revive
   the church that bears your name.
   And in your anger,
   Lord, remember mercy,
   O living God,
   whose mercy shall outlast the years.

3. Bend us, O Lord,
   where we are hard and cold,
   in your refiner's fire:
   come purify the gold.
   Though suff'ring comes
   and evil crouches near,
   still our living God
   is reigning, he is reigning here.

4. as verse 1

317 Rock of ages

Augustus Montague Toplady (1740-1778) alt.   Richard Redhead (1820-1901)

TUNE 1: PETRA (REDHEAD NO. 76) 77 77 77

1. Rock of a - ges, cleft for me, let me hide my - self in thee; let the wa - ter and the blood, from thy ri - ven side which flowed, be of sin the dou - ble cure: cleanse me from its guilt and pow'r.

2. Not the labours of my hands
   can fulfil thy law's demands;
   could my zeal no respite know,
   could my tears for ever flow,
   all for sin could not atone:
   thou must save, and thou alone.

3. Nothing in my hands I bring,
   simply to the cross I cling;
   naked, come to thee for dress;
   helpless, look to thee for grace;
   tainted, to the fountain fly;
   wash me, Saviour, or I die.

4. While I draw this fleeting breath,
   when mine eyelids close in death,
   when I soar through tracts unknown,
   see thee on thy judgement throne;
   Rock of ages, cleft for me,
   let me hide myself in thee.

Augustus Montague Toplady (1740-1778) alt

James Ward

TUNE 2: NEW CITY FELLOWSHIP 77 77 77

1. Rock of a-ges, cleft for me, let me hide myself in thee; let the wa-ter and the blood,
from thy ri-ven side which flowed, be of sin the
dou-ble cure: cleanse me from its guilt and
pow'r.

318 Salvation belongs to our God

Adrian Howard and Pat Turner

Adrian Howard and Pat Turner

1. Sal-va-tion be-longs to our God, who

sits on the throne, and to the

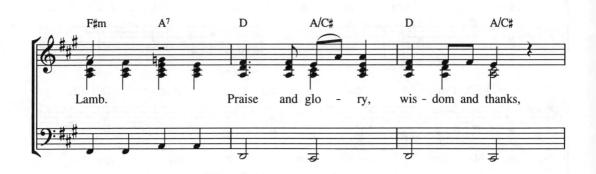

Lamb. Praise and glo-ry, wis-dom and thanks,

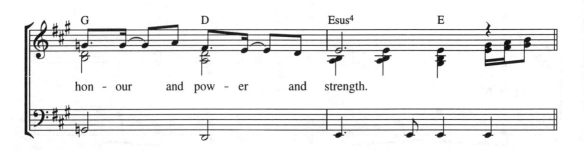

hon-our and pow-er and strength.

2. And we, the redeemed, shall be strong
   in purpose and unity,
   declaring aloud,
   praise and glory, wisdom and thanks,
   honour and power and strength.

319 Say the word

Stuart Townend

Stuart Townend

2. Say the word, I will be filled;
   my hands reach out to heaven,
   where striving is stilled.
   Say the word, I will be changed;
   where I am dry and thirsty,
   send cool, refreshing rain,
   say the word.

3. Say the word, I will be poor,
   that I might know the riches
   that you have in store.
   Say the word, I will be weak;
   your strength will be the power
   that satisfies the meek,
   say the word.

   The Lord will see the travail of his soul,
   and he and I will be satisfied.
   Complete the work you have started in me:
   O come, Lord Jesus, shake my life again.

320 See, amid the winter's snow

Edward Caswall (1814-1878)   John Goss (1800-1880)

OXFORD 77 77 and Refrain

Solo or Unison

1. See, a-mid the win - ter's snow, born for us on earth be - low,

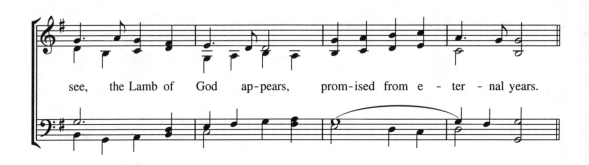

see, the Lamb of God ap-pears, prom-ised from e - ter - nal years.

Refrain
Harmony

Hail, thou e - ver - bles-sed morn! Hail, re-demp-tion's hap - py dawn!

Sing through all Je - ru - sa-lem: Christ is born in Beth - le - hem!

2. Lo, within a manger lies
   he who built the starry skies,
   he who, throned in heights sublime,
   sits amid the cherubim.

3. Say, ye holy shepherds, say,
   what your joyful news today;
   wherefore have you left your sheep
   on the lonely mountain steep?

4. 'As we watched at dead of night,
   lo, we saw a wondrous light;
   angels, singing peace on earth,
   told us of the Saviour's birth.'

5. Sacred infant, all divine,
   what a tender love was thine,
   thus to come from highest bliss,
   down to such a world as this!

6. Teach, O teach us, holy child,
   by thy face so meek and mild,
   teach us to resemble thee
   in thy sweet humility.

321 See him lying on a bed of straw

Michael Perry

Michael Perry (1942-1996)
arr. Stephen Coates

CALYPSO CAROL Irregular and Refrain

1. See him ly-ing on a bed of straw: a draugh-ty sta-ble with an o-pen door; Ma-ry cra-dl-ing the babe she bore – the Prince of Glo-ry is his name. O now car-ry me to Beth-le-hem to see the Lord of love a-gain: just as poor as was the sta-ble then, the Prince of Glo-ry when he

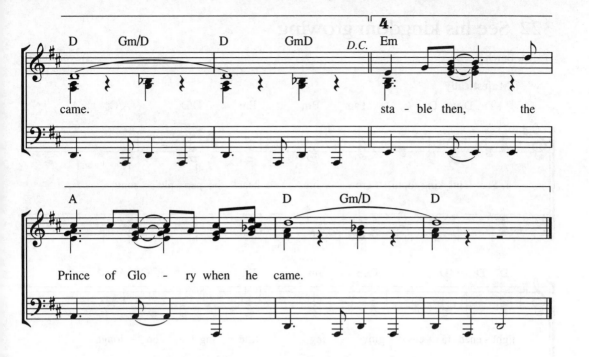

came. sta - ble then, the

Prince of Glo - ry when he came.

2. Star of silver, sweep across the skies,
   show where Jesus in the manger lies;
   shepherds, swiftly from your stupor rise
   to see the Saviour of the world!

3. Angels, sing again the song you sang,
   sing the glory of God's gracious plan;
   sing that Beth'lem's little baby can
   be the Saviour of us all.

4. Mine are riches, from your poverty;
   from your innocence, eternity;
   mine, forgiveness by your death for me,
   child of sorrow for my joy.

322 See his kingdom growing

Trevor Burch

Trevor Burch
arr. Susie Hare

1. See his king-dom grow - ing, hear the peo - ple's song;
light - ened fa - ces glow - ing, find - ing they be - long.
Liv - ing in his Spi - rit, filled with pow'r and grace,
work - ing for his com - ing, look - ing for his face.

Refrain
You are head, Lord Je - sus of your Church on earth,

bring-ing res-tor - a - tion, bring-ing us new birth; so Je - sus

bring your Church to glo - ry, pure be-fore your throne,

keep us faith - ful till the day that brings your king - dom in.

2. Build your Church, Lord Jesus,
   make your people strong,
   living lives of vict'ry,
   knowing they belong.
   Bring about your kingdom,
   reign in hearts and homes;
   through your Church responding
   let your will be done.

3. Jesus, build your kingdom,
   build, O Lord, in me
   as my roots go deeper,
   grafted to the tree.
   Purify my hands, Lord,
   mould my heart and will.
   When you come in glory,
   may I be serving still.

323 Should he who made the stars · *We sing your mercies*

Mark Altrogge

Mark Altrogge

1. Should he who made the stars be hung up-on a tree?
2. Should he who is the light be cast in-to the dark?

And should the hands that healed be
And should the Lord of love be

dri - ven through for me? Should he who gave us bread
pierced through his own heart? Should he who called us friends

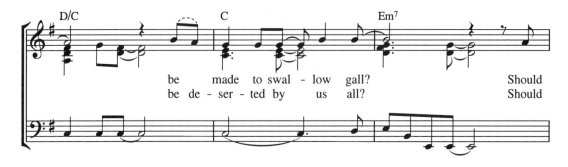

be made to swal - low gall? Should
be de - ser - ted by us all? Should

324 Show your power, O Lord

Graham Kendrick

Graham Kendrick (b.1950)

With energy

1. Show your pow'r, O Lord, de-mon-strate the jus-tice of your king-dom. Prove your migh-ty word, vin-di-cate your name be-fore a watch-ing world.

2. Show your pow'r, O Lord,
   cause your church to rise and take action.
   Let all fear be gone,
   powers of the age to come
   are breaking through.
   We your people are ready to serve,
   to arise and to obey.
   Show your pow'r, O Lord,
   and set the people free.

   Show your pow'r, O Lord,
   and set the people –
   show your pow'r, O Lord,
   and set the people –
   show your pow'r, O Lord,
   and set the people free.

The Bridge

325 Silent night

Joseph Mohr (1792-1848)
trans. John Freeman Young (1820-1885)

Franz Grüber (1787-1863)
arr. Colin Hand

STILLE NACHT Irregular

2. Silent night, holy night.
   Shepherds quake at the sight,
   glories stream from heaven afar,
   heav'nly hosts sing alleluia:
   Christ the Saviour is born,
   Christ the Saviour is born.

3. Silent night, holy night.
   Son of God, love's pure light,
   radiant beams from thy holy face,
   with the dawn of redeeming grace:
   Jesus, Lord, at thy birth,
   Jesus, Lord, at thy birth.

326 Sing to the Lord

Awaken the dawn

Stuart Garrard

Stuart Garrard

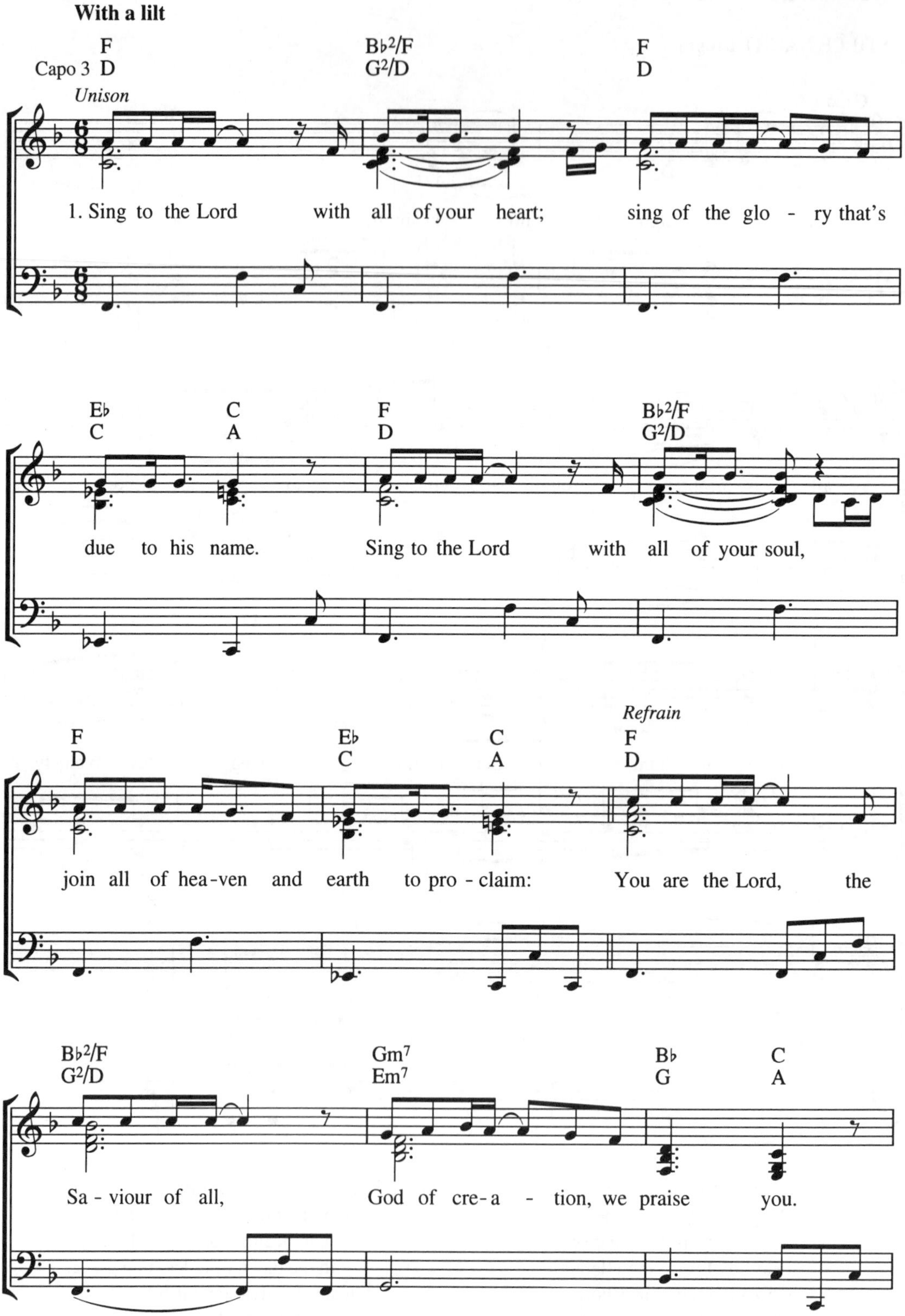
With a lilt
F
Capo 3 D
Bb2/F
G2/D
F
D
Unison
1. Sing to the Lord with all of your heart; sing of the glo - ry that's
Eb C F Bb2/F
C A D G2/D
due to his name. Sing to the Lord with all of your soul,
Refrain
F Eb C F
D C A D
join all of hea-ven and earth to pro - claim: You are the Lord, the
Bb2/F Gm7 Bb C
G2/D Em7 G A
Sa - viour of all, God of cre - a - tion, we praise you.

We sing the songs that a-wa-ken the dawn, God of cre-a - tion, we

praise you.

2. Sing to the Lord with all of your mind,
   with understanding give thanks to the King.
   Sing to the Lord with all of your strength,
   living our lives as a praise offering.

327 Soldiers of Christ, arise

Charles Wesley (1707-1788)
based on Ephesians 6:10-18

Edward Woodall Naylor (1867-1934)

TUNE 1: FROM STRENGTH TO STRENGTH DSM

1. Sol-diers of Christ, a - rise, and put your ar - mour on, strong in the strength which God sup - plies through his e - ter - nal Son. Strong in the Lord of hosts, and in his migh - ty pow'r; who in the strength of Je - sus trusts is more than con - que - ror.

2. Stand then in his great might,
   with all his strength endued;
   and take, to arm you for the fight,
   the panoply of God:
   to keep your armour bright,
   attend with constant care,
   still walking in your Captain's sight
   and watching unto prayer.

3. From strength to strength go on,
   wrestle and fight and pray;
   tread all the pow'rs of darkness down,
   and win the well-fought day;
   that, having all things done,
   and all your conflicts past,
   ye may o'ercome, through Christ alone,
   and stand entire at last.

Charles Wesley (1707-1788)
based on Ephesians 6:10-18

William Henry Monk (1823-1889)

TUNE 2: ST ETHELWALD SM

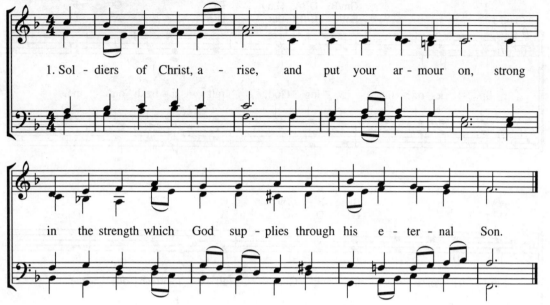

1. Sol - diers of Christ, a - rise, and put your ar - mour on, strong

in the strength which God sup - plies through his e - ter - nal Son.

2. Strong in the Lord of hosts,
   and in his mighty pow'r;
   who in the strength of Jesus trusts
   is more than conqueror.

3. Stand then in his great might,
   with all his strength endued;
   and take, to arm you for the fight,
   the panoply of God.

4. To keep your armour bright,
   attend with constant care,
   still walking in your Captain's sight
   and watching unto prayer.

5. From strength to strength go on,
   wrestle and fight and pray;
   tread all the pow'rs of darkness down,
   and win the well-fought day.

6. That, having all things done,
   and all your conflicts past,
   ye may o'ercome, through Christ alone,
   and stand entire at last.

328 Spirit of the living God

Daniel Iverson

Daniel Iverson (1890-1972)

329 Such love

Graham Kendrick

Graham Kendrick (b.1950)

2. Such love, stilling my restlessness;
   such love, filling my emptiness;
   such love, showing me holiness;
   O Jesus, such love.

3. Such love springs from eternity;
   such love, streaming through history;
   such love, fountain of life to me;
   O Jesus, such love.

330 Take my life, and let it be

Frances Ridley Havergal (1836-1879)

Wolfgang Amadeus Mozart (1756-1791) adapt.

TUNE 1: NOTTINGHAM 77 77

1. Take my life, and let it be con-se-cra-ted, Lord, to thee; take my mo-ments and my days, let them flow in cease-less praise.

2. Take my hands, and let them move
at the impulse of thy love;
take my feet, and let them be
swift and beautiful for thee.

3. Take my voice, and let me sing
always, only, for my King;
take my lips, and let them be
filled with messages from thee.

4. Take my silver and my gold;
not a mite would I withhold;
take my intellect, and use
ev'ry pow'r as thou shalt choose.

5. Take my will, and make it thine:
it shall be no longer mine;
take my heart: it is thine own;
it shall be thy royal throne.

6. Take my love; my Lord, I pour
at thy feet its treasure-store;
take myself, and I will be
ever, only, all for thee.

Frances Ridley Havergal (1836-1879)

Henri A. Cesar Malan
arr. Terry Butler

TUNE 2

2. Take my feet, and let them be
swift and beautiful for thee.
Take my voice, and let me sing
always, only, for my King,
always, only, for my King.

3. Take my lips, and let them be
filled with messages from thee.
Take my silver and my gold,
not a mite would I withhold,
not a mite would I withhold.

4. Take my love; my God I pour
at thy feet its treasure-store.
Take myself, and I will be
ever, only, all for thee,
ever, only, all for thee.

5. Take my life, and let it be
consecrated, Lord, to thee.
Take myself, and I will be
ever, only, all for thee,
ever, only, all for thee.

331 Teach me to dance

Graham Kendrick
and Steve Thompson

Graham Kendrick (b.1950)
and Steve Thompson

Lively

Unison
Refrain

Teach me to dance to the beat of your heart, teach me to move
Teach me to love with your heart of com - pas - sion, teach me to trust

in the pow'r of your Spi - rit, teach me to walk in the light of your pre -
in the word of your pro - mise, teach me to hope in the day of your com-

To repeat | *Last time*

- sence, teach me to dance to the beat of your heart.
- ing,

To verses

1. You wrote the rhy-thm of life,

cre- a - ted hea-ven and earth, in you is joy with-out mea - sure.

So, like a child in your sight, I dance to see your de-light, for I was made for your

plea - sure, plea - sure.

D.C.

2. Let all my movements express
   a heart that loves to say 'yes',
   a will that leaps to obey you.
   Let all my energy blaze
   to see the joy in your face;
   let my whole being praise you,
   praise you.

332 Tell out, my soul

Timothy Dudley-Smith (b.1926),
based on Luke 1:46-55

Walter Greatorex (1877-1949)

WOODLANDS 10 10 10 10

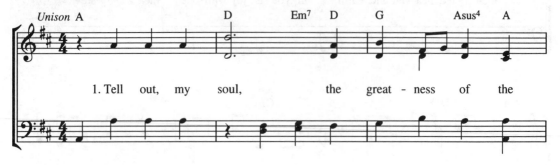

1. Tell out, my soul, the great-ness of the

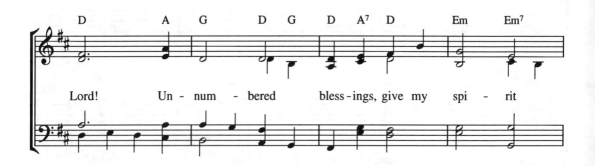

Lord! Un-num-bered bless-ings, give my spi-rit

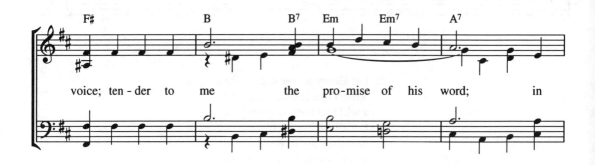

voice; ten-der to me the pro-mise of his word; in

God my Sa-viour shall my heart re-joice.

2. Tell out, my soul,
   the greatness of his Name!
   Make known his might,
   the deeds his arm has done;
   his mercy sure,
   from age to age the same;
   his holy Name,
   the Lord, the Mighty One.

3. Tell out, my soul,
   the greatness of his might!
   Pow'rs and dominions
   lay their glory by.
   Proud hearts and stubborn wills
   are put to flight,
   the hungry fed,
   the humble lifted high.

4. Tell out, my soul,
   the glories of his word!
   Firm is his promise,
   and his mercy sure.
   Tell out, my soul,
   the greatness of the Lord
   to children's children
   and for evermore!

333 Thank you for saving me

Martin Smith

Martin Smith

With a steady rhythm

1. Thank you for sav - ing me; what can I say?

You are my ev - 'ry - thing, I will sing your praise.

You shed your blood for me; what can I say?

You took my sin and shame, a sin - ner called by

name. Great

2. Mercy and grace are mine, forgiv'n is my sin;
   Jesus, my only hope, the Saviour of the world.
   'Great is the Lord,' we cry; God, let your kingdom come.
   Your word has let me see, thank you for saving me.

334 The church's one foundation

Samuel John Stone (1839-1900)   Samuel Sebastian Wesley (1810-1876)

AURELIA 76 76 D

2. Elect from ev'ry nation, yet one o'er all the earth,
   her charter of salvation, one Lord, one faith, one birth;
   one holy name she blesses, partakes one holy food,
   and to one hope she presses, with ev'ry grace endued.

3. 'Mid toil and tribulation, and tumult of her war,
   she waits the consummation of peace for evermore;
   till with the vision glorious her longing eyes are blest,
   and the great church victorious shall be the church at rest.

4. Yet she on earth hath union with God the Three in One,
   and mystic sweet communion with those whose rest is won:
   O happy ones and holy! Lord, give us grace that we
   like them, the meek and lowly, on high may dwell with thee.

335 The cross has said it all

Matt Redman and Martin Smith

Matt Redman and Martin Smith

With energy

Unison

1. The cross has said it all, the cross has said it all. I can't de-ny what you have shown, the cross speaks of a God of love; there dis-played for all to see, Je-sus Christ, our on-ly hope, a mes-sage of the Fa-ther's heart:

2. The cross has said it all, the cross has said it all. I ne-ver re-cog-nised your touch un-til I met you at the cross; we are fall-en, dust to dust, how could you do this for us? Son of God shed pre-cious blood,

336 The crucible for silver

Martin Smith

Martin Smith
arr. D.J. Langford

1. The

cru - ci - ble   for sil - ver,   and the fur - nace   for gold,   but the
2. Fa - ther, take   our off - 'ring,   with our song   we hum-bly praise you;   you have

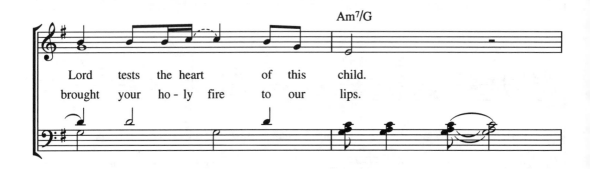

Lord   tests   the heart   of   this   child.
brought   your   ho - ly   fire   to   our   lips.

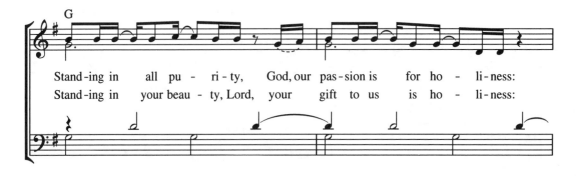

Stand-ing in   all pu - ri - ty,   God, our pas-sion is   for ho - li - ness:
Stand-ing in   your beau - ty, Lord,   your   gift to us   is ho - li - ness:

The Bridge

337 The day thou gavest, Lord, is ended

John Ellerton (1826-1893)

Clement Cotterill Scholefield (1839-1904)

ST CLEMENT 98 98

1. The day thou gav - est, Lord, is end - ed, the dark - ness falls at thy be - hest; to thee our morn - ing hymns a - scend - ed, thy praise shall san - cti - fy our rest.

2. We thank thee that thy Church unsleeping,
while earth rolls onward into light,
through all the world her watch is keeping,
and rests not now by day or night.

3. As o'er each continent and island
the dawn leads on another day,
the voice of prayer is never silent,
nor dies the strain of praise away.

4. The sun that bids us rest is waking
our brethren 'neath the western sky,
and hour by hour fresh lips are making
thy wondrous doings heard on high.

5. So be it, Lord! Thy throne shall never,
like earth's proud empires, pass away;
thy kingdom stands, and grows for ever,
till all thy creatures own thy sway.

338 The first Nowell

From William Sandys'
'Christmas Carols, Ancient and Modern' (1833) alt.

Traditional English melody
arr. John Stainer

THE FIRST NOWELL Irregular

1. The first No - well the an - gel did say was to cer - tain poor

shep-herds in fields as they lay: in fields where they lay

keep-ing their sheep, on a cold win-ter's night that was so deep.

Refrain

No - well, No - well, No - well, No - well,

born is the King of Is - ra - el!

2. They lookèd up and saw a star,
   shining in the east, beyond them far,
   and to the earth it gave great light,
   and so it continued both day and night.

3. And by the light of that same star,
   three wise men came from country far;
   to seek for a king was their intent,
   and to follow the star wherever it went.

4. This star drew nigh to the north-west,
   o'er Bethlehem it took its rest,
   and there it did both stop and stay
   right over the place where Jesus lay.

5. Then entered in those wise men three,
   full rev'rently upon their knee,
   and offered there in his presence,
   their gold and myrrh and frankincense.

6. Then let us all with one accord
   sing praises to our heav'nly Lord,
   who with the Father we adore
   and Spirit blest for evermore.

339 The God of Abraham praise

Thomas Olivers (1725-1799)
based on the Hebrew 'Yigdal', alt.

Traditional Hebrew melody

LEONI 66 84 D

1. The God of Ab-raham praise, who reigns en-throned a - bove, An -

cient of e - ver - last - ing Days, and God of love: Je -

ho - vah, great I Am, by earth and heav'n con - fessed; we

bow and bless the sa - cred name, for e - ver blest.

2. The God of Abraham praise,
   at whose supreme command
   from earth we rise, and seek the joys
   at his right hand:
   we all on earth forsake,
   its wisdom, fame and pow'r;
   and him our only portion make,
   our shield and tow'r.

3. The God of Abraham praise,
   whose all-sufficient grace
   shall guide us all our happy days,
   in all our ways:
   he is our faithful friend;
   he is our gracious God;
   and he will save us to the end,
   through Jesus' blood.

4. He by himself has sworn –
   we on his oath depend –
   we shall, on eagles' wings upborne,
   to heav'n ascend:
   we shall behold his face,
   we shall his pow'r adore,
   and sing the wonders of his grace
   for evermore.

5. The whole triumphant host
   give thanks to God on high:
   'Hail, Father, Son and Holy Ghost!'
   they ever cry:
   Hail, Abraham's God and ours!
   We join the heav'nly throng,
   and celebrate with all our pow'rs
   in endless song.

340 The grace of God

Judy Pruett

Judy Pruett

The grace of God up-on my life is not de-

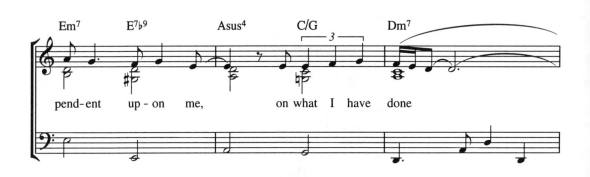

pend-ent up-on me, on what I have done

or de-served, but a gift of mer-cy from God

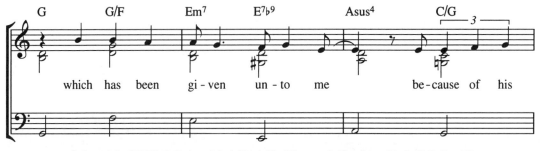

which has been gi-ven un-to me be-cause of his

341 The King of love my shepherd is

Henry Williams Baker (1821-1877)
based on Psalm 23

John Bacchus Dykes (1823-1876)

TUNE 1: DOMINUS REGIT ME 87 87

1. The King of love my shep-herd is, whose
good-ness fail-eth ne - ver; I no-thing lack if
I am his and he is mine for e - ver.

2. Where streams of living water flow
   my ransomed soul he leadeth,
   and where the verdant pastures grow
   with food celestial feedeth.

3. Perverse and foolish oft I strayed,
   but yet in love he sought me,
   and on his shoulder gently laid,
   and home, rejoicing, brought me.

4. In death's dark vale I fear no ill
   with thee, dear Lord, beside me;
   thy rod and staff my comfort still,
   thy cross before to guide me.

5. Thou spread'st a table in my sight,
   thy unction grace bestoweth:
   and O what transport of delight
   from thy pure chalice floweth!

6. And so through all the length of days
   thy goodness faileth never;
   good Shepherd, may I sing thy praise
   within thy house for ever.

Henry Williams Baker (1821-1877)
based on Psalm 23

Irish melody
(Petrie collection)

TUNE 2: ST COLUMBA 87 87

1. The King of love my shep - herd is, whose good - ness fail - eth ne - ver; I no - thing lack if I am his and he is mine for e - ver.

See over for another arrangement.

Irish melody (Petrie collection)
arr. Susie Hare

NEW ARRANGEMENT

Steadily building

2. Where streams of living water flow
   my ransomed soul he leadeth,
   and where the verdant pastures grow
   with food celestial feedeth.

3. Perverse and foolish oft I strayed,
   but yet in love he sought me,
   and on his shoulder gently laid,
   and home, rejoicing, brought me.

4. In death's dark vale I fear no ill
   with thee, dear Lord, beside me;
   thy rod and staff my comfort still,
   thy cross before to guide me.

5. Thou spread'st a table in my sight,
   thy unction grace bestoweth:
   and O what transport of delight
   from thy pure chalice floweth!

6. And so through all the length of days
   thy goodness faileth never;
   good Shepherd, may I sing thy praise
   within thy house for ever.

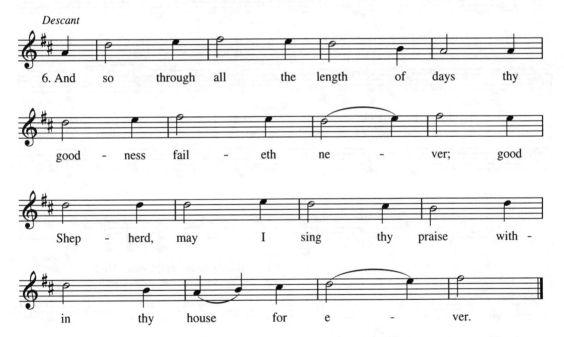

Descant

6. And so through all the length of days thy
good - ness fail - eth ne - ver; good
Shep - herd, may I sing thy praise with -
in thy house for e - ver.

342 The Lord is a mighty King

Creation creed

Graham Kendrick

Graham Kendrick (b.1950)

SHOUT:

For by him
all things were created.
Things in heaven
and on earth.
Visible and invisible.
Whether thrones
or powers
or rulers
or authorities;
all things were created by him,
and for him.

343 The Lord is marching out

O give thanks

Graham Kendrick

Graham Kendrick (b.1950)

1. The Lord is march-ing out in splen - dour,

in awe-some ma-jes-ty he rides, for truth, hu-mi-li-ty and

jus - tice, his migh-ty ar-my fills the skies. O give

thanks to the Lord for his love en - dures, O give thanks to the Lord for his

love en-dures, O give thanks to the Lord for his love en-dures for

e - ver, for e - ver.

1. **2.**

for e - ver,

2. His army marches out with dancing
   for he has filled our hearts with joy.
   Be glad the kingdom is advancing,
   the love of God, our battle cry!

344 The Lord reigns

Dan C. Stradwick

Dan C. Stradwick

2. The heav'ns declare his righteousness,
   the peoples see his glory;
   for you, O Lord, are exalted over all the earth,
   over all the earth.

345 The Lord's my shepherd

Stuart Townend, based on Psalm 23

Stuart Townend

2. He guides my ways in righteousness,
   and he anoints my head with oil;
   and my cup – it overflows with joy,
   I feast on his pure delights.

3. And though I walk the darkest path –
   I will not fear the evil one,
   for you are with me, and your rod and staff
   are the comfort I need to know.

346 The Lord's my shepherd

Psalm 23 from 'The Scottish Psalter' (1650)

Melody by Jessie Seymour Irvine (1836-1887)

CRIMOND CM

2. My soul he doth restore again,
   and me to walk doth make
   within the paths of righteousness,
   e'en for his own name's sake.

3. Yea, though I walk in death's dark vale,
   yet will I fear none ill.
   For thou art with me, and thy rod
   and staff me comfort still.

4. My table thou hast furnishèd
   in presence of my foes:
   my head thou dost with oil anoint,
   and my cup overflows.

5. Goodness and mercy all my life
   shall surely follow me.
   And in God's house for evermore
   my dwelling-place shall be.

347 The only power that cleanses me

Susie Hare

Susie Hare

Unhurried

1. The on - ly pow'r that clean - ses me is in the blood of
(2.) on - ly love that sets me free is in the heart of
(3.) ne - ver cease to be a - mazed that he should love so

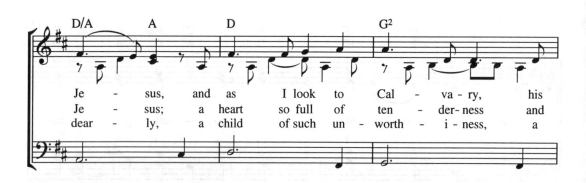

Je - sus, and as I look to Cal - va - ry, his
Je - sus; a heart so full of ten - der-ness and
dear - ly, a child of such un - worth - i - ness, a

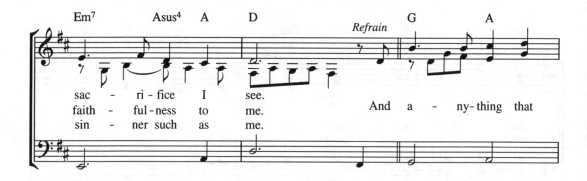

sac - ri - fice I see.
faith - ful-ness to me.
sin - ner such as me.

Refrain

And a - ny-thing that

I might give would al - ways be too small to

wor - ship you, be - cause you gave your life for me, be -

cause you gave me all.

rall.

The Bridge

348 The price is paid

Graham Kendrick

Graham Kendrick (b.1950)

Triumphantly

1. The price is paid, come, let us en-ter in to all that Je-sus died to make our own. For ev-'ry sin more than e-nough he gave, and bought our free-dom from each guil-ty stain. *Refrain* The price is paid, al-le-lu-ia, a-maz-ing grace, so strong and sure, and so with all my heart, my life in

ev - 'ry part, I live to thank you for the price you paid.

To verses

2. The price is

Last time

2. The price is paid,
see Satan flee away;
for Jesus crucified
destroys his pow'r.
No more to pay,
let accusation cease,
in Christ there is
no condemnation now.

3. The price is paid
and by that scourging cruel
he took our sicknesses
as if his own.
And by his wounds
his body broken there,
his healing touch
may now by faith be known.

4. The price is paid,
'Worthy the Lamb!' we cry,
eternity shall never
cease his praise.
The church of Christ
shall rule upon the earth,
in Jesus' name
we have authority.

The Bridge

349 There is a green hill far away

Cecil Frances Alexander (1818-1895) alt.

William Horsley (1774-1858)

HORSLEY CM

1. There is a green hill far a-way, out-
side a ci-ty wall, where the dear Lord was
cru-ci-fied, who died to save us all.

2. We may not know, we cannot tell,
   what pains he had to bear,
   but we believe it was for us
   he hung and suffered there.

3. He died that we might be forgiv'n,
   he died to make us good;
   that we might go at last to heav'n,
   saved by his precious blood.

4. There was no other good enough
   to pay the price of sin;
   he only could unlock the gate
   of heav'n, and let us in.

5. O, dearly, dearly has he loved,
   and we must love him too,
   and trust in his redeeming blood,
   and try his works to do.

350 There is a name I love to hear

F. Whitfield

W.M. Rudd

1. There is a name I love to hear, I love to speak its worth; it sounds like music in my ear, the sweet-est name on earth.

Refrain
Divisi
(1st voice) O how I love the Saviour's

(2nd voice) How I love the Saviour's

name,   O how I love the Sa - viour's name,

name,   how I love the Sa - viour's name, how I

O how I love the Sa - viour's name,

love, I love the Sa - viour's name, the

sweet - est name on earth. (on earth).

2. It tells me of a Saviour's love,
   who died to set me free;
   it tells me of his precious blood,
   the sinner's perfect plea.

3. It tells of one whose loving heart
   can feel my deepest woe;
   who in my sorrow bears a part
   that none can bear below.

4. It bids my trembling heart rejoice,
   it dries each rising tear;
   it tells me in a still, small voice,
   to trust and never fear.

See over for another arrangement.

W.M. Rudd
arr. Susie Hare

NEW ARRANGEMENT

1. There is a name I love to hear, I

love to speak its worth; it sounds like

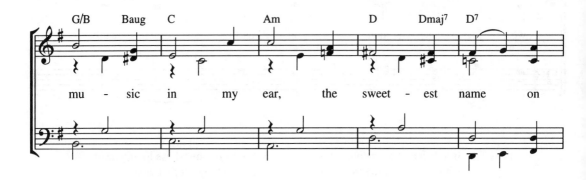

mu - sic in my ear, the sweet - est name on

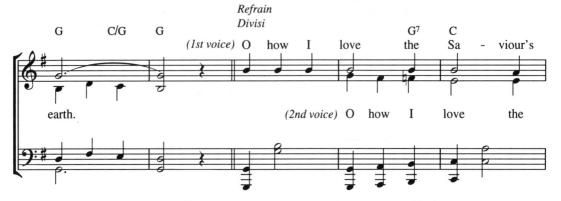

earth.

(1st voice) O how I love the Sa - viour's
(2nd voice) O how I love the

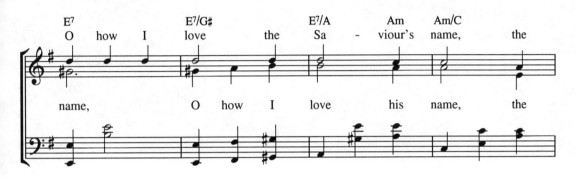

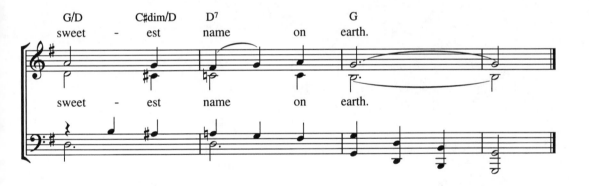

2. It tells me of a Saviour's love,
   who died to set me free;
   it tells me of his precious blood,
   the sinner's perfect plea.

3. It tells of one whose loving heart
   can feel my deepest woe;
   who in my sorrow bears a part
   that none can bear below.

4. It bids my trembling heart rejoice,
   it dries each rising tear;
   it tells me in a still, small voice,
   to trust and never fear.

The Bridge

351 There is a Redeemer

Melody Green

Melody Green

Hymn-like

1. There is a Re-deem-er, Je-sus, God's own Son,
pre-cious Lamb of God, Mes-si-ah, Ho-ly One.

Refrain
Thank you, O my Fa-ther, for giv-ing us your Son, and
leav-ing your Spi-rit till the work on earth is done. done.

2. Jesus, my Redeemer,
   Name above all names,
   precious Lamb of God, Messiah,
   O for sinners slain.

3. When I stand in glory,
   I will see his face.
   And there I'll serve my King for ever,
   in that Holy Place.

352 There is holy ground

Holy ground

Ian White

Ian White

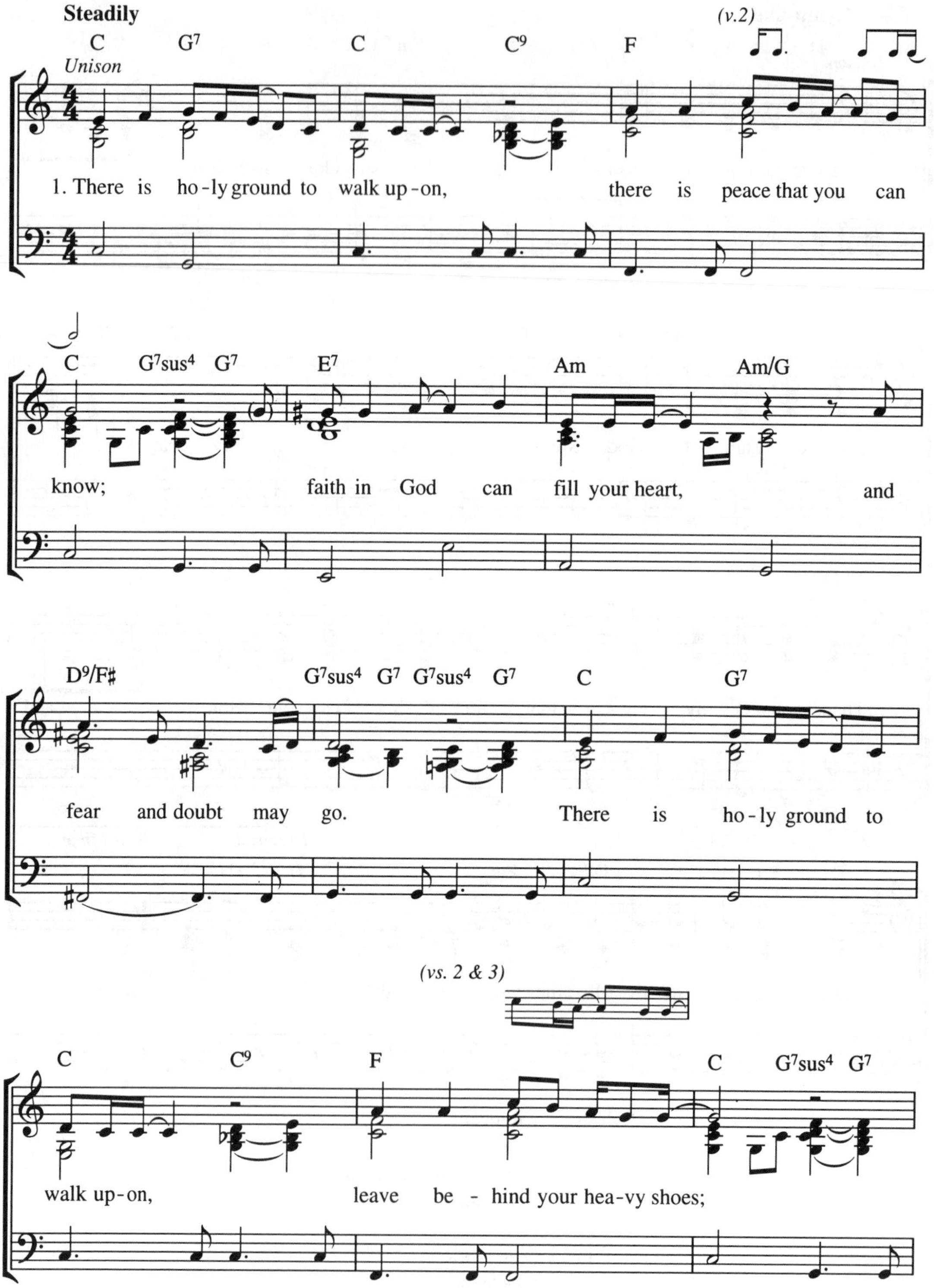
Steadily
C G7 C C9 F
Unison
(v.2)
1. There is ho-ly ground to walk up-on, there is peace that you can
C G7sus4 G7 E7 Am Am/G
know; faith in God can fill your heart, and
D9/F# G7sus4 G7 G7sus4 G7 C G7
fear and doubt may go. There is ho-ly ground to
(vs. 2 & 3)
C C9 F C G7sus4 G7
walk up-on, leave be - hind your hea-vy shoes;

2. There is holy ground to walk upon,
   hear him beckon to the lame;
   for there his healing pow'r may flow,
   and limbs find strength again.
   There is holy ground to walk upon,
   there is holy work to do;
   trusting in the words of life,
   that Jesus births in you.

3. There are holy dreams to dream upon,
   visions from the Lord on high;
   Jesus may be showing you,
   but will you turn your eyes?
   There is holy ground to walk upon,
   you can find the Jesus road;
   do not wait another day,
   but tell him you will go.

353 There is one name

Robert Critchley

Robert Critchley

Worshipfully, with strength

There is one name un-der hea-ven

by which men can be saved, Je - sus a-lone.

On - ly one name un-der hea - ven,

Je - sus, and Je - sus a - lone.

354 There is only one Lord

The strong name of Jesus

Morris Chapman and Claire Cloninger

Morris Chapman and Claire Cloninger

Strong 2-beat gospel feel

Capo 3 D
Unison

1. There is on - ly one Lord that we cling to,
2. Though a - part from him we can do no - thing,

there is on - ly one truth that we
by his Spi - rit we can do all

claim;
things;

there is on - ly one
co - vered by his blood

way that we walk in,
we are made right - eous,

there is on - ly pow - er in one name.
lift - ing up the name of Christ, our King!

355 There is power in the name of Jesus

Noel Richards

Noel Richards

Rocky

Unison

1. There is pow'r in the name of Je - sus;

we be-lieve in his name.

We have called on the name of Je - sus;

we are saved! We are saved!

At his name the de - mons flee.

2. There is pow'r in the name of Jesus,
   like a sword in our hands.
   We declare in the name of Jesus
   we shall stand! We shall stand!
   At his name God's enemies
   shall be crushed beneath our feet,
   for there is no other name that is higher
   than Jesus!

356 There's a place where the streets shine

Because of you

Paul Oakley

Paul Oakley

1. There's a place where the streets shine with the
   glo-ry of the Lamb. There's a way, we can
   go there, we can live there be-yond time. Be-cause of you,

pain, no more sad-ness, no more
suf-f'ring, no more tears. No more sin, no more
sick-ness, no in-justice, no more

joy e-ver-last-ing, there is
glad-ness, there is peace. There is wine e-ver-
flow-ing, there's a wed-ding, there's a

now we have this hope, be-cause of you.

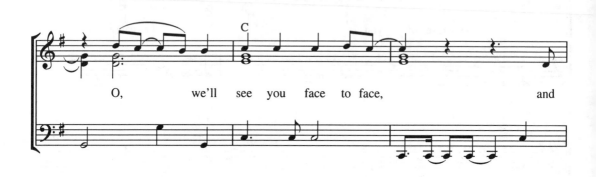

O, we'll see you face to face, and

we will dance to - ge - ther in the ci - ty of our God,

be-cause of you. 3. There is

The Bridge

357 There's a time coming nearer

Susie Hare

Susie Hare

Bright but steady

1. There's a time com-ing near - er that the world waits to see,
(2.) rides on the hea - vens and he shines like the sun,
(3.) jus - tice shall tri - umph o - ver dark - ness and sin

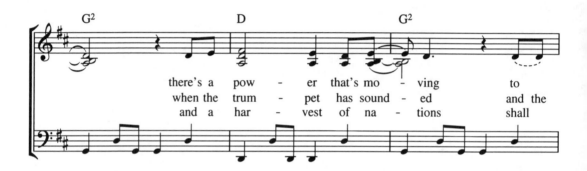

there's a pow - er that's mo - ving to
when the trum - pet has sound - ed and the
and a har - vest of na - tions shall

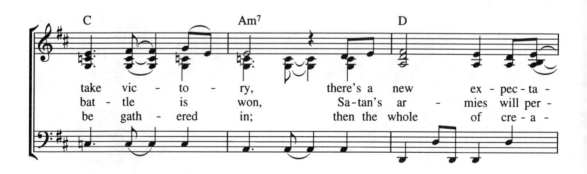

take vic - to - ry, there's a new ex - pec - ta -
bat - tle is won, Sa - tan's ar - mies will per -
be gath - ered in; then the whole of cre - a -

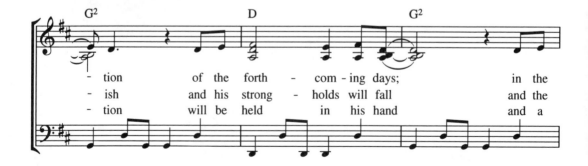

- tion of the forth - com - ing days; in the
- ish and his strong - holds will fall and the
- tion will be held in his hand and a

358 There's a wideness in God's mercy

Frederick William Faber (1814-1863) alt.

John Stainer (1840-1901)

CROSS OF JESUS 87 87

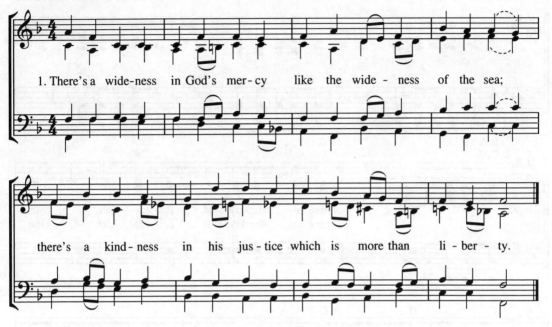

1. There's a wide-ness in God's mer-cy like the wide-ness of the sea;
there's a kind-ness in his jus-tice which is more than li-ber-ty.

2. There is no place where earth's sorrows
   are more keenly felt than heaven;
   there is no place where earth's failings
   have such gracious judgement giv'n.

3. There is plentiful redemption
   through the blood that Christ has shed;
   there is joy for all the members
   in the sorrows of the head.

4. For the love of God is broader
   than the measure of our mind,
   and the heart of the eternal
   is most wonderfully kind.

5. If our love were but more simple
   we should take him at his word,
   and our lives would be illumined
   by the glory of the Lord.

359 These are the days

Days of Elijah

Robin Mark

Robin Mark

1. These are the days of E-li-jah, de-clar-ing the word of the Lord; and these are the days of your ser-vant, Mo-ses, right-eous-ness be-ing re-stored. And though these are days of great tri-al, of fa-mine and dark-ness and

2. These are the days of E-ze-kiel, the dry bones be-com-ing as flesh; and these are the days of your ser-vant, Da-vid, re-build-ing a tem-ple of praise. These are the days of the har-vest, the fields are as white in the

The Bridge

360 The steadfast love of the Lord

Edith McNeil

Edith McNeil

361 The waves are breaking

To the ends of the earth

Dave Bilbrough

Dave Bilbrough

With anticipation

1. The waves are break-ing, the tide is turn-ing, God's Spi-rit is com-ing to this earth; the har-vest is wait-ing, and we have been called to go to the na-tions of this world. To the ends of the earth, to the ends of the earth, to the ends of the

earth we will go; bear-ing the mes- sage that our God can be known, to the ends of the earth we will go.

2. The fire is falling, the wind is blowing,
   the flame is spreading across our land;
   revival is coming, let the world hear,
   tell every woman, child and man.

3. The drums are beating, the trumpet is sounding,
   a warrior spirit he's put in our hearts;
   in the name of the Father, Spirit and Son,
   we'll take this word to ev'ryone.

362 The wonder of your mercy, Lord   *Covenant of grace*

Don Wallace

Don Wallace

The won-der of your mer - cy, Lord, the beau-ty of your

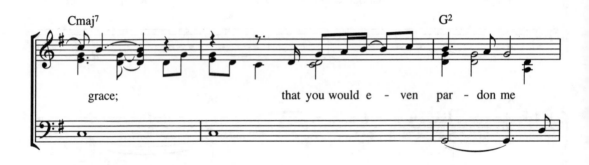

grace; that you would e - ven par - don me

and bring me to this place. I stand be-fore your

ho - li-ness, I can on -ly stand a - mazed:

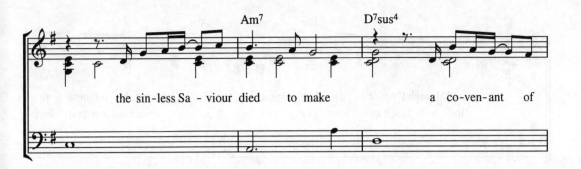

the sin-less Sa - viour died   to make   a co-ven-ant   of

Last time

grace.

To continue

grace.

1. I   on - ly want   to serve
2. You wel-come us   be-fore

you,
you,

bring ho-nour to   your   name,
in - to this ho - ly   place;

and though I've of - ten failed you,   your faith-ful-ness re -
the bril-liance of your glo - ry   de-mands our end - less

mains.   I'll glo - ry in my weak-ness,
praise.   The one, the on - ly Sa - viour

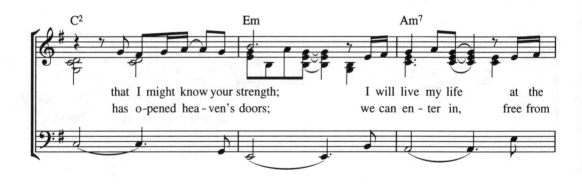

that I might know your strength;   I will live my life at the
has o-pened hea - ven's doors;   we can en - ter in, free from

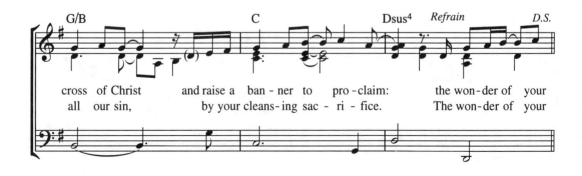

cross of Christ   and raise a ban - ner to pro - claim: the won-der of your
all our sin,   by your cleans-ing sac - ri - fice. The won-der of your

363 Thine be the glory

'A toi la gloire' by Edmond Louis Budry (1854-1932)
trans. Richard Birch Hoyle (1875-1939)

George Frideric Handel (1685-1759)

MACCABAEUS 10 11 11 11 and Refrain

1. Thine be the glo - ry, ri - sen, con - qu'ring Son,

end - less is the vic - t'ry thou o'er death hast won;

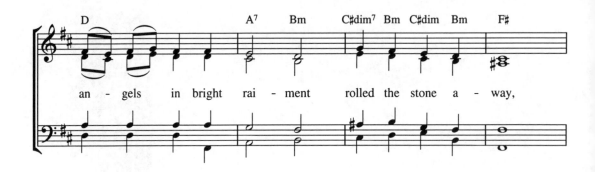

an - gels in bright rai - ment rolled the stone a - way,

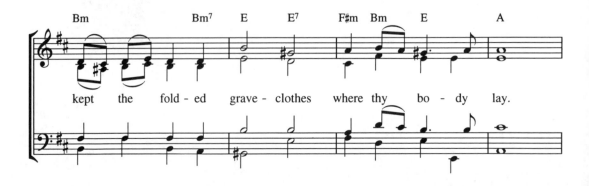

kept the fold - ed grave - clothes where thy bo - dy lay.

Refrain
Unison

Thine be the glo - ry, ri - sen, con - qu'ring Son,
end - less is the vic - t'ry thou o'er death hast won.

2. Lo! Jesus meets us, risen from the tomb;
   lovingly he greets us, scatters fear and gloom.
   Let the church with gladness hymns of triumph sing,
   for her Lord now liveth; death hast lost its sting.

3. No more we doubt thee, glorious Prince of Life;
   life is naught without thee: aid us in our strife.
   Make us more than conqu'rors through thy deathless love;
   bring us safe through Jordan to thy home above.

364 This Child

Graham Kendrick

Graham Kendrick (b.1950)

Calypso

1. This Child, se-cret-ly comes in the night, O this Child, hid-ing a hea - ven - ly light, O this Child, com-ing to us like a stran-ger, this hea - ven - ly Child.

Refrain

This Child, hea-ven come down now to be with us here, hea-ven - ly love

2. This Child, rising on us like the sun,
    O this Child, given to light everyone,
    O this Child, guiding our feet on the pathway
    to peace on earth.

3. This Child, raising the humble and poor,
    O this Child, making the proud ones to fall;
    O this Child, filling the hungry with good things,
    this heavenly Child.

365 This grace is mine

The power and the glory

Geoff Bullock

Geoff Bullock

The pow-er and the glo - ry of your name.

The pow-er and the glo - ry of your name,

the name of the Lord, the Son of

D.C. verse 3　　　　Last time

God.

2. This love is mine, so undeserved, this glorious name,
   this Son, this God, this life, this death, this vict'ry won,
   forgiveness has flowed and this grace that is mine finds my heart.

3. This life is mine, so perfect and so pure, this God in me,
   this glorious hope from earth to heaven, death to life,
   this future assured and secured by this love in my heart.

366 This is the air I breathe

Breathe

Marie Barnett

Marie Barnett
arr. Richard Lewis

367 This is the day

Rick Shelton

Rick Shelton

Lyrics:

1. This is the day that the Lord has made, I will re-joice and be glad in it; oh, this is the day that the Lord has made, I will re-joice and be glad in it. *Refrain* Re-joice in the Lord, re-joice

368 This means I love you

Matt Redman

Matt Redman

This means I love you, sing-ing this song, Lord I

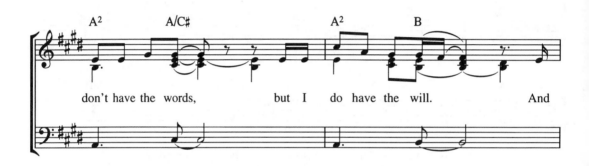

don't have the words, but I do have the will. And

this means I love you, that I take up my cross, I will sing

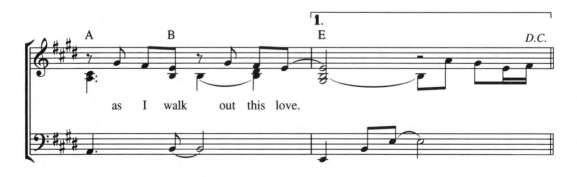

as I walk out this love.

1. Je - sus, this life   is   for you,
2. For these are the plans of my heart,

ev - 'ry - thing, Lord   that   I do;
yet of - ten I'm miss - ing the mark.

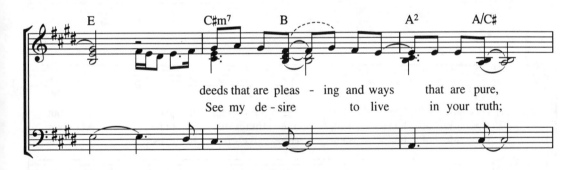

deeds that are pleas - ing and ways   that are pure,
See my de - sire   to live   in your truth;

Lord, may my life   bear this fruit.
this sure - ly means   I love you.

369 This side of heaven

O, what a day!

Susie Hare

Susie Hare

Easy ragtime style

1. This side of hea - ven we know just in part, but
2. This side of hea - ven, the things he has done are
3. This side of hea - ven we're fix - ing our eyes on

then we will know with all of our heart; for
pro - mi - ses now of what is to come; he's
run - ning the race and win - ning the prize; for

O what a song, O what a song we will sing

when we spend e - ter - ni - ty

Last time to Coda 1, 2.

wor - ship - ping Je - sus the King!

3. And no - thing we've earned can take

370 Thou didst leave thy throne

Emily Elizabeth Steele Elliot (1836-1897)
based on Luke 2:7,
adapted by Michael Forster (b.1946)

Timothy Richard Matthews (1826-1910)

MARGARET 10 8 11 8 and Refrain

1. Thou didst leave thy throne and thy king - ly crown when thou
cam - est to earth for me, but in Beth - le- hem's home was there
found no room for thy ho - ly na - ti - vi - ty. O
come to my heart, Lord Je - sus, there is room in my heart for thee.

Refrain

2. Heaven's arches rang when the angels sang
   and proclaimed thee of royal degree,
   but in lowliest birth didst thou come to earth
   and in deepest humility.

3. Though the fox found rest, and the bird its nest
   in the shade of the cedar tree,
   yet the world found no bed for the Saviour's head
   in the desert of Galilee.

4. Though thou cam'st, Lord, with the living word
   that should set all thy people free,
   yet with treachery, scorn and a crown of thorn
   did they bear thee to Calvary.

5. When the heav'ns shall ring and the angels sing
   at thy coming to victory,
   let thy voice call me home, saying, 'Heav'n has room,
   there is room at my side for thee.'

371 Thou, whose almighty word

John Marriott (1780-1825) alt.

Melody from Madan's 'Collection' (1769)
adapted by Felice de Giardini (1716-1796)

MOSCOW 664 6664

1. Thou, whose al - migh - ty word cha - os and dark - ness heard, and took their flight; hear us, we hum - bly pray, and where the gos - pel day sheds not its glo - rious ray, let there be light.

2. Thou, who didst come to bring
   on thy redeeming wing,
   healing and sight,
   health to the sick in mind,
   sight to the inly blind,
   O now to all mankind
   let there be light.

3. Spirit of truth and love,
   life-giving, holy Dove,
   speed forth thy flight;
   move on the water's face,
   bearing the lamp of grace,
   and in earth's darkest place
   let there be light.

4. Holy and blessèd Three,
   glorious Trinity,
   Wisdom, Love, Might;
   boundless as ocean's tide
   rolling in fullest pride,
   through the earth far and wide
   let there be light.

372 Through all the changing scenes of life

Psalm 34 in 'New Version'
(Tate and Brady, 1696)

George Thomas Smart (1776-1867)

WILTSHIRE CM

1. Through all the chang - ing scenes of life, in
trou - ble and in joy, the prai - ses of my
God shall still my heart and tongue em - ploy.

2. O magnify the Lord with me,
   with me exalt his name;
   when in distress to him I called,
   he to my rescue came.

3. The hosts of God encamp around
   the dwellings of the just;
   deliv'rance he affords to all
   who on his succour trust.

4. O make but trial of his love:
   experience will decide
   how blest are they, and only they,
   who in his truth confide.

5. Fear him, ye saints, and you will then
   have nothing else to fear;
   make you his service your delight,
   your wants shall be his care.

6. To Father, Son and Holy Ghost,
   the God whom we adore,
   be glory as it was, is now,
   and shall be evermore.

373 Through days of rage and wonder

Graham Kendrick

Graham Kendrick (b.1950)

1. Through days of rage and won - der we pur - sue the
2. Fix - ing our eyes on Je - sus, we will press on

end of time, to seize the day e - ter - nal,
day by day; this world's vain pas - sing plea - sures

the reign of love di - vine.
are not our des - ti - ny. Our an - cient

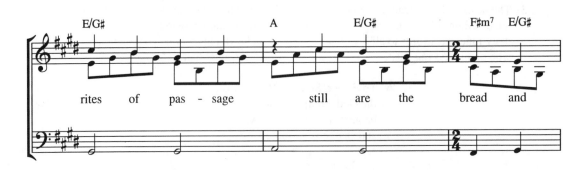

rites of pas - sage still are the bread and

wine: our   hope   a   cross   that   tow - ers

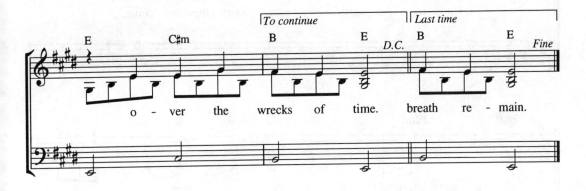

o - ver   the   wrecks   of   time.   breath   re - main.

3. Through days of rage and wonder,
   by the awesome pow'r of prayer
   God will shake ev'ry nation,
   secrets will be laid bare.
   And if his light increasing
   casts deeper shadows here,
   safe in his holy presence,
   love will cast out our fear.

4. Through days of rage and wonder
   you will give us grace to stand
   and seek a heav'nly city
   not built by human hands.
   Now is the only moment
   within our pow'r to change:
   to give back in obedience
   while life and breath remain.

374 Throughout the earth your glory will come

Lord, come and reign

James Wright

James Wright

Brightly, with a 'gospel' feel

Unison

1. Through-out the earth your glo-ry will come,
2. Up-on the earth may your king-dom come,

a day of pow'r, of sal - va - tion;
with - in our lives may your will be done;

to thirs-ty hearts your ri-vers will run, chang-ing
un-der the reign of Je-sus the Son we will

lives for the glo-ry of God.
live for the glo-ry of God.

2.

Lord, come and reign.

Lord, come and reign.

Lord, come and reign.

Lord, come and reign.

375 Thy hand, O God, has guided

Edward Hayes Plumptre (1821-1891) alt.

Basil Harwood (1859-1949)

THORNBURY 76 76 D

1. Thy hand, O God, has guid - ed thy flock, from age to age; the wond - rous tale is writ - ten, full clear, on ev - 'ry page; our fore - bears owned thy good - ness, and we their deeds re - cord; and both of this bear wit - ness: one

Church, one Faith, one Lord.

2. Thy heralds brought glad tidings
   to greatest, as to least;
   they bade them rise, and hasten
   to share the great King's feast;
   and this was all their teaching,
   in ev'ry deed and word,
   to all alike proclaiming:
   one Church, one Faith, one Lord.

3. Through many a day of darkness,
   through many a scene of strife,
   the faithful few fought bravely
   to guard the nation's life.
   Their gospel of redemption,
   sin pardoned, hope restored,
   was all in this enfolded:
   one Church, one Faith, one Lord.

4. And we, shall we be faithless?
   Shall hearts fail, hands hang down?
   Shall we evade the conflict,
   and cast away our crown?
   Not so: in God's deep counsels
   some better thing is stored:
   we will maintain, unflinching,
   one Church, one Faith, one Lord.

5. Thy mercy will not fail us,
   nor leave thy work undone;
   with thy right hand to help us,
   the vict'ry shall be won;
   and then by all creation,
   thy name shall be adored.
   And this shall be their anthem:
   One Church, one Faith, one Lord.

376 'Tis finished, the Messiah dies

Charles Wesley (1707-1788)

John Kelly
arr. Susie Hare

1. 'Tis fin-ished, the Mes-si-ah dies, cut off for sins, but not his own. Ac-com-plished is the sac-ri-fice, the great re-deem-ing work is done. 'Tis fin-ished, all the debt is paid; jus-tice di-vine is sat-is-fied, the grand and

full   a-tone-ment made, God   for   a   guil – ty   world   hath died.

2. The veil is rent, in Christ alone
    the living way to heav'n is seen.
    The middle wall is broken down
    and ev'ryone may enter in.
    The types and figures are fulfilled,
    exacted in the legal pain;
    the precious promises are sealed,
    the spotless Lamb of God is slain.

3. The reign of sin and death is o'er
    and all may live from sin set free.
    Satan hath lost his mortal pow'r,
    'tis swallowed up in victory.
    Saved from the legal curse I am,
    my Saviour hangs on yonder tree;
    see there the meek, expiring Lamb;
    'tis finished! He expires for me.

4. Accepted in the well-beloved
    and clothed in righteousness divine,
    I see the bar to heav'n removed
    and all thy merits, Lord, are mine.
    Death, hell and sin are now subdued,
    all grace is now to sinners giv'n,
    and lo, I plead th' atoning blood
    and in thy right I claim thy heav'n.

The Bridge

377 To be in your presence

My desire

Noel Richards

Noel Richards

With intimacy

1. To be in your pre - sence, to sit at your feet, where your love sur - rounds me, and makes me com - plete. This is my de - sire, O Lord, this is my de - sire. This is my de - sire, O Lord, this is my de - sire.

2. To rest in your presence, not rushing away,
to cherish each moment, here I would stay.

378 To God be the glory!

Frances Jane van Alstyne (Fanny J. Crosby) (1820-1915)

William Howard Doane (1832-1916)

TO GOD BE THE GLORY 11 11 11 11 and Refrain

1. To God be the glo-ry! great things he hath done; so loved he the world that he gave us his Son; who yield-ed his life an a-tone-ment for sin, and o-pened the life-gate that all may go in. Praise the Lord, praise the Lord! let the earth hear his

voice; praise the Lord, praise the Lord! let the peo - ple re -
joice: O come to the Fa - ther, through Je - sus the
Son, and give him the glo - ry; great things he hath done!

2. O perfect redemption, the purchase of blood!
   to ev'ry believer the promise of God;
   the vilest offender who truly believes
   that moment from Jesus a pardon receives.

3. Great things he hath taught us, great things he hath done,
   and great our rejoicing through Jesus the Son;
   but purer, and higher, and greater will be
   our wonder, our rapture, when Jesus we see.

379 We are marching

Traditional South African
v.1: trans. Anders Nyberg;
vs. 2 and 3: trans. Andrew Maries

Traditional South African

1. We are march - ing in the light of God, we are

march-ing in the light of God. We are

We are march-ing, march-ing, we are

march-ing, oh, we are march-ing in the light of God.

2. We are living in the love of God . . .

3. We are moving in the pow'r of God . . .

380 We believe

Graham Kendrick

Graham Kendrick (b.1950)

2. We believe he sends his Spirit
   on his church with gifts of pow'r.
   God, his word of truth affirming,
   sends us to the nations now.
   He will come again in glory,
   judge the living and the dead.
   Ev'ry knee shall bow before him,
   then must ev'ry tongue confess.

381 We come to you

All creation

Brian Doerksen and Steve Mitchinson

Brian Doerksen and Steve Mitchinson
arr. Richard Lewis

come to you with a heart of thanks, for your love, to
come to you with a song of praise, for your love; the

be a liv - ing sac - ri - fice, brought with love. We
mu - sic of our souls' de - light, brought with love. We

come to you with a heart of thanks, for your love; an
come to you with a song of praise, for your love;

of - fer-ing of all we are, brought with love.
sounds of joy and grate-ful - ness, brought with love.

All cre - a - tion, looks to you; all pro - vi - sion,

comes from you. In ev - 'ry sun - rise hope shines through.

For your mer - cy, we thank you. We we thank you.

2nd time Fine

All cre-a-tion looks to you. All pro-vi-sion comes from you. In
All cre-a-tion looks to you. All pro-vi-sion comes from you. In

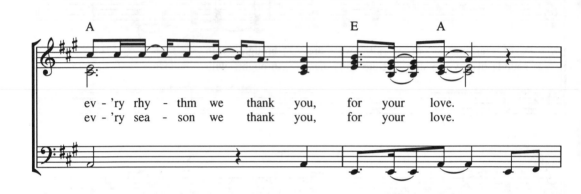

ev-'ry rhy-thm we thank you, for your love.
ev-'ry sea-son we thank you, for your love.

All cre-a-tion looks to you. All pro-vi-sion comes from you. In
All cre-a-tion looks to you. All pro-vi-sion comes from you. In

2nd time D.S. al Fine

ev-'ry rhy-thm we thank you, for your love.
ev-'ry sea-son we thank you, for your love.

382 We have a gospel to proclaim

Edward Joseph Burns (b.1938)

From William Gardiner's
'Sacred Melodies' (1815)

FULDA LM

1. We have a gos - pel to pro - claim, good news for all through - out the earth; the gos - pel of a Sa - viour's name: we sing his glo - ry, tell his worth.

2. Tell of his birth at Bethlehem,
   not in a royal house or hall,
   but in a stable dark and dim,
   the Word made flesh, a light for all.

3. Tell of his death at Calvary,
   hated by those he came to save;
   in lonely suff'ring on the cross:
   for all he loved, his life he gave.

4. Tell of that glorious Easter morn,
   empty the tomb, for he was free;
   he broke the pow'r of death and hell
   that we might share his victory.

5. Tell of his reign at God's right hand,
   by all creation glorified.
   He sends his Spirit on his Church
   to live for him, the Lamb who died.

6. Now we rejoice to name him King:
   Jesus is Lord of all the earth.
   This gospel-message we proclaim:
   we sing his glory, tell his worth.

383 We have sung our songs of victory

How long?

Stuart Townend

Stuart Townend

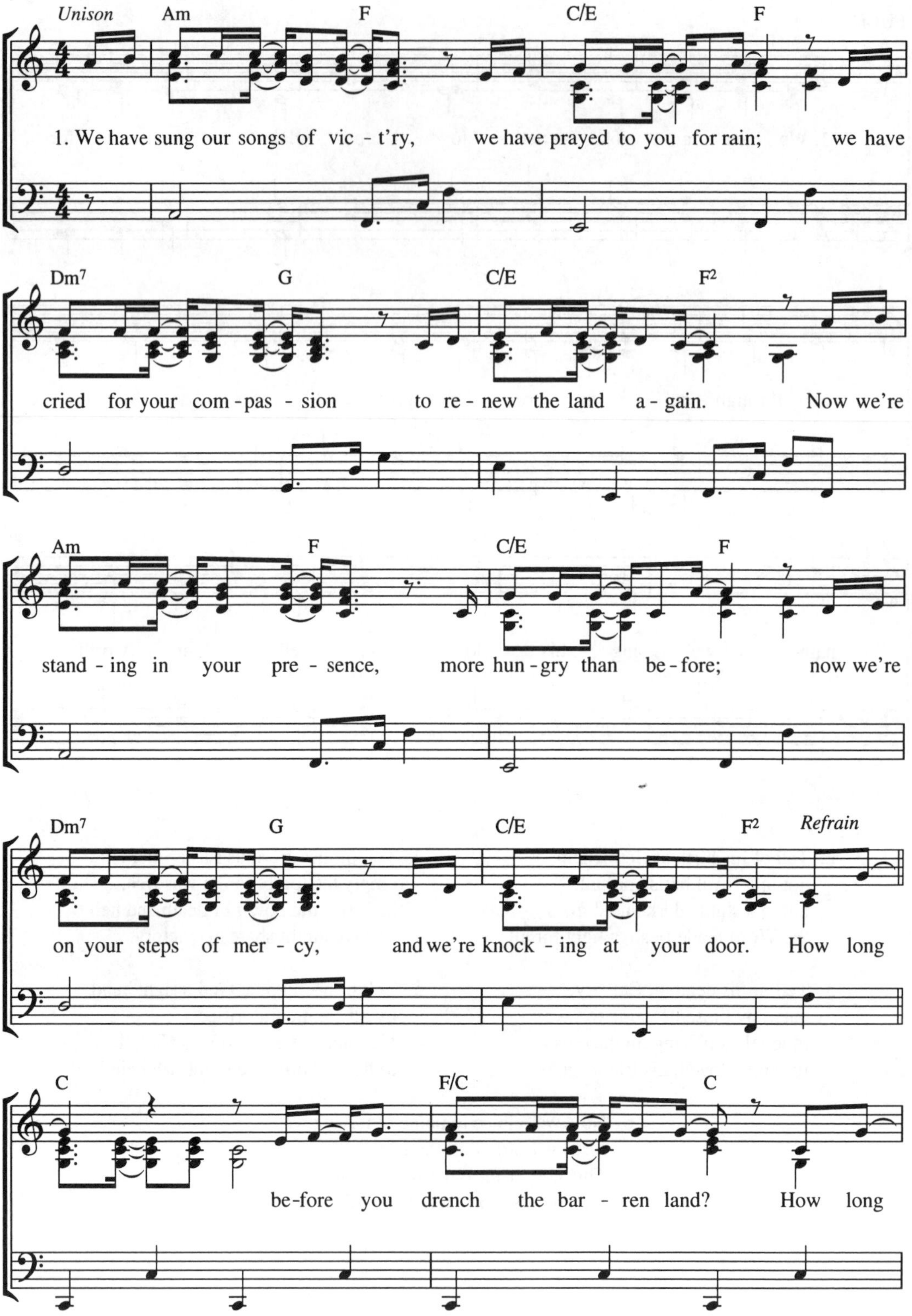

1. We have sung our songs of vic-t'ry, we have prayed to you for rain; we have cried for your com-pas-sion to re-new the land a-gain. Now we're stand-ing in your pre-sence, more hun-gry than be-fore; now we're on your steps of mer-cy, and we're knock-ing at your door. How long be-fore you drench the bar-ren land? How long

2. Lord, we know your heart is broken
   by the evil that you see,
   and you've stayed your hand of judgement
   for you plan to set men free.
   But the land is still in darkness,
   and we've fled from what is right;
   we have failed the silent children
   who will never see the light.

3. But I know a day is coming
   when the deaf will hear his voice,
   when the blind will see their Saviour,
   and the lame will leap for joy.
   When the widow finds a husband
   who will always love his bride,
   and the orphan finds a father
   who will never leave her side.

Final Refrain
How long before your glory lights the skies?
How long before your radiance lifts our eyes?
How long before your fragrance fills the air?
How long before the earth resounds with songs of joy?

384 We lift up our eyes

Isi de Gersigny, based on Psalm 121

Isi de Gersigny

We lift up our eyes a - bove the trou - bles in our land, and to - geth - er we stand to de - clare you as king. In times like these we choose to praise you, for it's you, it's you who real - ly mat - ter. You are wor - thy of all praise, and we will say that you are good, and all the

385 We'll walk the land

Let the flame burn brighter

Graham Kendrick

Graham Kendrick (b.1950)

With a strong rhythm

1. We'll walk the land with hearts on fire; and ev-'ry step will be a prayer. Hope is ris-ing, new day dawn-ing; sound of sing-ing fills the air.

years, and still the flame is burn-ing bright a-cross the land. Hearts are wait-ing, long-ing, ach-ing, for a-wak-'ning once a-gain.

truth, speak out for love; in Je-sus' name we shall be strong, to lift the fall-en, to save the child-ren, to fill the na-tion with your song.

2. Two thou-sand

Refrain

Let the flame burn bright-er in the heart of the dark-ness, turn-ing night to glo-rious

© Copyright 1989 Make Way Music, P.O. Box 263, Croydon, Surrey CR9 5AP, UK.
International copyright secured. All rights reserved. Used by permission.

386 We plough the fields and scatter

Matthias Claudius (1740-1815)
trans. Jane Montgomery Campbell (1817-1878) alt.

Johann Abraham Peter Schulz (1747-1800)
harm. John Bacchus Dykes (1832-1876)

WIR PFLÜGEN 76 76 D and Refrain

1. We plough the fields and scat – ter the good seed on the land, but
it is fed and wa – tered by God's al – migh – ty hand: he
sends the snow in win – ter, the warmth to swell the grain, the
breez – es and the sun – shine, and soft, re – fresh – ing rain.

Refrain

All good gifts a – round us are sent from heav'n a – bove; then

thank the Lord, O thank the Lord, for all his love.

2. He only is the maker
    of all things near and far;
    he paints the wayside flower,
    he lights the evening star;
    he fills the earth with beauty,
    by him the birds are fed;
    much more to us, his children,
    he gives our daily bread.

3. We thank thee then, O Father,
    for all things bright and good:
    the seed-time and the harvest,
    our life, our health, our food.
    Accept the gifts we offer
    for all thy love imparts,
    and, what thou most desirest,
    our humble, thankful hearts.

387 We rest on thee

Edith Gilling Cherry (1872-1897)   Jean Sibelius (1865-1957)

FINLANDIA 11 10 11 10 11 10

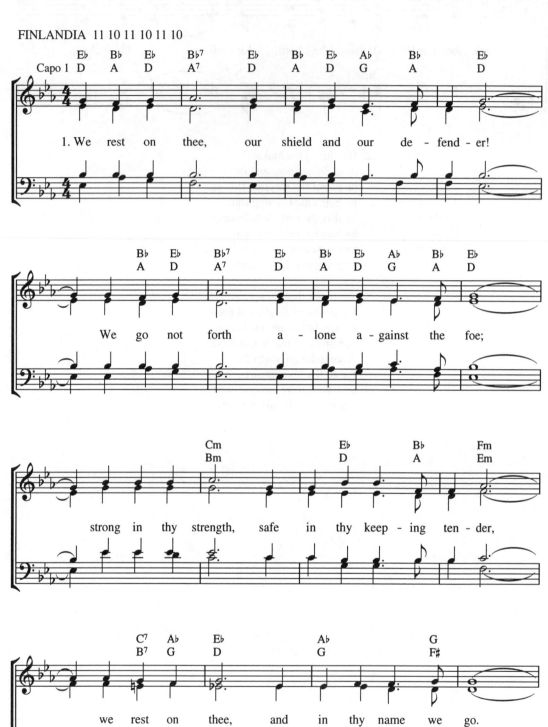

1. We rest on thee, our shield and our de - fend - er!
We go not forth a - lone a - gainst the foe;
strong in thy strength, safe in thy keep - ing ten - der,
we rest on thee, and in thy name we go.

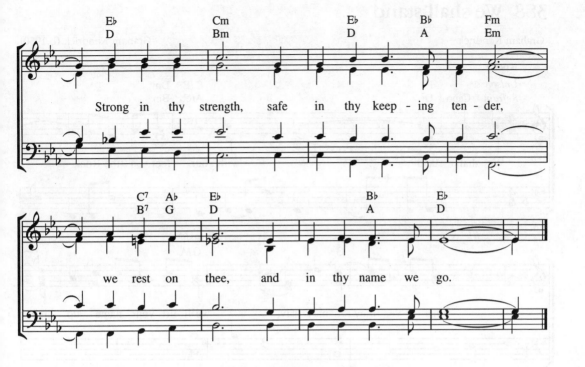

Strong in thy strength, safe in thy keep - ing ten - der,
we rest on thee, and in thy name we go.

2. Yes, in thy name, O captain of salvation!
   In thy dear name, all other names above;
   Jesus our righteousness, our sure foundation,
   our prince of glory and our king of love.
   Jesus our righteousness, our sure foundation,
   our prince of glory and our king of love.

3. We go in faith, our own great weakness feeling,
   and needing more each day thy grace to know:
   yet from our hearts a song of triumph pealing,
   'We rest on thee, and in thy name we go.'
   Yet from our hearts a song of triumph pealing,
   'We rest on thee, and in thy name we go.'

4. We rest on thee, our shield and our defender!
   Thine is the battle, thine shall be the praise;
   when passing through the gates of pearly splendour,
   victors, we rest with thee, through endless days.
   When passing through the gates of pearly splendour,
   victors, we rest with thee, through endless days.

388 We shall stand

Graham Kendrick

Graham Kendrick (b.1950)

We shall stand with our feet on the Rock.

What-e-ver they may say, we'll lift your name up high.

And we shall walk through the dark-

-est night; set-ting our fa - ces like flint,

we'll walk in-to the light.

2. Lord, as your witnesses
   you've appointed us.
   And with your Holy Spirit
   anointed us.
   And so I'll fight on through
   till I see you face to face.

The Bridge

389 We sing the praise

Thomas Kelly (1769-1855)

Ralph Harrison (1748-1810)

WARRINGTON LM

1. We sing the praise of him who died, of him who died up - on the cross; the sin-ner's hope let all de - ride, for this we count the world but loss.

2. Inscribed upon the cross we see
in shining letters, 'God is love';
he bears our sins upon the tree,
he brings us mercy from above.

3. The cross! it takes our guilt away,
it holds the fainting spirit up;
it cheers with hope the gloomy day
and sweetens ev'ry bitter cup.

4. It makes the coward spirit brave,
and nerves the feeble arm for fight;
it takes the terror from the grave,
and gilds the bed of death with light.

5. The balm of life, the cure of woe,
the measure and the pledge of love;
the sinner's refuge here below,
the angels' theme in heav'n above.

390 We want to see Jesus lifted high

Doug Horley

Doug Horley

Lively

Unison

We want to see Je - sus lift - ed high,

a ban - ner that flies a - cross this land,

that all men might see the truth and know

he is the way to hea - ven. We want to see,
(We're gon - na)

we want to see, we want to see Je - sus lift - ed high.
(we're gon - na) (we're gon - na)

391 We will seek your face

Touching heaven, changing earth

Reuben Morgan

Reuben Morgan

1. We will seek your face, al - migh - ty God,
Fa - ther, let re - vi - val start in us,

turn and pray for you to heal our land.
then ev - 'ry heart will know your king - dom come.

Lift - ing up the name of the Lord, in pow - er and in u - ni - ty.

We will see the na - tions turn. Touch - ing hea - ven, chang-

2. Never looking back we'll run the race,
   giving you our lives
   we'll gain the prize.
   We will take the harvest given us,
   though we sow in tears,
   we'll reap in joy.

392 What a friend we have in Jesus

Joseph Medlicott Scriven (1819-1886)

Charles Crozat Converse (1832-1918)

WHAT A FRIEND (CONVERSE) 87 87 D

1. What a friend we have in Je - sus, all our sins and griefs to bear!

What a pri - vi - lege to car - ry ev - 'ry-thing to him in prayer!

O what peace we of - ten for - feit, O what need-less pain we bear,

all be-cause we do not car - ry ev - 'ry- thing to God in prayer!

2. Have we trials and temptations?
   Is there trouble anywhere?
   We should never be discouraged:
   take it to the Lord in prayer!
   Can we find a friend so faithful,
   who will all our sorrows share?
   Jesus knows our ev'ry weakness –
   take it to the Lord in prayer!

3. Are we weak and heavy-laden,
   cumbered with a load of care?
   Jesus only is our refuge,
   take it to the Lord in prayer!
   Do thy friends despise, forsake thee?
   Take it to the Lord in prayer!
   In his arms he'll take and shield thee,
   thou wilt find a solace there.

See over for another arrangement.

Charles Crozat Converse (1832-1918)
arr. Susie Hare

NEW ARRANGEMENT

Ragtime

1. What a friend we have in Je - sus,

all our sins and griefs to bear!

What a pri - vi-lege to car - ry

ev - 'ry-thing to him in prayer!

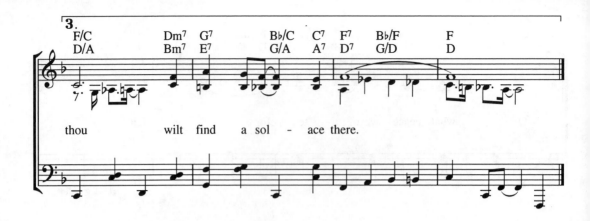

thou   wilt find   a sol - ace there.

2. Have we trials and temptations?
   Is there trouble anywhere?
   We should never be discouraged:
   take it to the Lord in prayer!
   Can we find a friend so faithful,
   who will all our sorrows share?
   Jesus knows our ev'ry weakness –
   take it to the Lord in prayer!

3. Are we weak and heavy-laden,
   cumbered with a load of care?
   Jesus only is our refuge,
   take it to the Lord in prayer!
   Do thy friends despise, forsake thee?
   Take it to the Lord in prayer!
   In his arms he'll take and shield thee,
   thou wilt find a solace there.

393 What a hope you have called us to

Bob Kauflin

Bob Kauflin

Unison

1. What a hope you have called us to, life for e-ver giv-ing glo-ry to you. A-wait-ing the day you make all things new; what a hope you have called us to.

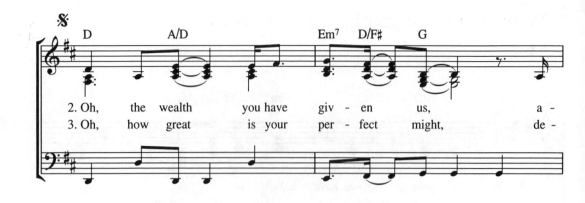

394 What a wonderful change

Rufus H. McDaniel (1850-1940)

Charles H. Gabriel (1856-1932)

SINCE JESUS CAME INTO MY HEART 12 8 12 8 and Refrain

1. What a won-der-ful change in my life has been wrought since

Je-sus came in-to my heart! I have light in my soul for which

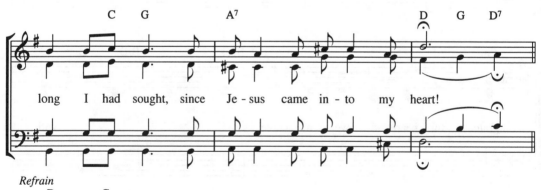

long I had sought, since Je-sus came in-to my heart!

Refrain

Since Je-sus came in-to my heart, since

Since Je-sus came in, came in-to my heart, since

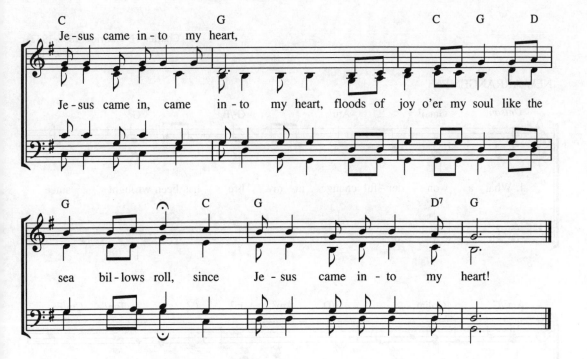

Je-sus came in-to my heart,
Je-sus came in, came in-to my heart, floods of joy o'er my soul like the
sea bil-lows roll, since Je-sus came in-to my heart!

2. I have ceased from my wand'ring and going astray
   since Jesus came into my heart!
   And my sins which were many are all washed away
   since Jesus came into my heart!

3. I'm possessed of a hope that is steadfast and sure,
   since Jesus came into my heart!
   And no dark clouds of doubt now my pathway obscure,
   since Jesus came into my heart!

4. There's a light in the valley of death now for me,
   since Jesus came into my heart!
   And the gates of the city beyond I can see,
   since Jesus came into my heart!

5. I shall go there to dwell in that city, I know,
   since Jesus came into my heart!
   And I'm happy, so happy, as onward I go,
   since Jesus came into my heart!

See over for another arrangement.

Charles H. Gabriel (1856-1932)
arr. Susie Hare

NEW ARRANGEMENT

heart, floods of joy o'er my soul like the
sea bil-lows roll, since Je-sus came in-to my heart.

2. I have ceased from my wand'ring and going astray
   since Jesus came into my heart!
   And my sins which were many are all washed away
   since Jesus came into my heart!

3. I'm possessed of a hope that is steadfast and sure,
   since Jesus came into my heart!
   And no dark clouds of doubt now my pathway obscure,
   since Jesus came into my heart!

4. There's a light in the valley of death now for me,
   since Jesus came into my heart!
   And the gates of the city beyond I can see,
   since Jesus came into my heart!

5. I shall go there to dwell in that city, I know,
   since Jesus came into my heart!
   And I'm happy, so happy, as onward I go,
   since Jesus came into my heart!

395 What kind of greatness

Graham Kendrick

Graham Kendrick (b.1950)

1. What kind of great-ness can this be, that chose to be made small? Ex-chang-ing un-told ma-jes-ty for a world so pi-ti-ful. That God should come as one of us, I'll ne-ver un-der-stand. The more I hear the sto-ry told, the more a-mazed

2. The One in whom we live and move
   in swaddling cloths lies bound.
   The voice that cried, 'Let there be light',
   asleep without a sound.
   The One who strode among the stars,
   and called each one by name,
   lies helpless in a mother's arms
   and must learn to walk again.

3. What greater love could he have shown
   to shamed humanity,
   yet human pride hates to believe
   in such deep humility.
   But nations now may see his grace
   and know that he is near,
   when his meek heart, his words, his works
   are incarnate in us here.

396 What kind of love is this

Bryn and Sally Haworth

Bryn and Sally Haworth

Gently

Unison

1. What kind of love is this that gave it-self for me? I am the guil - ty one, yet I go free. What kind of love is this, a love I've ne - ver

known? I did - n't e - ven know his name. What kind of love is this?

2. What kind of man is this
   that died in agony?
   He who had done no wrong
   was crucified for me.
   What kind of man is this
   who laid aside his throne,
   that I may know the love of God?
   What kind of man is this?

3. By grace I have been saved;
   it is the gift of God.
   He destined me to be his child,
   such is his love.
   No eye has ever seen,
   no ear has ever heard,
   nor has the heart of man conceived
   what kind of love is this.

397 What love is this?

I surrender

Dave Bilbrough

Dave Bilbrough

Slow and intense

1. What love is this, that took my place?

In-stead of wrath, you poured your

grace on me. What can I do but sim-ply come

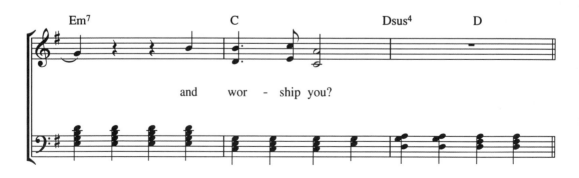

and wor - ship you?

2. What love is this,
   that comes to save?
   Upon the cross
   you bore my guilt and shame.
   To you alone
   I give my heart
   and worship you.

3. A greater love
   no man has seen;
   it breaks sin's pow'r
   and sets this pris'ner free.
   With all I have
   and all I am,
   I worship you.

398 What priceless treasures

Martin Leckebusch

Susie Hare

TUNWORTH 88 88 88

2. Forgiveness is the gift of God
   when harsher treatments would be right;
   the words which calm our gnawing guilt
   reveal the Father's chief delight –
   to tame and turn the rebel soul,
   to make the broken sinner whole.

3. If we deny our need of grace
   what foolish pride our words betray,
   since all the wrongs which we confess
   the blood of Christ will clean away:
   here justice and compassion meet –
   and here forgiveness is complete.

4. Released from sin's oppressive grasp,
   we make the way of grace our own
   as to each other we extend
   a pardon such as we have known:
   forgiven all, for ever free:
   what higher calling could there be?

399 When all thy mercies, O my God

Joseph Addison (1672-1719) alt.

Frederick Arthur Gore Ouseley (1825-1889)

CONTEMPLATION CM

1. When all thy mer - cies, O my God, my ris - ing soul sur - veys, trans - port - ed with the view, I'm lost in won - der, love and praise.

2. Unnumbered comforts to my soul
   thy tender care bestowed,
   before my infant heart conceived
   from whom those comforts flowed.

3. When in such slipp'ry paths I ran
   in childhood's careless days,
   thine arm unseen conveyed me safe,
   to walk in adult ways.

4. When worn with sickness oft hast thou
   with health renewed my face;
   and when in sins and sorrows sunk,
   revived my soul with grace.

5. Ten thousand thousand precious gifts
   my daily thanks employ,
   and not the least a cheerful heart
   which tastes those gifts with joy.

6. Through ev'ry period of my life
   thy goodness I'll pursue,
   and after death in distant worlds
   the glorious theme renew.

7. Through all eternity to thee
   a joyful song I'll raise;
   for O! eternity's too short
   to utter all thy praise.

400 When I look into your holiness

Wayne and Cathy Perrin

Wayne and Cathy Perrin
arr. Margaret Evans

Worshipfully

When I look in-to your ho - li - ness, when I gaze in -to your love - li -

ness, when all things that sur-round be- come sha - dows in the light of

you; when I've found the joy of reach -ing your

heart, when my will be-comes en-throned in your love, when all

things that sur-round be-come sha-dows in the light of you:

The Bridge

401 When I survey the wondrous cross

Isaac Watts (1674-1748)

Adapted by Edward Miller (1735-1807)

TUNE 1: ROCKINGHAM LM

1. When I survey the won-drous cross on which the Prince of Glo-ry died, my rich-est gain I count but loss, and pour con-tempt on all my pride.

2. Forbid it, Lord, that I should boast,
   save in the death of Christ, my God:
   all the vain things that charm me most,
   I sacrifice them to his blood.

3. See from his head, his hands, his feet,
   sorrow and love flow mingling down:
   did e'er such love and sorrow meet,
   or thorns compose so rich a crown?

4. Were the whole realm of nature mine,
   that were an off'ring far too small;
   love so amazing, so divine,
   demands my soul, my life, my all.

See over for another tune

Isaac Watts (1674-1748)

Somerset Folk song collected by
Cecil Sharp (1859-1924) arr. Susie Hare

TUNE 2: O WALY WALY LM

off- 'ring far too small; love so a- maz - ing, so di -
vine, de - mands my soul, my life, my all.

2. Forbid it, Lord, that I should boast,
   save in the death of Christ, my God:
   all the vain things that charm me most,
   I sacrifice them to his blood.

3. See from his head, his hands, his feet,
   sorrow and love flow mingling down:
   did e'er such love and sorrow meet,
   or thorns compose so rich a crown?

4. Were the whole realm of nature mine,
   that were an off'ring far too small;
   love so amazing, so divine,
   demands my soul, my life, my all.

402 When the music fades *The heart of worship*

Matt Redman Matt Redman

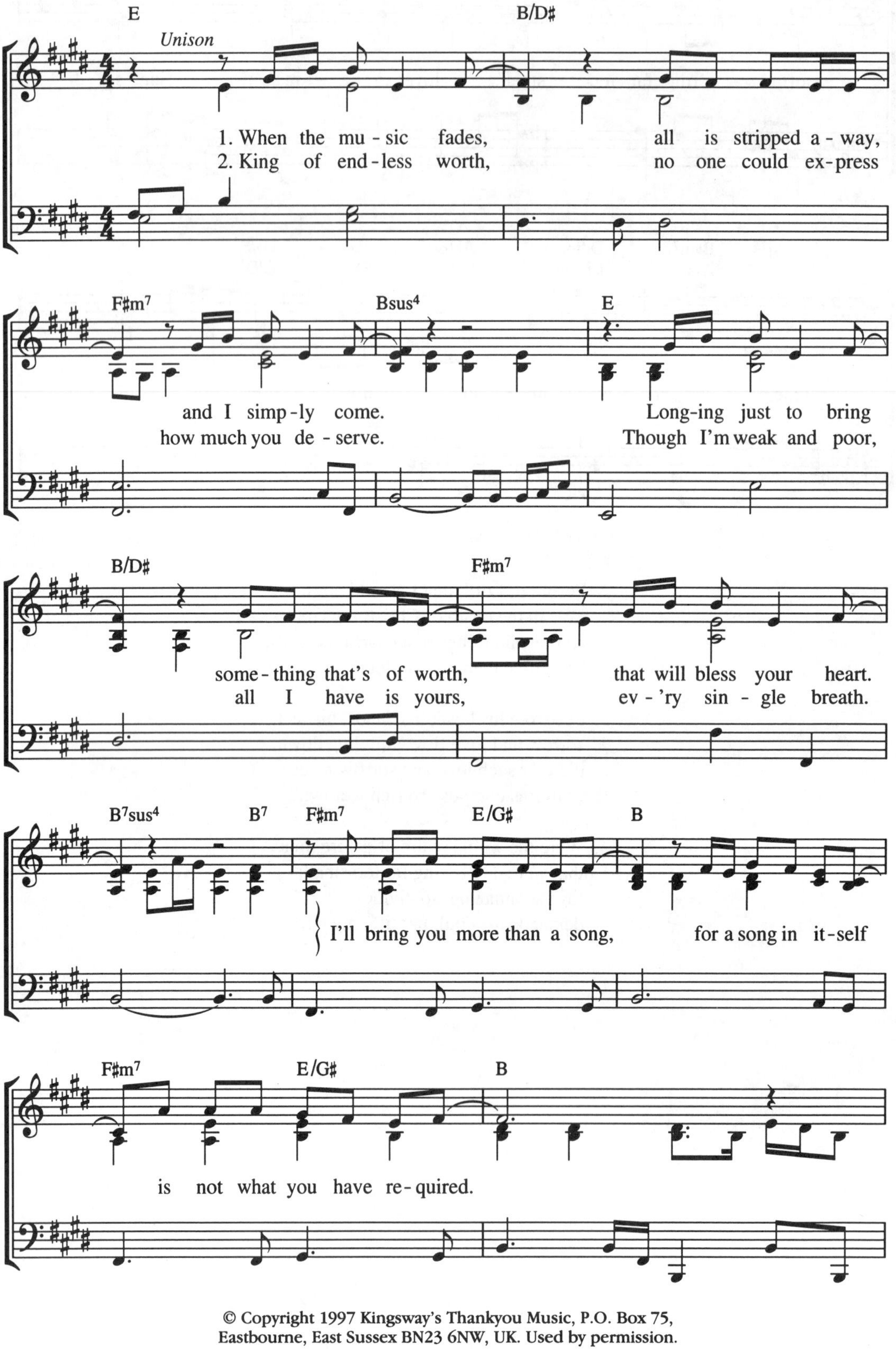

E
B/D♯
Unison
1. When the mu - sic fades, all is stripped a - way,
2. King of end - less worth, no one could ex - press
F♯m7
Bsus4
E
and I simp - ly come. Long - ing just to bring
how much you de - serve. Though I'm weak and poor,
B/D♯
F♯m7
some - thing that's of worth, that will bless your heart.
all I have is yours, ev - 'ry sin - gle breath.
B7sus4
B7
F♯m7
E/G♯
B
I'll bring you more than a song, for a song in it - self
F♯m7
E/G♯
B
is not what you have re - quired.

403 When this passing world is done

Robert Murray M'Cheyne (1813-1843)
adapted by Pam Haworth

Bryn Haworth

2. When I stand before the throne
   dressed in beauty not my own,
   when I see you as you are,
   I'll love you with unsinning heart;
   when the praise of heav'n I hear
   loud as thunder to the ear,
   then, Lord, shall I fully know,
   not till then, how much I owe.

3. Chosen not for good in me,
   wakened up from wrath to flee,
   hidden in the Saviour's side,
   by the Spirit sanctified;
   here on earth, as through a glass,
   Jesus, let your glory pass;
   teach me, Lord, on earth to show,
   by my love, how much I owe.

404 When we walk with the Lord

John Henry Sammis (1846-1919)

Daniel Brink Towner (1833-1896)
arr. Susie Hare

TRUST AND OBEY 66 9 and Refrain

1. When we walk with the Lord in the light of his word, what a glo-ry he sheds on our way! While we do his good will, he a-bides with us still, and with all who will trust and o-bey.

Refrain

Trust and o-bey, for there's no o-ther way to be

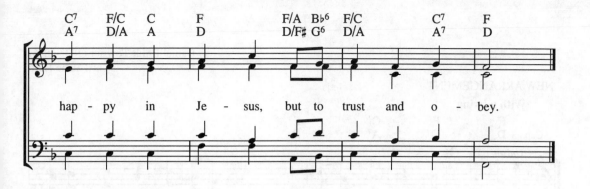

hap - py in Je - sus, but to trust and o - bey.

2. Not a shadow can rise,
   not a cloud in the skies,
   but his smile quickly drives it away;
   not a doubt nor a fear,
   not a sigh nor a tear,
   can abide while we trust and obey.

3. Not a burden we bear,
   not a sorrow we share,
   but our toil he doth richly repay;
   not a grief nor a loss,
   not a frown nor a cross,
   but is blest if we trust and obey.

4. But we never can prove
   the delights of his love
   until all on the altar we lay;
   for the favour he shows,
   and the joy he bestows,
   are for them who will trust and obey.

5. Then in fellowship sweet
   we will sit at his feet,
   or we'll walk by his side in the way;
   what he says he will do,
   where he sends we will go –
   never fear, only trust and obey.

See over for another arrangement.

Daniel Brink Towner (1833-1896)
arr. Susie Hare

NEW ARRANGEMENT

2. Not a shadow can rise,
not a cloud in the skies,
but his smile quickly drives it away;
not a doubt nor a fear,
not a sigh nor a tear,
can abide while we trust and obey.

3. Not a burden we bear,
not a sorrow we share,
but our toil he doth richly repay;
not a grief nor a loss,
not a frown nor a cross,
but is blest if we trust and obey.

4. But we never can prove
the delights of his love
until all on the altar we lay;
for the favour he shows,
and the joy he bestows,
are for them who will trust and obey.

5. Then in fellowship sweet
we will sit at his feet,
or we'll walk by his side in the way;
what he says he will do,
where he sends we will go —
never fear, only trust and obey.

405 Who can ever say they understand

For evermore

Dave Bilbrough

Dave Bilbrough

1. Who can e - ver say they un - der - stand all the won - ders of his mas - ter plan? Christ came down and gave him-self to man for e - ver - more.

2. He was

For e - ver - more we'll sing the

2. He was Lord before all time began,
   yet made himself the sacrificial lamb,
   perfect love reconciled to man
   for evermore.

3. He is coming back to earth again,
   ev'ry knee shall bow before his name,
   'Christ is Lord', let thankful hearts proclaim
   for evermore.

4. Who can ever say they understand
   all the wonders of his master plan?
   Christ came down and gave himself to man
   for evermore.

406 Who can sound the depths of sorrow

Graham Kendrick

Graham Kendrick (b.1950)

1. Who can sound the depths of sorrow in the Fa - ther heart of God, for the child - ren we've re - jec - ted, for the lives so deep - ly scarred? And each light that we've ex - tin - guished has brought dark - ness to our land:

up - on our na - tion, up - on our na - tion have

To repeat   *Last time*

mer - cy, Lord.   2. We have Lord.

2. We have scorned the truth you gave us,
   we have bowed to other lords.
   We have sacrificed the children
   on the altar of our gods.
   O let truth again shine on us,
   let your holy fear descend:
   upon our nation, upon our nation
   have mercy, Lord.

(Men)
3. Who can stand before your anger?
   Who can face your piercing eyes?
   For you love the weak and helpless,
   and you hear the victims' cries.
   (All)
   Yes, you are a God of justice,
   and your judgement surely comes:
   upon our nation, upon our nation
   have mercy, Lord.

(Women)
4. Who will stand against the violence?
   Who will comfort those who mourn?
   In an age of cruel rejection,
   who will build for love a home?
   (All)
   Come and shake us into action,
   come and melt our hearts of stone:
   upon your people, upon your people
   have mercy, Lord.

5. Who can sound the depths of mercy
   in the Father heart of God?
   For there is a Man of sorrows
   who for sinners shed his blood.
   He can heal the wounds of nations,
   he can wash the guilty clean:
   because of Jesus, because of Jesus
   have mercy, Lord.

Note: some congregations may wish to add to the effectiveness of this song by transposing the final verse up a semitone, into B♭ major.

407 Who, for my sake

Susie Hare

Susie Hare

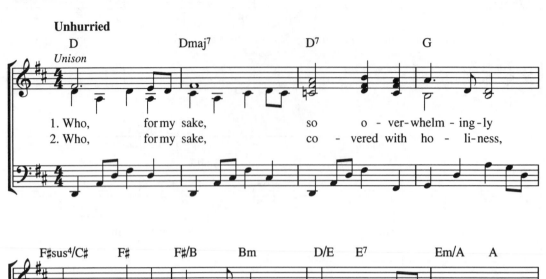

1. Who, for my sake, so o-ver-whelm-ing-ly
2. Who, for my sake, co-vered with ho-li-ness,

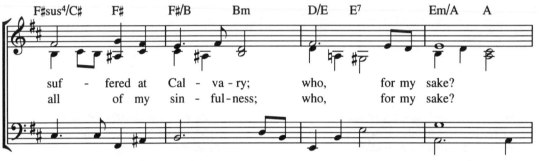

suf-fered at Cal-va-ry; who, for my sake?
all of my sin-ful-ness; who, for my sake?

Je-sus the Lamb, in all his pu-ri-ty,
Je-sus the King, God's per-fect sac-ri-fice,

slain on a cross to be Sa-viour of man.
yield-ed for me, his life, gave ev-'ry-thing.

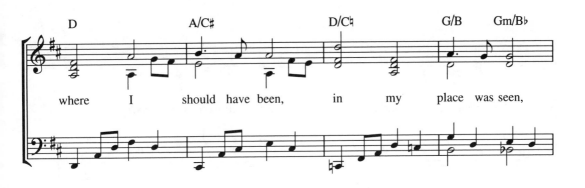

408 Who is on the Lord's side?

Frances Ridley Havergal (1836-1879)

Adapt. John Goss (1800-1880)

ARMAGEDDON 65 65 65 D

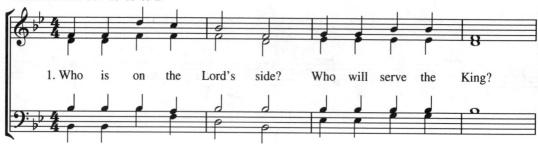

1. Who is on the Lord's side? Who will serve the King?

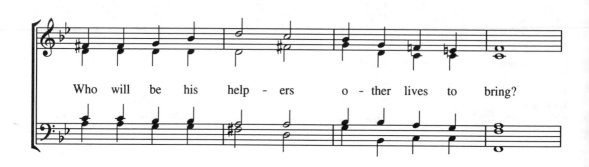

Who will be his help - ers o - ther lives to bring?

Who will leave the world's side? Who will face the foe?

Who is on the Lord's side? Who for him will go?

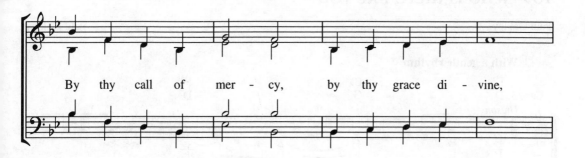

By thy call of mer - cy, by thy grace di - vine,

we are on the Lord's side, Sa - viour, we are thine.

2. Jesus, thou hast bought us
   not with gold or gem,
   but with thine own life-blood,
   for thy diadem.
   With thy blessing filling
   each who comes to thee,
   thou hast made us willing,
   thou hast made us free.
   By thy grand redemption,
   by thy grace divine,
   we are on the Lord's side,
   Saviour, we are thine.

3. Fierce may be the conflict,
   strong may be the foe,
   but the King's own army
   none can overthrow:
   round his standard ranging,
   vict'ry is secure;
   for his truth unchanging
   makes the triumph sure.
   Joyfully enlisting,
   by thy grace divine,
   we are on the Lord's side,
   Saviour, we are thine.

4. Chosen to be soldiers
   in an alien land,
   chosen, called, and faithful,
   for our captain's band;
   in the service royal
   let us not grow cold,
   let us be right loyal,
   noble, true, and bold.
   Master, thou wilt keep us,
   by thy grace divine,
   always on the Lord's side,
   Saviour, always thine.

409 Who is there like you

Paul Oakley

Paul Oakley

410 Who sees it all

Graham Kendrick

Graham Kendrick (b.1950)

1. Who sees it all, before whose gaze is dark-est night bright as the day; watch-ing as in the se-cret place his like-ness forms up-on a face?

all, the debt that's owed of lives un-lived, of love un-known? Who weighs the loss of in-no-cence, or feels the pain of our of-fence?

2. Who sees it
5. Whose bro-ken

1st and 4th times

2nd, 3rd and 5th times

3. Who knows the fears that drive a choice,
   unburies pain and gives it voice?
   And who can wash a memory,
   or take the sting of death away?

4. Whose anger burns at what we've done,
   then bears our sin as if his own?
   Who will receive us as we are,
   whose arms are wide and waiting now?

5. Whose broken heart upon a cross
   won freedom, joy and peace for us?
   Whose blood redeems, who ever lives
   and all because of love forgives?

The Bridge

411 With a clean heart

Chris Bowater

Chris Bowater

Worshipfully

With a clean heart I'll praise you, with a pure heart I'll ho-nour you, with a right spi-rit with-in me I will mag-ni-fy your name. I will mag-ni-fy your name, I will mag-ni-fy your name, with a heart that's full of love for you I will mag-ni-fy your name.

412 Wonderful grace

John Pantry

John Pantry

Smoothly

Unison

1. Won - der - ful grace, that gives what I don't de-serve,

pays me what Christ has earned, then lets me go free.

Won - der - ful grace, that gives me the time to change,

wash - es a - way the stains that once cov - ered me. And

2. Wonderful grace, that held in the face of death,
   breathed in its latest breath
   forgiveness for me.
   Wonderful love, whose pow'r can break ev'ry chain,
   giving us life again,
   setting us free.

The Bridge

413 Ye holy angels bright

Richard Baxter (1615-1691)
and John Hampden Gurney (1802-1862)

John Darwall (1731-1789)
harm. William Henry Monk (1823-1889)

DARWALL'S 148TH 66 66 44 44

1. Ye ho-ly an-gels bright, who wait at God's right hand, or through the realms of light fly at your Lord's com - mand, as - sist our song, for else the theme too high doth seem for mor - tal tongue.

2. Ye blessèd souls at rest,
   who ran this earthly race,
   and now, from sin released,
   behold the Saviour's face,
   God's praises sound,
   as in his sight
   with sweet delight
   ye do abound.

3. Ye saints, who toil below,
   adore your heav'nly King,
   and onward as ye go
   some joyful anthem sing;
   take what he gives
   and praise him still,
   through good or ill,
   who ever lives.

4. My soul, bear thou thy part,
   triumph in God above:
   and with a well-tuned heart
   sing thou the songs of love;
   let all thy days
   till life shall end,
   whate'er he send,
   be filled with praise.

414 Ye servants of God

Charles Wesley (1707-1788)

Charles Hubert Hastings Parry (1848-1918)

LAUDATE DOMINUM (PARRY) 10 10 11 11

1. Ye ser-vants of God, your Mas-ter pro-claim, and pub-lish a-broad his won-der-ful name; the name all vic-to-rious of Je-sus ex-tol; his king-dom is glo-rious, and rules o-ver all.

2. God ruleth on high, almighty to save;
   and still he is nigh, his presence we have;
   the great congregation his triumph shall sing,
   ascribing salvation to Jesus our King.

3. 'Salvation to God who sits on the throne',
   let all cry aloud, and honour the Son:
   the praises of Jesus the angels proclaim,
   fall down on their faces, and worship the Lamb.

4. Then let us adore, and give him his right –
   all glory and pow'r, all wisdom and might:
   all honour and blessing, with angels above;
   and thanks never-ceasing, and infinite love.

415 Yesterday, today, for ever

A. Simpson

J. Burke arr. Susie Hare

Yes-ter-day, to-day, for e - ver, Je-sus is the same; all may change, but Je-sus ne - ver, glo - ry to his name! Glo - ry to his name! Glo - ry to his name! All may change, but Je-sus ne - ver, glo - ry to his name!

NEW ARRANGEMENT

J. Burke arr. Susie Hare

416 You are a holy God

Brian Duane and Kathryn Scott

Brian Duane and Kathryn Scott
arr. Richard Lewis

You are a ho-ly God, an all con-sum-ing fire.
Your ways are not our ways. Your thoughts are high a-bove.

You're robed in ma-jes-ty, bright,
You are the foun-tain, Lord, of

shin-ing as the sun.
mer-cy, truth and

love. And we cry:

'Ho - ly, ho -

-ly, is the Lord God most

high'. And we cry: 'Ho -

ly, ho - ly

is the Lord most high'.

417 You are crowned with many crowns

John Sellers
John Sellers

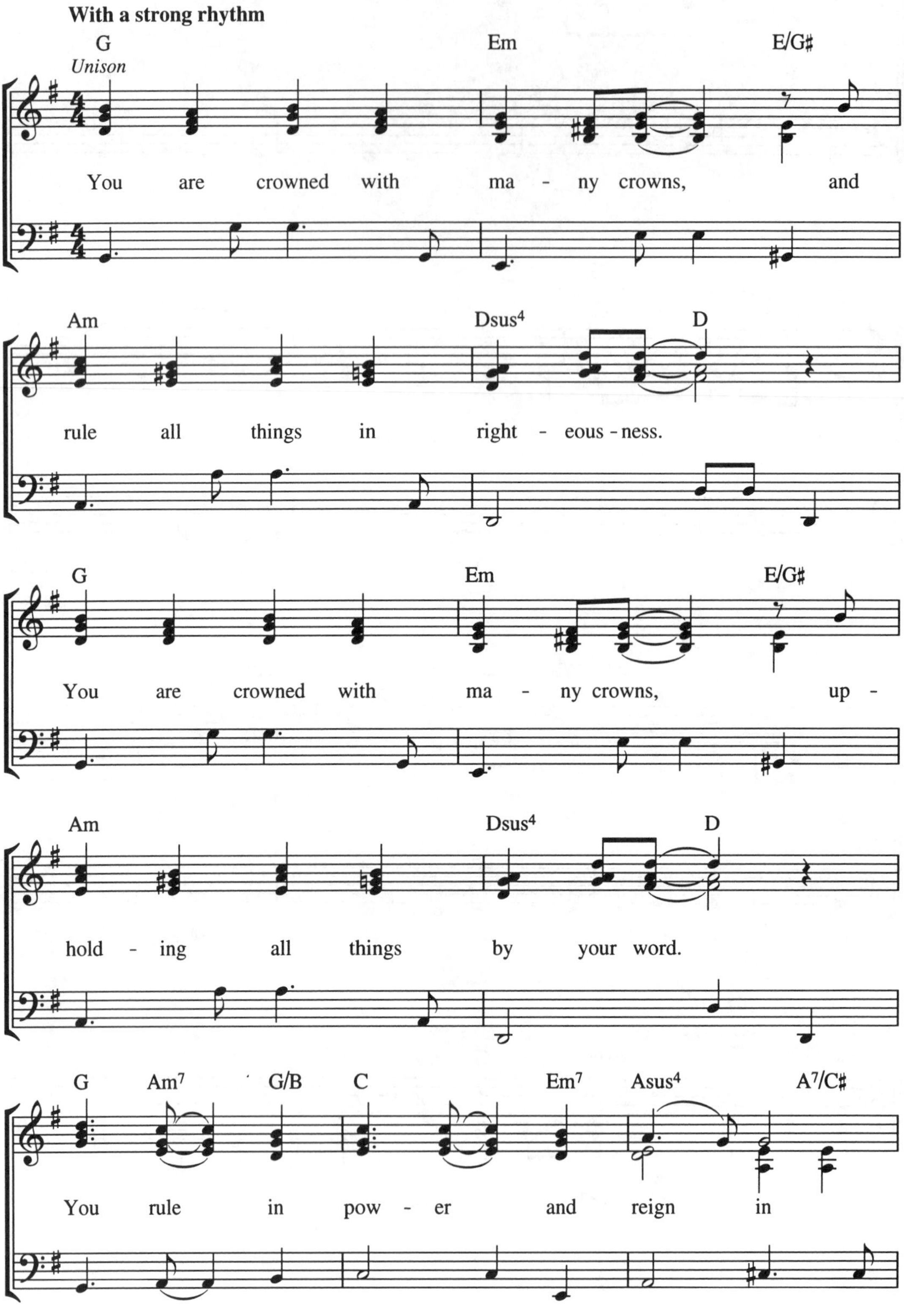

With a strong rhythm
G Em E/G♯
Unison
You are crowned with ma - ny crowns, and
Am Dsus4 D
rule all things in right - eous - ness.
G Em E/G♯
You are crowned with ma - ny crowns, up -
Am Dsus4 D
hold - ing all things by your word.
G Am7 G/B C Em7 Asus4 A7/C♯
You rule in pow - er and reign in

418 You are my love and my light

Don Moen

Don Moen

You are my love and my light, you are my pur-pose for liv-ing; you are my hope in the night, my rea-son for sing-ing. You bring a joy to my life, and you're mak-ing it bet-ter and bet-ter;

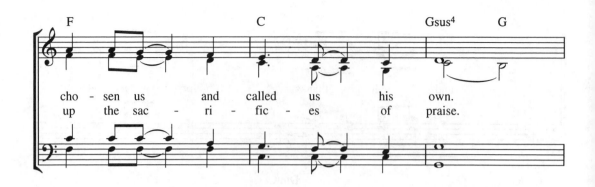

cho - sen us and called us his own.
up the sac - ri - fic - es of praise.

Flow - ing from his throne, there is a ri -
Teach us, Lord, we pray, to live in your pre -

- ver; bring - ing life and health wher -
- sence; make us more and more like

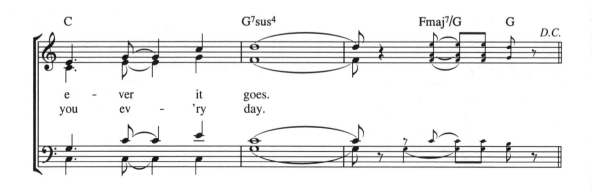

e - ver it goes.
you ev - 'ry day.

The Bridge

419 You are the King of Glory *Hosanna to the Son of David*

Mavis Ford

Mavis Ford

You are the King of Glo-ry, you are the Prince of Peace, you are the Lord of heav'n and earth, you're the Son of right-eous-ness. An-gels bow down be-fore you, wor-ship and a-dore, for you have the words of e-ter-nal life, you are Je-sus Christ the

420 You are the perfect and righteous God

I come by the blood

Steve and Vikki Cook   Steve and Vikki Cook

Moderately

1. You are the per - fect and right - eous God whose pre - sence bears no sin; you bid me come to your ho - ly place: how can I en - ter in when your pre - sence bears no sin? Through him who poured out his life for me, the a -

2. You are the high and ex - alt - ed King, the One the an - gels fear; so far a - bove me in ev - 'ry way. Lord, how can I draw near to the One the an - gels fear? Through him who laid down his life for me and as -

421 You are the sovereign 'I Am'

Your name is holy

Brian Doerksen

Brian Doerksen
arr. Richard Lewis

You are the sov-'reign 'I Am', your name is ho - ly.
You are the al - migh - ty one, your name is ho - ly.

You are the pure, spot - less lamb, your name is ho - ly.
You are the Christ, God's own Son, your name is ho - ly.

In your name there is mer - cy for sin,

there is safe - ty with - in, in your

The Bridge

422 You have become for us wisdom

All that we need

Mark Altrogge

Mark Altrogge

1. You have be-come for us wis - dom, you have be-come for us

right - eous-ness. You have be-come our sal-va - tion,

you have be-come all our ho - li-ness. All that we need is

found in you, oh, all that we need is in you.

All that we need is found in you; you are our all in all, you have be-come our all in all.

2. You have become our provision,
   in union with you we have victory.
   In you we have died and have risen,
   you are our great hope of glory.

423 You laid aside your majesty

I really want to worship you, my Lord

Noel Richards

Noel Richards

You laid a-side your ma-jes-ty, gave up ev-'ry-thing for me, suf-fer'd at the hands of those you had cre-a-ted. You took all my guilt and shame, when you died and rose a-gain; now to-day you reign, in heav'n and earth ex-alt-ed. I real-ly want to

424 You make your face to shine on me

And that my soul knows very well

Darlene Zschech and Russell Fragar

Darlene Zschech and Russell Fragar

1. You make your face to shine on me, and that my soul knows ve-ry well. You lift me up, I'm cleansed and free, and that my soul knows ve-ry well. When moun-tains fall

2. Joy and strength each day I find,
and that my soul knows very well.
Forgiveness, hope, I know is mine,
and that my soul knows very well.

425 You, O Lord

Mark Veary and Paul Oakley

Mark Veary and Paul Oakley

You, O Lord, rich in mer - cy, be-cause of your great love. You, O Lord, so lov'd us, e -ven when we were dead in our sins. You made us a- Christ, and live to - ge - ther with Christ, and

426 Your eye is on the sparrow

I will run to you

Darlene Zschech

Darlene Zschech

Your eye is on the spar-row, and your hand, it com-forts me. From the ends of the earth to the depths of my heart, let your mer-cy and strength be seen. You call me to your pur-pose, as an - gels un - der - stand. For your glo - ry may you draw all men, as your love and grace de-mands.

427 Your love

Pour over me

Stuart Townend

Stuart Townend

1. Your love, shin-ing like the sun, pour-ing like the
   grace frees me from the past, it purg-es ev-'ry
   come and lay my bur-den down glad-ly at your

rain, rag-ing like the storm, re-fresh-ing me a-gain; oh,
sin, it pu-ri-fies my heart and heals me from with-in; oh,
feet. I'm op-'ning up my heart, come make this joy com-plete; oh,

I re-ceive your love.
I re-ceive your grace.
I re-ceive your grace.

2. Your

Pour o-ver me, pour o-ver me,

The Bridge

Indexes

The Bridge

Index of Composers, Arrangers and Sources of Music

Index of Authors and Sources of Text

Alphabetical Index of Tunes

Metrical Index of Tunes

Scriptural Index

GENESIS

1:1	The Lord is a mighty King	342
1:1-4	Lord, the light of your love	222
	O Breath of Life	263
	Thou, whose almighty word	371
1:26	The Lord is a mighty King	342
2:7	Breathe on me, Breath of God (Fellingham)	40
	Breathe on me, Breath of God	41
	O Breath of Life	263
3:4	The Lord is a mighty King	342
3:15	Abraham's Son	3
4:7	Restore, O Lord	316
8:22	We plough the fields and scatter	386
11:9	It came upon the midnight clear	159
18:17	I want to serve the purpose of God	165
22:12	O Lord, my God	278
22:14	Who is there like you	409
22:16	The God of Abraham praise	339
28:10-19	Beneath the cross of Jesus	32
	Blessed assurance, Jesus is mine	37
49:24	Rock of ages	317

EXODUS

3:5	Be still, for the presence of the Lord	33
	There is holy ground	352
3:6	The God of Abraham praise	339
3:14	I lift my hands	146
	Let every tribe and every tongue	203
	Lord of lords	220
	The God of Abraham praise	339
13:21	Glorious things of thee are spoken	92
	Guide me, O thou great Redeemer	106
16:4	Glorious things of thee are spoken	92
20:3	I lift my hands	146
	Make way, make way	232
28:36	Holiness unto the Lord	124
32:26	Who is on the Lord's side?	408
33:22	Rock of ages	317
34:6	Praise, my soul, the King of heaven	307
34:24	O, that you would bless me	292
39:30	Holiness unto the Lord	124

LEVITICUS

6:13	O thou who camest from above	295
18:21	Who can sound the depths of sorrow	406
25:10	These are the days	359

NUMBERS

6:25	You make your face to shine on me	424
14:18	Praise, my soul, the King of heaven	307
21:4-9	Beneath the cross of Jesus	32
20:8-11	Lord, enthroned in heavenly splendour	211

DEUTERONOMY

5:7	I lift my hands	146
	Make way, make way	232
6:5	I will worship	172
	My life is in you, Lord	248
	Sing to the Lord	326
7:9	Lord, I come before your throne of grace	214
10:17	Alleluia, sing to Jesus!	5
32:4	Lord, I come before your throne of grace	214

JOSHUA

1:5	Abide with me	1
3:7	Guide me, O thou great Redeemer	106
3:16	Thine be the glory	363
6:2	Rejoice!	314
6:7	Rejoice!	314
5:14	Join all the glorious names	197
	We rest on thee	387

Joshua

24:15	O happy day	271
	Who is on the Lord's side?	408

JUDGES

1:20	See his kingdom growing	322
1:24	I come into your presence, Holy King	140

1 SAMUEL

3:10	Master speak! Thy servant heareth	234
17:47	In heavenly armour	151

2 SAMUEL

6:12	These are the days	359
6:14	Teach me to dance	331
7:12-13	These are the days	359
7:16	Rejoice, the Lord is King!	315
	The day thou gavest, Lord, is ended	337
22:2	For all the saints	79

1 KINGS

8:27	In the bleak mid-winter	153
8:30-40	Christ is made the sure foundation	47
18:36-39	O God of burning, cleansing flame	270
18:41-44	We have sung our songs of victory	383
19:9-18	Dear Lord and Father of mankind	60

1 CHRONICLES

16:25	I sing praises	156
16:29	The crucible for silver	336

2 CHRONICLES

7:14	We have sung our songs of victory	383
	We will seek your face	391
14:11	We rest on thee	387
20:12	I will worship	172
20:25	In heavenly armour	151

NEHEMIAH

8:10	In every circumstance	150

JOB

3:4	Breathe on me, Breath of God (Fellingham)	40
38:7-11	Angels from the realms of glory	20
	O little town of Bethlehem	276

PSALMS

2:1-2	My song is love unknown	251
3:5	Lord, how majestic you are	213
4:7	Almighty God, my Redeemer	15
	Come on and celebrate	54
5:11	You are the sovereign 'I Am'	421
7:1	O righteous God	290
7:9-10	O righteous God	290
7:17	Lift up your heads	207
	O righteous God	290
8:1	Lord, how majestic you are	213
8:1-2	O Lord our God	279
8:1-9	O Lord, my God	278
8:2	Jesus shall reign	186
9:7-8	O Lord our God	279
10:14	Abide with me	1
16:5	Be thou my vision	36
	The God of Abraham praise	339
16:10	He has risen	113
16:11	All my days	11
	Lord, I come before your throne of grace	214

JOHN

ACTS

Key Word Index

Index of First Lines